AN INTRODUCTION TO
STATISTICS
FOR CANADIAN SOCIAL SCIENTISTS

Second Edition

AN INTRODUCTION TO
STATISTICS
FOR CANADIAN SOCIAL SCIENTISTS

Michael Haan

OXFORD
UNIVERSITY PRESS

OXFORD
UNIVERSITY PRESS

Oxford University Press is a department of the University of Oxford.
It furthers the University's objective of excellence in research, scholarship,
and education by publishing worldwide. Oxford is a registered trade mark of
Oxford University Press in the UK and in certain other countries.

Published in Canada by
Oxford University Press
8 Sampson Mews, Suite 204,
Don Mills, Ontario M3C 0H5 Canada

www.oupcanada.com

Library and Archives Canada Cataloguing in Publication

Haan, Michael, 1974-
An introduction to statistics for Canadian social scientists/Michael Haan. — 2nd ed.

Includes bibliographical references and index.
ISBN 978-0-19-544125-3

1. Social sciences—Statistical methods—Textbooks. I. Title.

HA29.H22 2013   300.72'7   C2012-906699-0

Cover image: (c)iStockPhoto.com/aleksandarvelasevic
All screen shots in SPSS Lab Manuals, Reprint Courtesy of International Business
Machines Corporation © International Business Machines Corporation.
(SPSS ® Inc. was acquired by IBM ® in October 2009.)

All screen shots in STATA Lab Manuals, Reprint Courtesy StataCorp. 2011.
Stata Statistical Software: Release 12. College Station, TX: StataCorp LP.

This book is printed on permanent (acid-free) paper ∞.

Printed and bound in Canada
2 3 4 — 15 14 13

CONTENTS

PART III | MULTIVARIATE TECHNIQUES   197

LIST OF BOXES

EVERYDAY STATISTICS

PREFACE

When I began writing the first edition of this text back in the fall of 2006, I had a very specific goal in mind: to produce a uniquely Canadian textbook to introduce undergraduates to the topic of social statistics. That undertaking was successful enough to warrant this second edition, which now includes new content and features that reflect the evolving needs of the country's young social scientists.

Most undergraduate social science students are required to take at least one statistics course as part of their training, usually in their second or third year. Traditionally, there has been a shortage of high-quality, non-technical Canadian textbooks in this area, and professors have almost invariably chosen an American text for their courses. The upside of this is that they have had a wide choice of excellent examples from which to choose; the downside is that the substantive content is largely foreign to students—examples and datasets are almost always from the United States. I believe that this is one of the reasons that students complain about the difficulty and, of greater concern, the irrelevance of statistics for their studies.

But it's not just students who suffer. Using a US text compounds the dismay of professors of subsequent courses about the overall lack of familiarity among students with the basic statistical characteristics of Canadian society. Things like age distributions, city populations, median income, population changes over time, etc., could easily be used to exemplify statistical terms and concepts (like means, medians, variances, normal distributions, etc.), but with so many textbook offerings, students learn these characteristics about US society. Teaching students with Canadian content promotes greater familiarity with these topics, while at the same time teaching the universal language of statistics. It has been quite satisfying to discover, then, that its ground-up development as a Canadian text has been one of the features instructors and students have liked best about *An Introduction to Statistics for Canadian Social Scientists*. This second edition includes a new feature, the "Everyday Statistics" box, which furthers the mission of presenting students with unique Canadian content.

Since the best way to learn statistics is "hands-on" (particularly with the ongoing proliferation of computers in social science departments), a "knowledge-through-discovery" approach is ideal. Instead of providing the platform for lectures with little or no application, effective pedagogy require students to apply what they learn in each chapter through practice questions and laboratory exercises (included in the built-in manual for SPSS and STATA, two of the most popular statistical software packages). Additional chapter-end questions, revised lab manuals that use real data from the 2009 Alberta Survey, and a text-wide technical review for accuracy ensure the second edition thoroughly engages the knowledge-through-discovery approach.

Finally, in this second edition I also wanted to continue to offer a text that fits students' budgets. Several statistical textbooks retail for over $200 CDN, an exorbitant amount, made worse when instructors don't come close to covering all of the topics in a semester. To remedy this, I've kept the text to such a length that there is approximately enough material to fill one semester. Consequently, the second edition is shorter than most other introductory statistics texts, yet there is still plenty of material for a semester- or year-long course.

What I didn't understand when I began writing the first edition of this text was how hard it would be to fulfill the goals I had set for myself. I had thought that teaching statistics through a textbook would require minimal modifications from my in-class lectures. I became acutely aware of just how different textbook instruction is to lecturing. Perhaps the most noticeable difference is that it's impossible to stop at certain points to ask students if the explanations are clear. The advantage to publishing a second edition of this text is that the feedback of both instructors and students who used the original edition has been taken into account and woven into the pages of this text that you hold in your hands.

This text is broad enough to be used in several social science departments. Although I'm trained as a sociologist, my goal has been to keep examples diverse enough to be of interest to both sociologists and non-sociologists. I hope you'll enjoy (or at least not loathe) what I consider to be one of the most fascinating and useful topics in academia today.

HIGHLIGHTS OF THE SECOND EDITION

- **"Everyday Statistics" boxed feature.** Developed to demonstrate how statistics figure into the day-to-day workings of Canadian society, "Everyday Statistics" looks at topics such as the use of bivariate statistics by the media during election campaigns and the consequences of cancelling the long-form Canadian Census. This new feature also concludes with a probing questions crafted to stimulate critical thinking.

- **Expanded end-of-chapter practice questions.** Additional questions at the end of each chapter, with answers found in the end-of-text answer key, provide students with more opportunities to put their learning to the test.

- **Revised lab manuals.** Both the SPSS and STATA lab manuals found at the conclusion of the text have been revised, keyed to real data collected in the 2009 Alberta Survey. Working with real data affords students the opportunity to see actual social science in action.

- **Quick-reference guides.** Located on the inside front and back covers, guides to frequently used formulas and symbols serve as handy reference tools placed right at students' fingertips.

- **Technical check.** Equations, solutions, and concepts throughout the text have undergone a technical check to ensure an edition that is as accurate as possible.

- **Augmented ancillaries suite.** New to this edition is a fully automated test generator and instructor's manual, as well as revised PowerPoint slides. Students will be aided by new key concept cue cards and further statistical resources located on the text's companion site.

ABOUT THE AUTHOR

Michael Haan is an Associate Professor of Sociology and Canada Research Chair in Population and Social Policy at the University of New Brunswick. Professor Haan's recent research focuses on the economic and social implications of migration within and international migration to Canada. He teaches demography and public policy courses at the University of New Brunswick and co-directs (with Ted McDonald) the New Brunswick Institute for Research, Data, and Training, a state-of-the-art facility for working with government administrative statistical data.

ACKNOWLEDGEMENTS

Since writing the first edition, I have moved to the University of New Brunswick from the University of Alberta. As a result, I had to enlist an almost entirely new "village" of bright young people (only Julie Hudson continued to work with me on this second edition, and has once again singlehandedly produced the lab manuals) to help with this new edition. Ashley Calhoun and Kayla Power worked diligently and efficiently on producing the test bank, website materials, and some of the practice questions (please blame me, not them, if the questions on your exams are too difficult). I have also been lucky enough to work with John Calhoun, Alison Luke, Sasha McEachern Caputo, and Donna Safatli on different projects. Their competence, independence, and diligence provided me with enough free enough time to complete the draft manuscript for this second edition.

Jodi Lewchuk from Oxford University Press also joined as developmental editor on the second edition, and has been incredibly patient and encouraging throughout the process.

Dale Ballucci has remained a strong source of support with this edition. Finally, our daughters, Evelyn and Abigail, have made our lives a little bit busier and lot more interesting, all the while providing the details for some of the practice questions in this text.

PART I | INTRODUCTION AND UNIVARIATE STATISTICS

CHAPTER 1

Why Should I Want to Learn Statistics?

LEARNING OBJECTIVES

This chapter will help you to understand why you should want to take a statistics course. It will accomplish this by:

- describing some of the concerns that might be causing you to dread this course;
- putting each of these concerns into context;
- discussing the merits of learning to think statistically;
- linking exercises and practice questions to material.

INTRODUCTION

I bet you're reading this book involuntarily. You've probably enrolled in introductory social statistics in one of the social science departments (history, political science, psychology, sociology, etc.) at your college or university. The course is likely required for your degree or diploma. If you're like most other students, you've dreaded taking statistics for some time now. I'd also bet that you wouldn't be taking this course if it wasn't required. You may be in the final year of your program, even though the course is listed as a second- or third-year course.

You're not alone. Very few people actually *want* to learn statistics. I didn't, and neither did most of my colleagues (some of whom now teach statistics courses). Like you, we were forced by our university bureaucracies to enroll in stats. In my case, I'd never met the person, or people, who made this decision for me; they didn't follow my progress through the course, and after I'd finished they didn't ask me if I agreed with their decision to require me to take the course.

That was probably a good thing, because I likely would have told them that I dreaded statistics more *after* taking the course than I did before. Sure, I'd learned a few things, but the information was so abstract and boring that it didn't seem relevant to my day-to-day life. Up to that point, I'd survived without knowing what a standard deviation or a z-score was, and I was quite certain that I would have continued to survive without that knowledge. After completing my undergraduate statistics course, I still hated statistics. So did most of the people in my class.

WHY DO SO MANY PEOPLE HATE STATISTICS?

Looking back, I think I had at least four reasons for disliking statistics. First, I found it to be little more than useless math and equations, which made the material impenetrable and unintelligible for me. In my mind, the abstract equations discussed in class bore very little relevance to the *practice* of doing statistics. Second, I found the logic, and the assumptions, to be shaky at times. Why, for example, did we often have to assume that variables are normally distributed (we'll discuss what this means later), when this is so rarely true? Third, if statistics are so important and "objective," how can people on both sides of a debate use them to support their claims to knowledge? Finally, my professor (who will remain nameless), though a capable statistician, was not very good at, or perhaps not very interested in, making assumptions, concepts, and equations palatable to me when I was 19 years old. To this day, I remain convinced that it was his decision alone to schedule the class at 8:00 a.m. on Mondays, Wednesdays, and Fridays.

You may share some, or all, of these reasons for hating statistics. It is likely, however, that someone in your college or university has decided that that you too should learn statistics, making the debate about whether you "should" learn statistics moot. This brings us to our discussion of whether you should *want* to learn statistics.

Let's see if this is going to be as bad as you fear. You're probably dreading the math and the equations, but they're not as hard as you may think. We'll review the necessary math in Chapter 2, but for now I can assure you that to use statistics well you don't need to know a lot of math or to understand equations that you didn't learn in elementary or high school. That is not to say that the math underlying statistics isn't difficult, only that we are going to be focusing on the basics here. Similarly, while some of the equations look complex, the principles behind them are generally quite easy to understand. Whenever a new equation is introduced in the text, I try my best to explain, in everyday language, what that equation does. These explanations should be easy to understand because most social statistics concepts are "results driven." That is, once you understand what a certain procedure is designed to do, using it will be easier.

The second reason many people hate statistics is that they don't trust them. Darrell Huff's *How to Lie with Statistics* (1954) is the bestselling statistics book of all time, so statistical doubters are plentiful. Sure, statistics can mislead, but this can be said about any type of argument (how many athletes have claimed to be "the best there ever was and there ever will be" over the years, even though at most only one of them can be correct?). It is your responsibility to assess the validity of any claim, and you can only do that if you understand the tools (be they statistics, rhetoric, logic, etc.) that are being used. Statistics is a tool for constructing a narrative, and one of the goals of a college or university education is to help you use that tool and know if others are using it effectively.

Let me illustrate with an example. Say that your friend tells you that he believes all people from Moose Jaw are affluent. Before believing his claim, you might want to analyze it yourself. You might ask yourself:

1. Do I accept the definitions being used? (What exactly is "Moose Jaw"? Does it include the outlying suburbs? What does "affluent" mean? How much of the population of Moose Jaw must be considered affluent before Moose Jaw can be called affluent?)

2. Do I agree with the underlying assumptions? (Is "affluence" a meaningful concept? Can I determine the affluence of one place without comparing it to the affluence of other places?)

3. Do I accept the methods that are being used to arrive at the claim? (e.g., which residents of Moose Jaw answered questions about their affluence when the data were being collected?)

4. Do I believe that there is a population for whom the claim is assumed to be valid (e.g., who lives in Moose Jaw, what are the boundaries of this population).

You might choose to reject your friend's claim about the affluence of Moose Jaw because you are not satisfied with the answers to one or more of those questions. That is the point of using statistics in the social sciences: to provide a framework for assessing claims in a systematic manner. People do lie with statistics, but that makes it *more* important for you to understand statistics, so you can identify how the claim was made and decide whether you agree with it. Statistics is just a set of tools and concepts that help you do what you already do countless times every day.

Finally, statistics is just as hard to teach as it is to learn. Students aren't in class because they want to be there, and teaching students who would rather be just about anywhere else is difficult. A quick check of www.ratemyprofessor.com shows that statistics professors often receive the harshest criticisms. For this reason, I believe that many professors don't bother trying to make the subject matter more bearable because they don't think that they can get students to like the class no matter what they do.

So, to liven things up, I have used the most interesting and/or relevant examples I could find. Canadian introductory statistics courses are often hurt by the use of US texts, which contain examples that Canadian students can't always relate to. I have tried to rely exclusively on Canadian examples and content, with the hope that you will find the examples relevant.

Each chapter starts with a list of its objectives. Words that you may find unfamiliar will be **highlighted** throughout the text. You can find the definition of each highlighted word in the glossary of statistical terms at the back of the book. If you still find the material difficult and require further help, there are several soothing reads on statistics, including *Statistics Without Tears* (Rowntree, 2000) and *Statistics for the Terrified* (Kranzler and Moursund, 1999). However, as long as you read this text and listen to your professor's lectures, I hope you won't need those resources.

This book adopts a "knowledge-through-discovery" approach. Instead of studying abstract lessons on statistics with little or no application, you will apply what you learn in each chapter with laboratory exercises using Canadian data sets (such as the 1881 Census of Canada, the Canadian Community and Health Survey, or one of the General Social Surveys). I hope that they will help you see the links between what you learn in the classroom and what you do in the lab. That will close the gap between the theory of statistics and its practice.

LEARNING TO THINK STATISTICALLY

Using statistics as a toolkit to make claims about the world has only become common practice in the last 200 years or so. In 1975, Ian Hacking, a prominent Canadian philosopher of science, published an influential book titled *The Emergence of Probability* (Hacking, 1975). Hacking claims that one of the defining characteristics of the nineteenth century was that people began to see the world less in terms of indeterminism and chance, and more in terms of laws and **probabilities**. One of the consequences of this was what Hacking refers to as the onset of an "avalanche of printed numbers." In fewer than 20 years (from around 1820 to 1840), there was "an exponential increase in the number of numbers being published" (186). The newfound popularity of numbers caused a shift in the public's view, and understanding, of the world.

Hacking documented the change from not collecting statistics to collecting them, and, more important, the change in the nature of knowledge. He showed that the adoption of statistical methodology changed the dominant way of thinking, learning, and, ultimately, knowing about the world.

Learning statistics is thus as much about learning a new way of thinking as it is about introducing new subject matter.

UNDERSTANDING THE WORLD WITH NUMBERS

Since that "avalanche" began roughly 200 years ago, the topics of statistical inquiry have ranged widely. Numbers and statistics form the basis for many of our understandings: aging, Americanization, apartheid, apple growth patterns, astronomy . . . you name it. Although the focus here is on social statistics, or those that are used to understand the behaviours and characteristics of people, the sheer diversity of topics that statistics are used to study shows that the world can be understood from within the framework of stats.

Consider a study of cellular phone usage among teenage girls (Campbell, 2006). Teenagers in North America crave style, friendship, and individuality. Companies that sell cell phones are well aware of this, and present their product to teens as a way to *enhance* individuality, while at the same time promoting conformity to the norms of teens' peer groups. Most teenagers can choose whether or not to have a cell phone, and they see their choice as an act of individuality (Campbell, 2006). They and many of their friends have already chosen to have a cell phone—in 2003, the year the study data were collected, roughly half of all teens had a cell phone (that number is certainly higher now). Social scientists try to explain this sort of social behaviour. Statistics may or may not help.

IF I DON'T EVER PLAN TO USE STATISTICS IN MY CAREER, SHOULD I STILL LEARN ABOUT THEM?

Of course you should! Within your discipline, there are conversations occurring between several communities. Some of them will assume that you have a certain level of statistical competency. To understand those discussions you need to be at least somewhat statistically savvy.

I also have a philosophical reason for believing that everyone should learn some statistics. Often there are internal divisions within Canadian social science departments—those who don't use statistics in their research do not engage with those who do use statistics (and vice versa). This division hurts all of us within the academic community. It stymies the intellectual cross-pollination that occurs when different methodological allegiances are combined. To prevent these "disciplinary silos" from forming, and get people with different methodological beliefs to read each other's work, it's important to understand how and what all members of your discipline think. It is equally important, and beneficial, to learn how more theoretically oriented and qualitative researchers think.

ORGANIZATION OF THE BOOK

The next chapter looks at some of the mathematical concepts you'll need to learn statistics. Many of these are basic, but you should still take the time to review them. They are the building blocks for the course, and they will help you decode and demystify the subsequent chapters. The topics of Chapter 2 (logarithms, exponents, order of operations, fractions, and decimals) are all commonly used in statistics, and it is crucial for you to become familiar with them.

We'll look at univariate (one variable) statistics in Chapter 3, probability in Chapter 4, and the Gaussian or normal curve in Chapter 5. The methods discussed in Chapter 3 (frequencies, percentiles, etc.) are used to give vital information about a particular variable, including the arithmetic average (mean), the median, or the mode. This information can be an end in itself—for example, it is useful to tell people that the median total income of individuals in Canada in 2004 was $24,400 (Statistics Canada, 2006). Once we begin to think in terms of distributions, as we do in Chapters 5 through 7, we begin to think about further analysis of data.

Assessing variable distribution allows us to determine if we can extend conclusions from a sample to an entire population. Statistics can explain trends in certain populations—such as the population of Kelowna, Bathurst, or all of Canada—but because it's almost impossible to talk to everyone in a population, we often only use data on a portion of the population. Sometimes this results in a "mismatch" between the group being used in analysis (the sample) and the entire population. This is known as **sampling error**. There will almost always be some sampling error, but there are ways to reduce it. These strategies will form the basis for Chapter 8. Chapter 9 will focus on techniques that can help to determine how closely a sample resembles the population it was drawn from. It will also cover the different ways to extract a sample from a population.

EVERYDAY STATISTICS

Canadian Census

In 2010, the Government of Canada announced that it would no longer issue the long-form version of the 2011 census. One of the biggest concerns, which subsequently led to the resignation of Chief Statistician Munir Sheikh, was that the government maintained that the data from a voluntary survey would not be of poorer quality than a mandatory census. In other words, the claim was that there would be no difference in sampling error.

. . . .

Q: Do you agree with this statement? Can you think of why sampling error would differ between a voluntary and mandatory survey?

Once you understand how to describe single variables, the next logical step is to begin identifying relationships between variables. This is known as hypothesizing relationships, and in Part Two of this book we'll look at how to cast and test hypotheses with statistics. You probably already hypothesize and test for the existence of relationships all the time, but in Chapter 10 we'll begin to look at how to do this a little more systematically.

Chapter 10 also covers methods to test for relationships between two variables (such as gender and income, skin colour and alcohol consumption, rural/urban living and pickup truck ownership). These methods are useful, because they allow you to establish the existence of relationships. They also allow you to quantify the magnitude and direction of those relationships—Canadian men, on average, earn more money than Canadian women do, but how much more? White people consume more bottles of beer in a year than East Asian people do, but how many more?

Since we're almost always dealing with samples, we need the skills to determine whether the difference between two groups is statistically significant—that is, does it accurately depict the entire population? Assessing statistical significance allows you to determine whether the differences you observe in your samples are due to peculiarities in the data (such as sampling error), or if you could expect to find similar differences in the total population. This will be the focus of Chapters 10 through 15.

Chapter 16 will cover techniques for moving beyond studying two variables, and focus on multivariate statistics. Multivariate statistics are often superior to bivariate statistics because they allow you to control for the effect of one or more other variables. For example, you could use multivariate statistics to determine if men make a higher average wage than women because of differences in their educations. On average, people with a higher level of education earn more money, so maybe men earn more than women because they go to school longer or get more advanced degrees (they don't). Alternatively, maybe people who live in the country are more likely to own pickup trucks because many of them are farmers. Since pickup trucks are useful on farms, perhaps the rural/urban difference in vehicle choice disappears when we "control" for occupation choice (it doesn't). Chapter 16 will also look at multivariate techniques for continuous outcomes, allowing us to answer questions like: are gender pay differentials due to an education gap across genders?

Chapter 17 will focus on qualitative or binary outcome variables, that is, variables with only two possible answers. An example of a binary variable would be whether a person owns a pickup truck or not. Chapter 18 discusses techniques for diagnosing regression results, which compare many variables at once. Finally, Chapter 19 covers techniques for dealing with missing data, a situation that occurs when an individual is unable or unwilling to provide you with some, or all, of the information you request in a survey.

After you have worked through these chapters, the statistics that you have learned will allow you to perform rudimentary analyses on most data sets and understand much of what is published in the journals of your discipline. Since there is a lot to absorb, each chapter except this one has a series of practice questions and exercises, both at the end and scattered throughout each chapter. In addition to the main body of the text, there are a series of appendices. These are critical to understanding the information in several chapters.

This second edition includes several improvements on the first edition. New text boxes labelled "Theory in Practice" appear, intended to outline the theory behind the exercises: why are you being asked to complete a series of exercises, and how do they relate to the subject of each chapter? Also new to the second edition are "Everyday Statistics" activities taken from statistical interpretations in newspapers, magazines, and government reports. There are also more practice questions and exercises, and countless other improvements made possible by the comments and helpful suggestions I've received since writing the first edition.

GLOSSARY TERMS

Probabilities (p. 5)   Sampling error (p. 6)

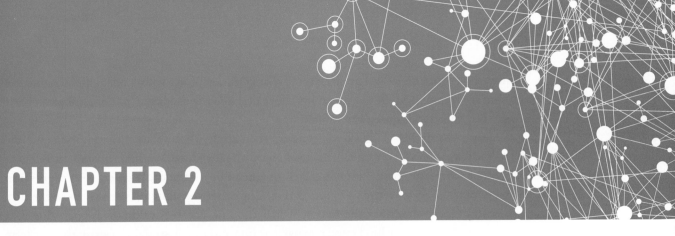

CHAPTER 2

How Much Math Do I Need to Learn Statistics?

LEARNING OBJECTIVES

To learn statistics you will need some background knowledge. Luckily, most of you have already been exposed to in your other courses the information you will need. In this chapter, we'll cover:

- the order of operations;
- fractions, decimals, and logarithms.

BEDMAS AND THE ORDER OF OPERATIONS

Mathematics is the foundation of statistics and has its own internal logic that is not always intuitive; why, for example, must you multiply before you add? One of the most basic of all mathematical principles is the **order of operations**. We'll review it briefly here, because it will provide a roadmap for solving problems and equations.

For example, the following equation predicts the average number of hours per month that a teenager in Canada spends at the mall:

# of hours at mall = 0.2 * # of friends + (0.01 * disposable income − 4 * age) − 0.2
$$* \text{ \# of security guards at mall} + 2 \qquad (1)$$

At first, this equation seems daunting, but it can be reduced to something much simpler—the slope y-intercept form:

$$Y = ax + b \qquad (2)$$

I hope this equation looks familiar; you probably learned it in high school as an introduction to linear algebra. Both of the equations above describe the characteristics of a trend. In basic statistics, this trend is usually a straight line.

First, let's discuss the second equation, then apply what we learn to the first equation. Typically, a and b are constants whose value you already know. The first constant, b, refers to the value where the trend line (also called the **line of best fit** or the **least-squares regression** line) crosses the y-axis when x is set to zero. The other constant, a, is the slope of the line, meaning that it describes the rate at which the line goes up or down as the value of x increases. The relationship between equations one and two is straightforward; the last term in both (the number "2" in equation one and the "b" in equation two) represents the same thing: the value of Y (our outcome of interest) when x is set to zero (meaning that a is multiplied by zero). You can see the proof for this if you imagine that in the second equation x is equal to zero. No matter what the value of a is, the product of $a * x$ is zero; therefore Y would equal zero.

Let's apply these principles to equation two. The value of b is 2 (it's the last term in equation one), and in equation two, ax corresponds to everything else on the right side of equation one (0.2 * # of friends + [0.01 * disposable income − age * 4] − 0.2 * # of security guards at mall); a is replaced by four known values (0.2, 0.01, 4, and 0.2) to collectively become the slope term; "# of friends," "disposable income," "age," and "# of security guards at mall" represent x. The big difference between equations one and two is that the slope terms in equation one are expressed by a single term in equation two. Finally, Y in equation two is equal to what you are interested in predicting in equation one: the number of hours at the mall.

The goal of both statistics and linear algebra is often just to simplify equations as much as possible to derive values of interest—that is, points on the line for individuals that you want to know something about. In other words, you seek a unique solution for Y (# of hours at mall) and try to use factors that you think will help you do this (# of friends, disposable income, age/4, and # of security guards at mall). These variables are related to one another and can be found in equations trying to express the relationship. To ensure that these equations are calculated properly, you need to be familiar with the order of operations.

To solve the equations, you will need to use BEDMAS, an acronym that tells you what order to perform each operation in an equation. BEDMAS stands for Brackets, Exponents, Division, Multiplication, Addition, and Subtraction. For multiplication and division, the order in which you solve the problem doesn't matter. The same applies for addition and subtraction, so BEDMAS could just as easily be BEMDAS, BEMDSA, BEDMSA, etc. It is still important to remember that multiplication and division must be done before addition and subtraction. To illustrate, let's solve equation one for a person who has three friends, makes $10,000 per year, is 20-years-old, and is at a mall that has 25 security guards.

Following BEDMAS, we know that the first part of the equation to solve is the portion in brackets (0.01 * disposable income − age * 4). Within these brackets, there are two multiplication terms (0.01 * disposable income, and age * 4), and a subtraction term (disposable income − age). Using BEDMAS again, we know that the first problem to solve in the brackets is the multiplication. Once you've solved for disposable income and age, you can do the subtraction.

Now that you've solved everything in the brackets, if there was an exponent (the "E" in BEDMAS), you would need to calculate that. At this point, we're going to ignore exponents. Substituting our known values for the unknowns, the right-hand side of the original equation:

$$0.2 * \text{\# of friends} + (0.01 * \text{disposable income} - 4 * \text{age}) - 0.2 * \text{\# of security guards at mall} + 2$$

becomes:

$$0.2 * 3 + (0.01 * 10{,}000 - 20 * 4) - 0.2 * 25 + 2$$

then:

$$0.6 + (100 - 80) - 5 + 2$$

and finally:

$$0.6 + 20 - 3 = \textbf{17.6 hours per month}$$

This equation predicts that a person with the observed characteristics (three friends, income of $10,000 per year, age 20, at a mall that has 25 security guards) will spend 17.6 hours per month at a mall.

If we believe that our equation does a good job estimating our outcome of interest, we could use it to predict the number of hours for a 45-year-old earning $50,000 at the West Edmonton Mall, a 100-year-old who earns $5,000 per year at Square One, a five-year-old at Scotia Square Mall . . . just about anyone. We'll learn more about how to do this in later chapters.

EVERYDAY STATISTICS

An Order of Operations by Any Other Name . . .

In the United States, the order of operations is often abbreviated as PEMDAS, which stands for parentheses, exponents, multiplication, division, addition, and subtraction. In the United Kingdom, BODMAS is often the acronym used for the order of operations, which stands for brackets, orders, division, multiplication, addition, and subtraction. Although these differ from the ordering of BEDMAS in Canada, all of the variations in the order of operations mean the same thing.

FRACTIONS AND DECIMALS

In the example, we had to use decimals to find the predicted value. The product of the parts of the equation that involved decimals (the constant for number of friends, and number of security guards) is not usually a round number—that is, it is a non-integer. To use non-integers you have to be comfortable with fractions and decimals. You should note that decimals and fractions are just different ways of stating the same thing. For example, the fraction ¼ is equal to 0.25. You'll probably prefer to work with decimals because they're easier to use in these equations.

EXPONENTS

To successfully use statistics, you also need to understand exponents. They are typically used to simplify calculations, and take the following form: X^m, where m (the exponent) stands for how many times X is being multiplied by itself. The exponent always appears in the top right-hand corner. The larger character, X, is called the base. Using exponents is also called "raising to a power," where the exponent is the "power." It would not be uncommon to hear X^m referred to as "X raised to the power of m," or "X raised to the mth power." To illustrate, if $m = 3$, then $X * X * X$ would be represented as X^3.

If you're working with two or more exponents with identical bases, and you need to multiply them, you can add the exponents together. Rather than relying extensively on multiplication, you can rely more heavily on addition. For example, $X^a * X^b$ is the same as X^{a+b}. This can only be done when the bases are the same. $X^a * Y^b$ is not the same as XY^{a+b}.

The **inverse function** of an exponent is the root: $2^2 = 4$, then $\sqrt{4} = 2$.

LOGARITHMS

A logarithm is a special form of exponent, where the base is either 10 or 2.718 (the transcendental number). Transcendental numbers are not algebraic numbers nor are they numbers that are expressed in any form of fraction, therefore they can also be considered irrational numbers. When the base is 10, we're dealing with common logarithms, whereas a base of 2.718 brings us to natural logarithms, which is what we will use in this text. As an example, let's look at the logarithm of 1,000. Usually, in mathematics, if the base is not stated, it is assumed to be 10, so it could be expressed as $\log 1000 = 3$ or $\log_{10} 1000 = 3$. In this example, the logarithm is a way of stating that when 10 is the base it must be multiplied by itself 3 times (10^3) to obtain the product of 1,000.

For now, you only have to remember that, just as the inverse function of an exponent is the root, the inverse of a log is the base. We'll return to these in Chapter 17 when we discuss logistic regression.

BOX 2.1

Logarithms: History of a Term

Scottish Baron John Napier (1550–1617), a prominent politician and Protestant advocate (Hald, 1990), introduced logarithms in 1614. Logarithms were a hugely significant advance in arithmetic: they provided the tools for scientific progress in a number of fields. Logarithms make calculations much simpler and faster. Logarithmic identities and derivatives allow complex operations to be simplified, and aid in integration and differential calculations. They are also useful for surveying, navigation, astronomy, and anything else requiring complex calculations.

For logarithms to be useful, one needs *logarithmic tables*, huge reference tomes that contain logarithms for lists of whole numbers. Napier and Henry Briggs (1561–1630), a math professor at Oxford, developed base 10 logarithms. Napier spent 20 years constructing logarithmic tables, as did Briggs, who eventually published the *Arithmetica Logarithmica* (1624), which includes the logarithms of the natural numbers from 1 to 20,000 and from 90,000 to 100,000 to 14 decimal places (Hald, 1990: 17). Adriaan Vlacq (1600–1667) was a Dutch mathematician who also contributed to these tables, occupying himself with the logarithms for numbers 20,000 to 90,000, completing Briggs's tables.

Consider that Briggs began his *Arithmetica Logarithmica* in 1617, after publishing his first table of logarithms, then worked out 30,000 cases over the next seven years. That amounts to just over 11 per day, every day, from the time he was 56 to the time he was 63!

LEVELS OF MEASUREMENT

When looking at the world statistically, it is useful to think of information as falling into four categories, or **levels of measurement**. These categories are nominal, ordinal, interval, and ratio. The primary distinction between the levels stems from the relationship that exists between the different possible values of the variable. For example, take the numbers on the jerseys of the BC Lions. The Lions have retired the jersey numbers of Jamie Taras (#60) and Jim Young (#30). You can't use the jersey numbers to argue that Taras was twice as good a player as Young. In fact, you can't use the numbers for any purpose other than identification. It is not possible to rank players or judge playing ability by looking at jersey numbers alone. (Although you could assert that players who wear #13 are likely to be less superstitious than average.) Variables with those characteristics are called **nominal**—that is, the numbers are really only names of things. With nominal data, it isn't possible to rank subjects based on value, or to usefully measure the distances between response categories. For statistical purposes, nominal variables, such as religion, social insurance number, or hair colour, are used to distinguish among respondents.

The next level of measurement is **ordinal**: data that can be placed into an order. A good example of this is the order that students finish in a foot race. If you knew how a person placed, you would be able to assess how well they did relative to other students, but you would *not* be able to assess the differences in their athletic skill. The first-place student could have finished a second ahead of the last-place student, or a month ahead. Ordinal variables can be ranked, but not the exact distance or difference between the values of the variable. Without knowing exactly how long a person took to complete the race, you can't accurately compare the runners' athletic ability.

Another example of ordinal data: when you respond to a telephone survey on the degree to which you agree, for example, that *Survivor* is the best television show ever, you might encounter a scale from 1 (strongly disagree) to 5 (strongly agree). This is an ordinal-level question (the intermediate scores would represent more moderate levels of agreement or disagreement). We know that there is a difference in the level of agreement between "strongly agree" and "strongly disagree," but we cannot accurately measure this distance.

Interval data can be organized into an order and can be added or subtracted but not multiplied or divided. Interval data cannot be multiplied or divided because, although there are equal distances or intervals between a pair of values, you cannot say that a value of four is twice as much of what happens to be measured than a value of two. Examples of interval data are counts, such as the number of Conservative votes or the number of chapters read by students before an exam. Temperatures in Celsius are also interval data, because the zero point is statistically arbitrary. If the temperature is zero degrees, it does not make sense to say that there is no temperature. When measuring temperature in Celsius, zero has the same qualitative meaning that one does. Interval levels of measurement are much less common than those at the ratio level.

With **ratio** data, it is possible to rank individuals and to accurately measure the distance between them. You can add, subtract, multiply, or divide ratio data. In ratio data, zero means that there is none of what you are measuring. Ratio data can be in fractions or decimals—they don't have set intervals, like some kinds of interval data. In the racing example above, a variable revealing the time it took to complete the race contains this information. Before a race begins, the stop watch is set to zero because no time has yet passed in the race. The measurement of how long it took a competitor to win the race can be considered a ratio measure because the zero has statistical meaning. With ordinal data, it is not possible to measure how close the first- and second-place contestants were when they finished. Knowing the time of completion, however, allows us to not only identify the first- and second-place finishers, but to determine how big the gap between them was. As with the other levels of measurement, examples of ratio data abound: age, income, body temperature, airfare ticket prices . . . the list of ratio variables is almost endless. See Table 2.1 for a chart showing the different levels of measurement.

TABLE 2.1 | Descriptions of Levels of Measurement and Examples

Level of measurement	Description	Example
Nominal	Identifies observations but does not allow them to be ranked or the difference between observations to be calculated	How many marathon runners are from each country?
Ordinal	Provides information about how each observation is ranked	Who came in first, second, and third place in the marathon?
Interval	Allows for the difference between observations to be measured but the value of zero has no qualitative difference when compared to the value of one	On a scale from one (very unhappy) to five (very happy), how did each competitor feel as they crossed the finish line?
Ratio	Has a meaningful zero value and allows for the exact difference between observations to be measured	How much time did it take to cross the finish line?

WHEN FOUR LEVELS OF MEASUREMENT BECOME THREE . . . OR EVEN TWO

Many believe that maintaining the four levels of distinction is excessive. Few people see any purpose in maintaining the distinction between interval and ratio levels, so these variables are often collapsed, leaving nominal, ordinal, and interval/ratio variables.

Others collapse the levels even further, only making the distinction between categorical and continuous variables. Categorical variables include the nominal level of measurement, and continuous variables include interval and ratio levels of measurement. Ordinal variables can be considered either categorical or continuous, depending on the situation (often ordinal variables with two or three levels are considered to be categorical, whereas those with greater than three values are continuous, although this generalization can be problematic). To help you get a better sense of how this works, consider Table 2.2.

The motivation, and justification, for doing this is largely procedural. For most statistical techniques, the type of analysis used depends on the data available. We'll discuss these distinctions more when we get down to doing some analysis.

TABLE 2.2	**Levels of Measurement and Their Classifications**		
Level of measurement	**Can you rank response categories?**	**Can you measure distances between response categories?**	**How else might this variable be described?**
Nominal	No	No	Categorical
Ordinal	Yes	No	Categorical, Continuous
Interval	Yes	Yes	Continuous, Interval/Ratio
Ratio	Yes	Yes	Continuous, Interval/Ratio

GLOSSARY TERMS

Interval — level of measurement (p. 14)

Least squares regression line (p. 10)

Levels of measurement (p. 13)

Nominal — level of measurement (p. 13)

Order of operations (p. 9)

Ordinal — level of measurement (p. 13)

Ratio — level of measurement (p. 14)

PRACTICE QUESTIONS

Please replace the question marks below with the appropriate answers:

1. 10 + 15 = ?

2. 10 + 15 − 5 = ?

3. $10 - (-2) = ?$

4. $(10 + 15) - 5 = ?$

5. $(10 - 15) - 2 = ?$

6. $10 * 15 = ?$

7. $10 * 15 - 5 = ?$

8. $10 * (15 - 5) = ?$

9. $10 * 15 - 15/5 = ?$

10. $10/5 * 15 - 5 = ?$

11. $(X * Y)^a + b = X^? * Y^? + ?$

12. $(X^a)(X^b) = X?$

13. $\sqrt{x} = x^?$

14. If $\ln 5 = 1.61$, then $e^{1.61} = ?$

Identify the levels of measurement (nominal, ordinal, interval, or ratio) for the following:

15. Percentage scores on a math exam.

16. Letter grades on a math exam.

17. Flavours of ice cream.

18. Fitness training levels on an exercise machine classified as Easy, Difficult, or Impossible.

19. Ethnic origins.

20. Political parties.

21. Commuting distances to school in kilometres.

22. Years between important historical events.

23. Age (in years).

24. Amount of money in your savings accounts.

25. Temperature on the moon, measured in degrees Celsius.

Answers to the practice questions for Chapter 2 can be found on page S-1.

CHAPTER 3

Univariate Statistics

FREQUENCIES

In this course, you will learn how to make large, unwieldy sets of numbers more understandable, or intuitive, allowing for comparisons of data to be made. Part of your role as a social statistician is to do exactly this, to be a numerical translator. It is your job to turn numbers that only a few people can understand into something that's easy to explain to anyone.

One of the most basic translation tools is the **frequency** table. Typically used for nominal or ordinal data, frequencies tell us the number of times an item, or a response category, comes up in a sample. If, for example, we wanted to know how many males and females there are in Canada, a good way to present this information would be in the form of a frequency table such as Table 3.1 on the next page.

There are five columns of information in the table. The first, labelled "Sex," is the name of the variable: the sex of the respondent. Since "Sex" is a nominal variable, the order in which the response categories are presented is arbitrary (the information for males could appear before females, although it is good practice to present your data in alphabetical order). The next column provides the frequencies for each of the categories. Now we know that as of 16 May 2006 (the census reference date), there were 16,136,930 females and 15,475,970 males living in Canada. As the column "%" tells us, this translates into 51.05 per cent of the Canadian population being female and 48.95 per cent being male. "Cumulative frequency" is a running total of the frequency of observations in each category (thus, the 31,612,895 beside male equals the

TABLE 3.1	Number of Males and Females in the Canadian Population, 2006 Census of Canada			
Sex	**Frequency**	**%**	**Cumulative frequency**	**Cumulative %**
Female	16,136,930	51.05	16,136,930	51.05
Male	15,475,970	48.95	31,612,895	100.00

Source: 2006 Census of Canada
Note: Includes all Canadian citizens and landed immigrants who have a usual place of residence in Canada, or who are abroad either on a military base or attached to a diplomatic mission.

total number of males *and* females), and "Cumulative %" tells us the same about the percentage of observations in each category (since everyone is either male or female in the census, the total beside male is 100 per cent).

There are several ways to present the same data. In Figures 3.1 and 3.2, bar charts are used instead of numbers. Many people prefer that format because it provides a visual aid that can be quickly and easily understood. Figure 3.1 shows the number of observations in each category.

Figure 3.2 shows the percentage of observations in each category. As you can see, the horizontal, or ***x*-axis**, is the same for both graphs (sex of respondent), as is the height of the bars. The only real difference between the two charts is that Figure 3.1 has the number of observations in each category as the unit for the vertical or ***y*-axis**, and Figure 3.2 has the per cent of total population as the *y*-axis.

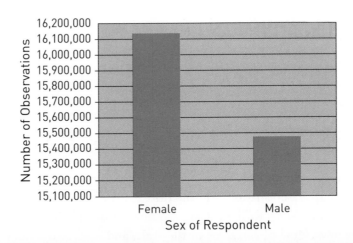

FIGURE 3.1 | Bar Chart of the Number of Males and Females in the Canadian Population, 2006 Census of Canada

Source: 2006 Census of Canada
Note: Includes all Canadian citizens and landed immigrants who have a usual place of residence in Canada, or who are abroad either on a military base or attached to a diplomatic mission.

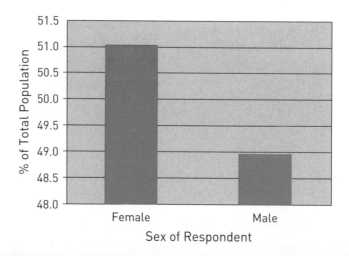

FIGURE 3.2 | Bar Chart of the Percentage of Males and Females in the Canadian Population, 2006 Census of Canada

Source: 2006 Census of Canada
Note: Includes all Canadian citizens and landed immigrants who have a usual place of residence in Canada, or who are abroad either on a military base or attached to a diplomatic mission.

In both of the charts it appears as though females outnumber males because the bar that corresponds with the frequency, or percentage, of women is almost three times higher than the bar for males. This is deceptive. A more representative chart would begin the *y*-axis at zero, or zero per cent.

RULES FOR CREATING BAR CHARTS

You need to know a few things about using bar charts.

First, the response categories should always appear on the *x*-axis, and the frequencies (whether stated as a percentage or as the number of observations) should always be on the *y*-axis.

Second, the title should only describe the output and the data sets; it should not impose an interpretation of the data. **Axis titles** should be brief and non-repetitive. For example, it would not be necessary to use "sex of respondent in the Canadian census" as the *x*-axis for Figure 3.2, because that information is in the title of the chart. **Axis scales** should present data as efficiently as possible, without using too many numbers. In Figure 3.1, it would be acceptable to remove some of the zeros in the scale, and express the numbers in units of 10,000, 100,000, or even 1,000,000—so the first number would be 14,300, then 1,430, then 14.3, respectively. When the numbers on the *y*-axis are smaller, they become easier to interpret. However, you will need to do some mental math to interpret the data using either the full or the reduced number.

Third, the numbers should be listed in equal increments, so that the scale is consistent for each axis. For example, a *y*-axis should never be 0, 2, 4, 20, 100, 10,000, etc. If you see a chart that looks like that, be suspicious! **Legends** often appear alongside bar charts and are always

EVERYDAY STATISTICS

History of the Bar Chart

William Playfair first developed the bar chart in his 1786 book *The Commercial and Political Atlas*. In this book, Playfair was interested in graphing the imports and exports from different countries over a period of several years. Accordingly, the first bar chart was a representation of Scotland's imports and exports to and from several different countries in 1781.

. . . .

Q: Why do you think that a bar chart would be helpful to graph Playfair's observations?

useful. In Figures 3.1 and 3.2, the nominal variable has only two categories, and the data were simple enough that a legend was not necessary. Later examples will use legends to help clarify the data.

Fourth, list the data source, usually in a smaller font, below the chart. Readers will need to know the source of the numbers if they want to replicate the results. If there are notes about your sample, include those too. Notice the notes regarding the section of the population included in the sample at the bottom of Figures 3.1 and 3.2.

Data can also be presented in a pie chart, as in Figure 3.3. The rules for bar charts also apply to pie charts. Legends are helpful, titles should be brief and descriptive, and data sources should be listed beneath the figure.

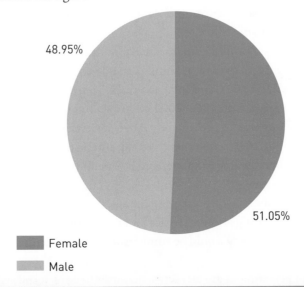

48.95%

51.05%

■ Female
■ Male

FIGURE 3.3 | Pie Chart of the Percentage of Males and Females in the Canadian Population, 2006 Census of Canada

Source: 2006 Census of Canada
Note: Includes all Canadian citizens and landed immigrants who have a usual place of residence in Canada, or who are abroad either on a military base or attached to a diplomatic mission.

TRANSLATING FREQUENCIES

Frequencies can often be misleading and/or difficult to work with. The numbers are often large and difficult to simplify. Presenting data in percentages, as in Figures 3.2 and 3.3, is one method of simplifying frequencies. Percentages are a good way to translate simple statistics because it's easier to remember that 51.05 per cent of all Canadians are female than it is to recall the number 16,136,930.

RATES AND RATIOS

Two other numerical translation tools are **rates** and **ratios**. A ratio is the number of observations in one category compared to the number of observations in another category. For example, we could report the 2006 census data as a ratio and say that there are 16,136,930 women for every 15,475,970 men in Canada but we would probably want to reduce these numbers to make them easier to digest. That can be done by expressing the numbers as fractions and cancelling out common factors in the numerator and denominator. By dividing the number of men and of women by 100,000, 155 can replace 15,475,970 and 161 can be substituted for 16,136,930 (16,136,930/100,000 ≈ 161; 15,475,970/100,000 ≈ 155). Thus, we would have a ratio of 161:155.

Rates are closely related to ratios, but the denominator is usually a round number (1,000, 100,000, etc.) or an intuitive number (kilometres per hour, heartbeats per minute, GDP per capita, etc.). For example, we could say that there are approximately 511 women for every 1,000 Canadians. Ratios can be used to compare categorical and continuous data, while rates are usually used to present continuous data. Categorical data allow for responses to be sorted into categories but do not allow for a measurement of difference between responses or a ranking as continuous data would. Rates are one of the most common methods in the social sciences for presenting univariate data; examples include crime rates, death rates, birth rates, fertility rates, unemployment rates, and inflation rates. To further illustrate rates, look at the Canadian crime rate for the period 1962–2002, as shown in Figure 3.4.

In 1962, the crime rate was approximately 2,800 for every 100,000 people. It continued to inch upward until about 1993, when there was a dramatic reversal. As of 2002, the rate was still declining and stood just below 8,000 per 100,000 people, about three times as high as in 1962.

Rates are a more elegant way of presenting data because they use the same denominator (100,000 in this case). Presenting crime statistics (or birth statistics, death statistics, unemployment statistics, etc.) as a frequency would be cumbersome, because a more detailed explanation would be necessary.

Rates, ratios, and percentages are attractive because they are **standardized**. That is, they use the same unit of measurement, and can be compared across countries, over time, or any other way you choose. When using rates, ensure that the denominator is the same across

Rate per 100,000 Population

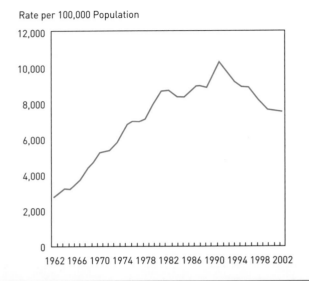

FIGURE 3.4 | Crime Rate, 1962 to 2002

Source: 2002 *Juristat* (Canadian Centre for Justice Statistics, 2003)

comparison groups (i.e., make sure that all ratios that you compare are based on the same "per *X* population"). With percentages that are already done for you, the denominator is always 100.

PERCENTILES

The *Canadian Oxford Dictionary* defines percentile as "one of 99 values of a variable dividing a population into 100 equal groups as regards the value of that variable." You determine the percentiles by slicing your sample into 100 groups, making sure that each group has exactly the same number of people (the best you can, without slicing a person in half). If there were 30,000,000 people in Canada and we were sorting them by age, each group would have 300,000 people. Each of those groups would represent one percentile, and the age values used to delineate the 100 groups would form the cut-points of the percentile, the points at which each percentile is differentiated.

Returning to the 2006 census, the age value for the first percentile is zero because of all the babies who haven't had a birthday yet. Showing all 100 percentiles in a table makes for a very big, clumsy table, so you usually only show a few of them, as in Table 3.2. It is also common to show deciles (10, 20, . . .) or quartiles (25, 50, 75, and 100). Table 3.2 shows that age 19 is at the 25th percentile (or first quartile), meaning 25 per cent of the total population is below the age of 19. The 50th percentile (where the Canadian population is evenly divided in half), is at age 40.

TABLE 3.2 | The Age of the Canadian Population by Percentile Cut-Offs, 2006 Canada

Percentile	Value
1	0
25	19
50	40
75	54
100	85

Source: 2006 Census of Canada

The 50th percentile is the median, since half of the population is at or above 40, and half is below. The 75th percentile is those who are at, or over, the age of 54, and the 100th percentile cutoff is age 85. This number is lower than you might expect because Statistics Canada recodes all values above age 85 so that those who are 85 and those who are older are all labelled as being 85, to ensure confidentiality.

Here's an example of percentiles that you are very familiar with: test scores. If you scored 91 per cent on a test, you would know that you were 9 percentage points from 100, and 91 points from zero. This would give you an idea of how you did on the test. Let's suppose that lots of people did well on the test, and that 91 per cent was actually the score for the 50th percentile (or the median). You could be proud that you beat half of your classmates, but the other half would also have tied or beaten your score. Depending on the measure of central tendency (the average or typical score for those who wrote the test), your 91 per cent might only be average, not the exceptional grade that you thought it was. Percentiles rank you in relation to your peers, not just on a scale of 100 that doesn't relate you to anyone else. They are often used in standardized testing, such as the Scholastic Aptitude Test (SAT), the Law School Admission Test (LSAT), the Graduate Record Examination (GRE), the Medical College Admission Test (MCAT), or the American College Test (ACT).

GLOSSARY TERMS

Axis scales (p. 20)
Axis titles (p. 20)
Frequency (p. 18)
Legends (p. 21)
Rates (p. 22)

Ratios (p. 22)
Standardized (p. 23)
x-axis (p. 19)
y-axis (p. 19)

PRACTICE QUESTIONS

A. Jorge placed 113th out of 1,432 people in a national spelling bee by correctly spelling 37 of the 40 words he was given.
   1. What is the ratio of correct to incorrect responses?
   2. What is his score stated as a percentage?
   3. What is his rank in percentiles?

B. Ethel is conducting a telephone survey to determine the approximate number of people who are interested in lobbying the federal government about recent changes to the Canada Pension Plan. Over the course of a week, she calls 541 people. Of those people, she contacts 432 and identifies 112 individuals who are willing to participate in the lobbying effort.
   1. What is her contact rate per 1,000 people?
   2. What is her contact/non-contact ratio in lowest terms?
   3. What is her lobbying participation rate as a percentage, using only contacted individuals?

C. Charles, a woodchuck with ego problems, thinks that he can chuck more wood than any other woodchuck. But he is insecure and decides that he'll ask 30 of his closest wood-chuck friends if they agree. To his chagrin, he only reaches 22 of his friends, and only 5 agree with him. Although he didn't reach 8 of his woodchuck friends, he is certain that they'd agree that he's the best woodchucker out there. To celebrate his accomplishment, he decides to make a poster to hang on the wall of his dwelling, but doesn't know how to calculate any univariate statistics. Help Charles out by calculating (1) the number, (2) the percentage, and (3) using Charles' assumption, the ratio of woodchucks who think he is the king of all woodchucks.

D. As of August 2, 2010, at 5:35 pm EST, Canada's population was estimated to be 34,194,937 (http://www.statcan.gc.ca/ig-gi/pop-s-eng.htm). This number is subject to change from many sources, but most importantly it declines because of deaths and migration out of Canada, and increases because of births and migration into Canada. When these things are considered simultaneously, the country's growth rate is 1.283% per year. Demographers typically calculate population growth using the following equation:

$$\text{Population}_{tn} = \text{Population}_{t0} * (1 + GR)^{n}$$

Where:

Population_{tn} = Population at desired point in time (time n).
Population_{t0} = Starting Population

GR = Growth rate

n = The number of growth terms (often years)

This gives the total population after the number of years have elapsed. If you are interested in the growth component alone (expressed as a per cent), the corresponding equation would be $(1 + GR)^n$. Given this,

1. What will the population be in exactly one year?
2. What will it be in 10 years, assuming no change in growth rate?
3. Assuming the same growth rates over time, what was Canada's population exactly ten years ago?
4. How much time elapses between the addition of a new person? (Hint: it is less than an hour.)

Answers to the practice questions for Chapter 3 can be found on page S-2.

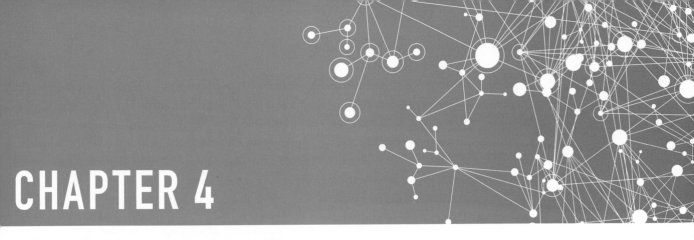

CHAPTER 4

Introduction to Probability

LEARNING OBJECTIVES

Learning statistics relies on a knowledge of basic probabilities. In Chapter 4, we'll cover:

- the law of large numbers;
- empirical and theoretical probabilities;
- discrete probabilities;
- mutually exclusive probabilities;
- non-mutually exclusive probabilities;
- the addition rule;
- the multiplication rule.

INTRODUCTION

A standard deck of cards has four suits (spades, hearts, diamonds, and clubs) and 13 cards in each suit (ace through king). Let's assume there are no jokers in the deck. If each card is equally likely to be drawn, is it possible to calculate the likelihood of drawing a particular card?

The answer is yes. Any time you identify how likely an event is to occur, what you're really doing is calculating a probability. A **probability** is a number between zero and one (or zero to 100 per cent, when stated as a percentage), where zero refers to an event that never occurs and one to an event that definitely occurs. The event can be anything imaginable, from a coin landing heads-up, to a car accident on the way home from work. It doesn't really matter. What does matter is that a calculable chance, or probability, can be attached to the competing outcomes.

The short answer to this question is that probabilities are central to both sampling distributions and hypothesis testing. Since we are typically working with a population subset, we use probabilities to determine the likelihood that the trends we see in our dataset (which usually isn't the entire population) would also be seen in our population of interest. For example, the census of Canada is based, roughly, on a 3 per cent sample of the entire Canadian population. Without probabilities, we'd have no way of knowing how closely the sample approximates all Canadians. In the next few chapters we'll investigate why this is the case. First, we'll start with a discussion of what probabilities are and how to calculate them. Then, we'll discuss the normal curve before moving on to how these things relate to one another.

This chapter will cover the basic types of probabilities, and identify some of the laws that make probabilities work in statistics.

SOME NECESSARY TERMINOLOGY

To discuss probabilities, you need to know the vocabulary. These concepts will be used throughout the text, so it is important to understand them.

Sample Space

A **sample space** contains all of the theoretically possible outcomes of an event. Each probability is a fraction of the sample space. The sum of the probabilities of all possible outcomes equals one. The probability of the occurrence of an event is one minus the probability that it won't occur.

If the probability of picking a green apple from a barrel containing 44 green apples and 56 red apples is 44/100, or 11/25, then the probability *of not* picking a green apple is equal to 1 – 11/25, or 14/25. When there are only two possible outcomes (picking a green apple or a red apple), 14/25 is also the probability of picking a red apple. The probability of picking a red apple plus the probability of picking a green apple is 14/25 + 11/25, or 25/25. If you pick an apple, you can be certain that it will either be green or red. That is why the sum of all probabilities of an outcome should always be one.

Random Variables

What makes a variable "random" is that the value is subject to variation from known or unknown sources. The value of a random variable is not predictable, strictly speaking, but the probability of certain values can often be calculated. A random variable has a value that is the result of a process or experiment, such as tossing a coin or splitting an atom. Like other types of variables, random variables can take on different values, but the entire sample space is usually already known.

Imagine a coin tossing experiment. Create a variable (let's call it X) for whether the coin will come up heads or tails. Since it was (1) created by a particular process or experiment (tossing a coin), (2) has a known sample space (heads and tails), and (3) it is not possible to predict outcomes perfectly (that is, whether a toss lands heads or tails), we know that we are dealing with a random variable.

Trials and Experiments

Discussions about probability, or statistics, are usually conducted in terms of trials and experiments. A trial is an individual exercise that, when taken alongside other exercises, will collectively form the data for the experiment. A trial is part of an experiment. Suppose you were calculating the probability of randomly selecting a person with a Ph.D. in your student union building. The exercise would form the experiment, and each person selected would count as a trial. If you did this 100 times, the point of the experiment would be to calculate the probability of randomly selecting a person with a Ph.D., and the results would include the data from the 100 trials.

The Law of Large Numbers

The **law of large numbers** states that if you repeat a random experiment (such as tossing a coin or rolling a die) many, many times, your outcomes will approach a level of "stability." Pretend that you have a coin and that you tossed it in the air 100 times. How many heads would you expect to get? In a 100-toss event, you wouldn't be able to determine that perfectly, but you could make a pretty good "guess." Let's say that you predicted the coin would turn up heads half the time.

One hundred is a lot of tosses. It's also a boring way to spend your time. The law of large numbers states that you'll probably turn up heads closer to half of the time tossing it 100 times than if you only tossed 10 times. The law also states that if you tossed it 100,000 times, you would get even closer to your predicted ratio. The more times you toss the coin, the closer you'll be to your calculated theoretical probability value of half heads. This is because empirical and theoretical probabilities, both discussed below, converge as the number of trials increases.

TYPES OF PROBABILITIES

There are numerous types of probabilities—so many that there are university courses dedicated just to that subject. We won't cover all of them. Instead, we'll focus on some of the more common types.

Empirical versus Theoretical Probabilities

There are two ways to calculate the probability of an event.

First, you can conduct an experiment, and use the results to calculate the probability. If, for example, you wanted to know the probability of drawing a spade from a full deck of well-shuffled cards, you could draw single cards over and over again, and use your results to calculate the probability of drawing a spade. If you conducted 100 draws, and pulled a spade 26 times, you could conclude that the probability of pulling a spade is equal to roughly 26/100, or 26 per cent. Since you are using real data, that number is known as an **empirical probability**.

Second, you can calculate a **theoretical probability** using your powers of deduction. Instead of conducting an experiment, you could determine the total number of spades in a deck (13) relative to the total number of cards (52). That would yield the theoretical probability of 13/52, or 25 per cent. This means that you should expect to pull a spade about 25 per cent of the time.

You can see that there is a difference in the results for the empirical and theoretical probabilities. This can be due to either a random or a non-random error in the empirical probability. An example of non-random error could be if the deck of cards happened to be missing a few cards, or contained more or less of a suit than you had initially believed. The probability would be affected because of the poor design of the experiment, which is not random. Perhaps the deck wasn't shuffled perfectly, or there weren't enough draws. If there were more trials (draws), the law of large numbers says that the empirical probability will converge with the theoretical probability.

For now, to make things simple, let's pretend that we always have a sample large enough to make the differences between empirical and theoretical probabilities negligible. We'll discuss what to do when sample size becomes an issue in Chapter 9 and beyond, but for now let's pretend that it doesn't exist.

Discrete Probabilities

A discrete probability has clearly defined, non-overlapping outcomes. These variables often have an equal probability of occurrence for each value. For example, the roll of a single die has six discrete possible outcomes (turning up as 1, 2, 3, 4, 5, or 6). We can assign equal probabilities to each outcome. In this case, the probability would be 1/6, the frequency of each outcome over the total possible number of outcomes.

Tossing a coin is another example of a discrete outcome. The coin will either land heads or tails, and if there is no reason to suspect that the coin will come up more often one way than the other, we can assign the probability of 1/2 to each of the outcomes. The outcomes are discrete because a coin that comes up heads cannot also come up tails.

In both examples, each outcome has an equal probability, but it isn't hard to imagine examples of where this isn't so. For example, if there is a 15 per cent chance of rain, we assign a probability of 0.15 to the chance of rain and a probability of 0.85 to no rain. Once again, the occurrence of rain is discrete because it either rains or it doesn't.

Discrete probabilities are easy to work with because of their intuitiveness. If all of the possible outcomes are known, the sum of probabilities will equal one (that is, at least one event in the sample space will occur). For example, the die-tossing scenario has six outcomes, each with a probability of 1/6. If we sum the values of our sample space, we get 1/6 + 1/6 + 1/6 + 1/6 + 1/6 + 1/6, which equals 6/6, or 1.

Even when probabilities are not equal, the sum is usually one. The chance of rain in the earlier example is 0.15 and the chance of no rain is 0.85, so the probability of either rain or no rain is 1 (0.15 + 0.85 = 1). State the probability as a percentage and it's 100 per cent.

In reality, the calculated probabilities never quite total one because of the possibility of unforeseen, very unlikely, events: a bird swoops down and catches your coin; the planet explodes

EVERYDAY STATISTICS

Probability and Car Insurance

Often, car insurance companies set premiums based on the probability that a customer will make a claim against their insurance. The perceived amount of risk that an individual poses is influenced by their age, their sex, the length of time they have had a licence, etc. Based on the probability obtained by the insurance company, a profitable rate is calculated to charge the customer.

. . . .

Q: What types of probabilities do you think insurance companies would use? Why?

before you can determine whether it rained; your friend gets tired of you rolling dice and throws them out the window before your experiment is over. These events are rare, but they do suggest the need at times to account for the unexpected. You might consider them the statistical analogs to your parents or guardians suggesting you wear clean underwear in case of an accident; the accident is unlikely and unforeseen, but the possibility exists nonetheless.

Discrete probabilities are also called simple probabilities, because they involve only one set of outcomes. In scenarios where more than one outcome is likely, calculating probabilities is more difficult.

The Probability of Unrelated Events

If one event does not affect the probability of another event, the events are **independent**. Suppose you're calculating the probabilities of two unrelated activities. An example would be rolling two sixes in a row with a six-sided die. The probability of rolling a single six would be equal to 1/6. But what about rolling two sixes in a row?

BOX 4.1

The Steps: Calculating a Discrete, Theoretical Probability

1. Identify the experiment of interest (coin tossing, card drawing, etc.), and be sure that the outcomes are mutually exclusive.
2. Determine the sample set, or the total number of possible outcomes. This will be the denominator of your probability calculations.
3. Determine the frequency of occurrence of your outcome of interest (a coin landing on heads, drawing a spade, etc.). This will be the numerator of your calculation.
4. Divide the numerator by the denominator to determine the discrete probability.
5. Convert the probability to a percentage by multiplying the number by 100 if you wish, or leave it as a decimal.

First, calculate the two discrete probabilities, p(A) and p(B). Then use the **multiplication rule of probabilities**, which states that observing two independent outcomes in succession is equal to the product of the probability of the two individual outcomes. In our example, we have two independent probabilities, p(A) and p(B), with respective probabilities of 1/6 and 1/6. Each of these refers to the independent probability of rolling a six, whereas multiplying the two together provides the probability of the two events occurring in succession. To identify the probability of rolling two successive sixes, we multiply these numbers together:

$$p(A \text{ and } B) = p(A) * p(B)$$
$$= 1/6 * 1/6$$
$$= 1/36$$
$$= 0.028$$

The equation yields 0.028, so there's about a 3 per cent (0.028 * 100 ≅ 3%) chance of rolling two sixes in a row.

The Probability of Related Events

In the example above, the events are independent because rolling a six on the first toss has no impact on the outcome of the second toss. This runs contrary to what you may think. If, for example, you are at a slot machine, hoping to hit a jackpot, you might continue feeding the machine because you believe that your ongoing losses must eventually affect the odds of getting a winner (you may even tell yourself that you are "due" for some good luck!). This isn't true, though, and is perhaps one of the greater misconceptions of gambling. The fact is, gambling outcomes are independent of one another.

If one event affects the probability of another event, then the events are **dependent**. Solving problems involving related events is more complicated because an intermediate calculation is required. Let's use a bag containing 40 marbles to illustrate. Ten of the marbles are green, 10 red, 10 yellow, and 10 blue. Suppose that we wanted to know the probability of pulling out a green marble, then pulling out a red marble. How would you figure it out?

Pulling out the red marble is only of interest when the first marble that's pulled out is green. Additionally, the number of marbles changes across experiments, from 40 to 39, thereby altering our probability calculations. Event A is pulling out a green marble first. Since 10 of the 40 marbles are green, p(A) = 10/40 = 1/4. If the first marble is green, what is the probability that the second marble will be red? Of the 39 remaining marbles, 10 are red, so p(B|A), or the probability of B given A, is 10/39. The probability of A then B is therefore equal to

$$p(A \text{ then } B) = p(A) * p(B|A) \text{ (this is read as the probability of } B \text{ given } A)$$
$$= 1/4 * 10/39$$
$$= 10/156$$
$$= 0.064$$

There's a 6.4 per cent chance of pulling a green and then a red marble in succession.

Dependent probabilities like this can be thought of as successive, because interest in the second outcome is contingent on the outcome of the first. If your first marble isn't green, you don't really care what happens next, because your first condition wasn't met.

Mutually Exclusive Probabilities That Are Interchangeable

To determine the probability of either of two mutually exclusive events occurring, you need to add the independent probabilities. If you wanted to know the probability of a die roll yielding *either* a one or a six, you would need to sum the two independent probability calculations:

$$p(one) = 1/6$$
$$p(six) = 1/6$$
$$p(one \text{ or } six) = 1/6 + 1/6 = 1/3$$

This is the **addition rule of probabilities** and is useful for calculating outcomes when you don't care what the outcome is. Suppose, for example, that you wanted to calculate the probability of getting either an A or a B in statistics, and that you didn't care which grade you received (perhaps your university requires you to keep at least a B average for you to retain your extremely prestigious scholarship). Let's suppose that the possible outcomes in the course are A, B, C, D, or F, then the probability would be calculated as

$$p(A) = 1/5$$
$$p(B) = 1/5$$
$$p(A \text{ or } B) = 1/5 + 1/5 = 2/5$$

Naturally, underpinning this calculation is the assumption that the grades assigned to you are completely random, even though we know they're not. Studying hard in the course tips the balance toward an increased probability of receiving As and Bs. So, 2/5 is an underestimation of what you'd receive in the course if you spent a lot of time working through the practice questions, the labs, and the exercises that your instructor provides.

Non–Mutually Exclusive, or Interchangeable, Probabilities

When two events can occur simultaneously, they are considered non-mutually exclusive, or interchangeable, probabilities. With non-mutually exclusive categories, there is a danger of double-counting. When that occurs, values that have been double-counted need to be subtracted. Of the probabilities that we'll cover, this is the most difficult type to grasp.

Consider the following scenario: In Dodge City in 1810—a town with a population of 200—there are 40 people who smoke but don't drink and 60 people who drink but don't smoke. There are also 98 people who both smoke and drink. What is the probability of randomly picking a smoker p(A), a drinker p(B), a smoker and a drinker p(A and B), or a smoker or a drinker p(A or B)?

BOX 4.2

How to Calculate Probabilities for Non-Mutually Exclusive Events

1. Calculate the probability of event A.
2. Calculate the probability of event B.
3. Subtract the number of duplications.
   The formula takes the form:

   $$p(A \text{ or } B) = p(A) + p(B) - p(A \text{ and } B)$$

4. If you prefer to see probabilities expressed as percentages, multiply the result by 100.

- For a smoker, the outcomes are independent of one another (a person either smokes or doesn't smoke). So, $p(A)$ is 138/200 (40 smokers, and 98 smokers and drinkers).
- For a drinker, the outcomes are once again independent, so $p(B)$ is equal to 158/200 (60 drinkers, and 98 smokers and drinkers).
- For a smoker and a drinker, we are already given the information in the description. It is $p(A \text{ and } B)$, which is equal to 98/200.
- For a smoker or a drinker, it becomes more complicated because of the risk of double-counting. In that case, we'd need to add $p(A)$ to $p(B)$, then subtract the duplicates $p(A \text{ and } B)$, yielding

$$
\begin{aligned}
p(A \text{ or } B) &= p(A) + p(B) - p(A \text{ and } B) \\
&= 138/200 + 158/200 - 98/200 \\
&= (138 + 158 - 98)/200 \\
&= 198/200 \\
&= 0.99
\end{aligned}
$$

These are also called cumulative probabilities, because the outcomes overlap to some extent.

Continuous Probabilities

There is another class of probabilities for variables that don't have exact values, such as time or height, called continuous probabilities. There are no discrete, exact measures of these variables—you can always measure them more precisely. There are an infinite number of possible values. Consequently, the probabilities are also continuous. Although it is possible to calculate continuous probabilities, these are beyond the focus of this text.

CONCLUSION

To check the plausibility of your calculations, keep in mind the following:

1. The probability of an event that cannot occur is zero.
2. The probability of an event that must occur is one.

3.   Every probability is a number between zero and one, inclusive. As a percentage, it will range between zero per cent and 100 per cent.

4.   The sum of the probabilities of all possible outcomes of an experiment is one.

5.   When thinking about probabilities, remember what Aristotle said: "The probable is what usually happens."

It is useful to think of statistics as an elaborate way of calculating probabilities.

GLOSSARY TERMS

Addition rule of probabilities (p. 33)

Dependent (p. 32)

Empirical probability (p. 29)

Independent (p. 31)

Law of large numbers (p. 29)

Multiplication rule of probabilities (p. 32)

Probability (p. 27)

Sample space (p. 28)

Theoretical probability (p. 30)

PRACTICE QUESTIONS

1.   Which of the following is the sample space when two coins are tossed?
     a.   H, T, H, T
     b.   H, T
     c.   HH, HT, TH, TT
     d.   H, H, T, T

2.   At the University of Regina, three out of five students graduate with a Bachelor of Arts degree. The remainder receive a different degree, such as a Bachelor of Science. What is the probability that a randomly chosen graduating student will *not* be getting a Bachelor of Arts degree?

3.   A pair of dice is rolled. What is the probability of getting a sum of two?

4.   There are 2 soccer teams in Winnipeg with 30 players in total. One team (Team A) has 16 players and the other (Team B) has 14. Five of these players are left forwards, 3 of whom are on Team A. If a player is chosen at random, what is the probability of choosing someone on Team A, or a left forward?

5.   In Canada, roughly 52 per cent of people wear a seat belt while driving. If 2 people are chosen at random, what is the probability that both of them are wearing a seat belt?

6.   Three cards are chosen at random from a deck *without* being replaced. What is the probability of getting a 3, a 9, and a jack, in that order?

7. In poker, one of the better hands is a flush. A flush is 5 cards of the same suit (all hearts, all clubs, etc.). Calculate the likelihood of being dealt 5 consecutive cards of the same suit (hint: there are 4 suits in total, 13 cards to a suit, and 52 cards in a standard deck). State the likelihood as a decimal, rather than a fraction.

8. Ryan only had time to study six of the eight essay questions that could be on his sociology exam. His professor will be choosing two of the eight questions for the exam. What are the chances that both of the questions that Ryan didn't study will appear on the exam?

9. Every year, Julie usually dresses up as either a male pirate or a female pirate for Halloween. So rarely does she stray from her costume that you believe it's possible to predict her costume for the coming year before even seeing her. Since you know that of the last 10 Halloweens, she was a male pirate 5 times, a female pirate 3 times, a dog once, and a llama the other time, what is the probability that Julie will appear this year dressed up as something other than a pirate?

10. Suppose that you have few friends, but that you've decided to use your newly acquired statistical knowledge to make some. Since you like to gamble, you decide to head to the casino to try to meet people at the craps table. What would you say to people who say the following?
    a. "I haven't had any luck all night! I'm due for some good fortune!"
    b. "Nobody around me is winning!"
    c. "The probability of both of these two dice turning up fives is nil!"

    Answers to the practice questions for Chapter 4 can be found on page S-3.

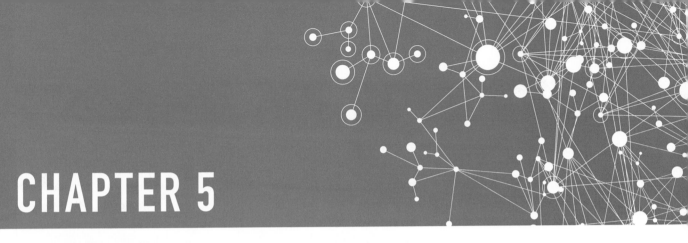

CHAPTER 5

The Normal Curve

LEARNING OBJECTIVES

Now that you've learned about probabilities and how to describe data, Chapter 5 will expand on those topics. You will learn:

- how data are distributed;
- principles of the normal distribution;
- how probability is related to the normal curve.

THE HISTORY OF THE NORMAL (GAUSSIAN) DISTRIBUTION

Imagine that you're a gambler and want to know how frequently an outcome (such as the number of times a coin will turn up heads in 100 tosses) will occur. A safe guess would be to predict 50 per cent of the time. Usually that's pretty accurate, but gamblers make money by betting on something *other* than the most obvious outcome. Since coin tossing is a **random process**, the outcome won't always be the most obvious or intuitive one, although it is the most likely one. There could be 53 heads and 47 tails in one set of tosses, 65 heads and 35 tails in another, and 75 heads and 25 tales in yet another. It is theoretically conceivable that you could get 95 heads and 5 tails in one round of tosses. Anything between zero heads and 100 tails, and 100 heads and zero tails is possible.

Imagine that you've been hired to predict the likelihood of outcomes for an avid gambler, someone not schooled in how probabilities work. Your gambler boss wants to know the probability of the outcome that you think would be most likely (and therefore which outcome he/she should bet on). Depending on how risk averse your boss is, you probably wouldn't suggest choosing 95 heads and 5 tails, given the over-representation of heads and the low likelihood of that outcome. Instead, you might suggest placing a bet on a more evenly divided outcome because it makes more sense to you, and everyone else, which is also why it wouldn't pay as well

BOX 5.1

The Normal Curve: History of a Term

The reason the normal curve is sometimes called the bell curve is because of its bell-like shape. It is often (mistakenly) called the Gaussian curve, to pay tribute to Carl Friedrich Gauss's work on the distribution of errors in an ordinary least squares regression equation. This equation fits a line on top of data that best represents the relationship between variables (this will be covered in greater detail in Chapter 16). Gauss argued that the distribution of errors in the equation is random, and that their shape therefore assumes a normal distribution. Since it was Abraham de Moivre who used the curve first, it should bear his name. The fact that it doesn't follows the "law of eponymy," coined by statistician Stephen Stigler, which states that "no scientific discovery is named after its original discoverer."

as a more extreme bet. By considering these possibilities, you're applying some of the general principles of probability: the **central limit theorem** and the **normal curve**.

Applying the principles of probability is what de Moivre, one of the Western world's earliest statisticians, did for a living. He was born in 1667 in Vitry-le-François, France, and moved to London around 1685. There, in addition to being a tutor and mathematician, he served as a gambling consultant at a local coffeehouse. It is likely that de Moivre frequently faced problems like the coin toss example above, because he derived an equation that allowed him to estimate the probability of any of the 100 possible outcomes. He could do that because he noticed that when the number of events (coin flips) increased, the distribution of outcomes approached a smooth and predictable bell-like curve. This observation later became known as the central limit theorem, and the curve he saw is known today as the **Bell, Gaussian**, or **normal curve**.

ILLUSTRATING THE NORMAL CURVE

Although de Moivre's equation actually calculates probabilities, it's not yet important to understand how the probabilities we studied in the last chapter relate to the normal curve. Instead, let's look at the central limit theorem and determine its relation to the normal curve. A simplified version of the central limit theorem states that if any variable (such as one that contains the number of times a coin toss shows heads) has a known range, then it will increasingly approximate the normal curve as the number of samples increases.

To illustrate the normal curve, let's continue using the coin toss example. You would start out with a small exercise, such as performing 100 tosses once.[1] Once you've flipped the coin 100 times (say it yielded 55 heads and 45 tails), you have completed one **experiment**. This probably took some time to do, but it is not even *close* to the number of tosses needed to see the normal curve. In fact, in Figure 5.1, the 100-toss experiment was repeated 100 times (that's 10,000 tosses!).

EVERYDAY STATISTICS

How "Normal" Is Normal?

Some researchers have suggested that the normal distribution is problematic because abnormalities such as outliers occur in normal samples but are not taken into account. One alternative to the normal distribution is an application of a "heavier-tailed" family of distributions (those with more than 5 per cent of observations ±3 deviations from the mean). This alternative has many of the properties associated with the normal distribution but allows for the inclusion of a larger number of extreme values.

· ·

Q: Do you think there is a problem with the proposed alternative to the normal distribution?

The type of graph in Figure 5.1 is a histogram. Histograms are often used to assess **distributions**. The x-axis represents the frequency with which heads was observed in each experiment; the values on the y-axis are the proportion of the experiments where each frequency of heads was observed. The y-value of the tallest bar (which is the mode, and has an x-value of 49 heads) is 0.09, meaning that in 100 experiments, 49 heads were observed 9 per cent of the time, that is, in 9 experiments. On either side of this value are shorter bars with values of 0.07, meaning that 48 and 50 heads were observed in 7 experiments.

The thin black curvy line in Figure 5.1 represents the normal curve. The normal curve will be bell-shaped, as the black line shows. As de Moivre noted in the central limit theorem,

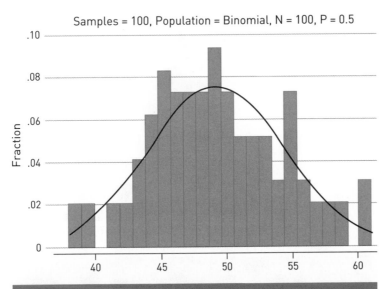

FIGURE 5.1 | Results from 100 Coin Toss Experiments, 100 Tosses per Experiment

the fewer the number of tosses, the farther away or worse the approximation of the normal curve will be, creating more gaps between the bars of the histogram and the normal curve line. Figure 5.1 represents 100 sets of tosses, each set containing 100 tosses. You can see that the tails are thicker than the normal curve would suggest and that there are several instances where the bars don't align with the curve. The values of 40 and 59 don't even occur. In Figure 5.2, the number of samples is increased to 1,000 (each experiment still contains 100 tosses). Notice how much closer the distribution of data is in the normal curve.

There are far fewer gaps between the normal curve and the data in Figure 5.2, but the graph still doesn't follow the curve exactly.

When the number of samples is increased to 10,000 (Figure 5.3), the fit shows even more improvement. There is very little difference between the results and the overlaid normal curve.

As the exercise demonstrates, the distribution of data, in this case the proportion of heads in each set of 100 tosses, resembles the normal curve more closely as sample size increases. This is the crux of the central limit theorem, which states that observed data approach the normal curve as the number of observations increases. Knowing this made it possible for de Moivre to predict how often a set of tosses would return any combination of heads and tails. The curve can also be used to predict other kinds of outcomes. If there are enough trials, it's possible for the distribution *within* a sample to approach normal distribution.

As Figure 5.3 suggests, the normal curve can also be used as an **asymptotic** approx-

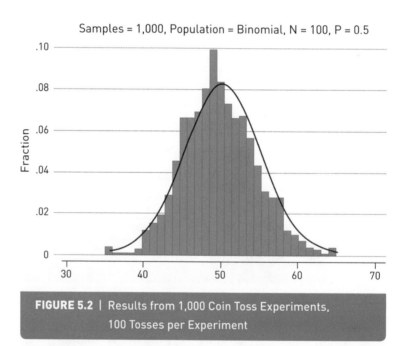

FIGURE 5.2 | Results from 1,000 Coin Toss Experiments, 100 Tosses per Experiment

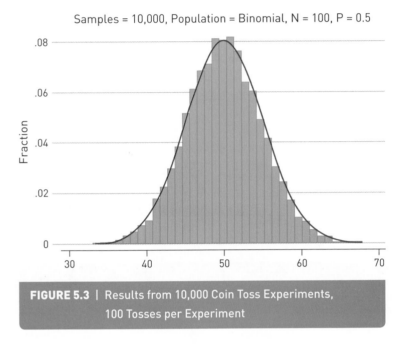

Samples = 10,000, Population = Binomial, N = 100, P = 0.5

FIGURE 5.3 | Results from 10,000 Coin Toss Experiments, 100 Tosses per Experiment

imation of outcome for a finite set of coin-toss trials. It can also approximate the distribution of a continuous variable, such as income. There are some necessary qualifiers for income, though. Since it has a wider range of values than the coin toss, one large sample can approach the normal curve. Also, unless you are self-employed, it is difficult to earn less than $0. Finally, a few people in Canada earn a lot more money than could be randomly predicted. These people (such as the Thomsons, Galen Weston, the Irving brothers, Jim Pattison) are known as **outliers**, because their earnings are sufficiently unique that they will never fall within the parameters of the normal distribution (perhaps that is why they are in

BOX 5.2

What Is an Asymptote?

"Asymptote" comes from the Greek word *asymptotos*, which means "never falling together." In statistics, this term is often used to describe the shape of a distribution with a large sample and an infinite number of trials. If we were tossing coins, for example, and got a distribution like Figure 5.1 above, we would say that although the distribution is not yet normal, it would become increasingly so, but would never fully reach normal, if we kept going. Asymptotic normality is just a fancy way of saying that a distribution is normal, but only with an infinite amount of coin tossing. Making this assumption allows us to use the suite of statistical techniques and principles that are designed for use with normal distributions.

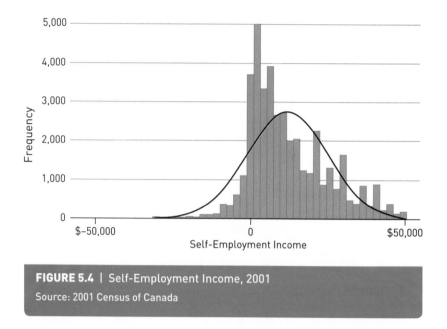

FIGURE 5.4 | Self-Employment Income, 2001
Source: 2001 Census of Canada

the news so often!). Those who earn less than $0 are also outliers.

Some of the difficulties with examining income can be resolved by focusing only on the self-employed (since it is possible to lose money if you're self-employed) and by eliminating the wealthy.

Figure 5.4 is a histogram of income for the approximately 130,000 people in Canada who were self-employed in 2001. Once again, the normal curve is overlaid. There are considerable gaps in the plot versus the normal curve. Ideally, the number of observations would be increased to produce a better fit, but that option is not available; everyone who was self-employed in Canada in 2001 is already included.

The example shows that there will almost always be a level of misfit between observed data and the normal curve. However, we often decide that our data are close enough to normal that the same statistics would be used to assess and describe a variable that is normally distributed, such as averages in a coin toss.

SOME USEFUL TERMS FOR DESCRIBING DISTRIBUTIONS

Below are several useful terms for describing histograms:

a. **Symmetrical**: Exactly half of the scores fall above the mean, and exactly half of them fall below the mean. Both sides of the mean have the same pattern of distribution (see Figure 5.5).

b. **Skewness**: The opposite of symmetrical. Occurs when there are more scores on one

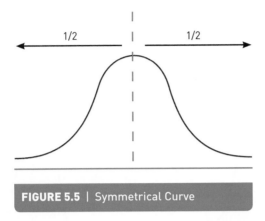

FIGURE 5.5 | Symmetrical Curve

side of the mean than on the other, resulting in one of the tails of the histogram being longer than the other. If the right tail is longer than the left (meaning that high values are more spread out than lower values, as in Figure 5.4), we say that the histogram is positively skewed (see Figure 5.6a), or skewed to the right. Histograms with a longer tail of lower values are negatively, or left, skewed (see Figure 5.6b).

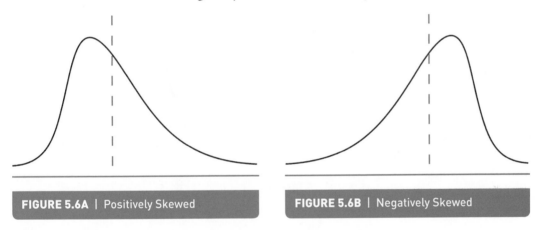

FIGURE 5.6A | Positively Skewed

FIGURE 5.6B | Negatively Skewed

c. **Kurtosis**: Refers to how flat or peaked a distribution is. If a distribution is flatter than usual, it has negative kurtosis; if it is more peaked than normal, it has positive kurtosis.

d. **Unimodal**: A distribution is unimodal when there is only one mode (the most frequently occurring value in your data set, on a variable of interest). Histograms of unimodal distributions will have only one major "hump" in them (see Figure 5.7). The income histogram (Figure 5.4) is a good example of this.

e. **Bimodal**: A distribution with two modes is bimodal, and will have two major "humps" (see Figure 5.8).

f.   **Multimodal**: Any distribution that has more than two modes (see Figure 5.9).

g.   **Bell curve**: As shown in Figure 5.10, the normal curve is shaped like a bell, so it is often called a bell curve.

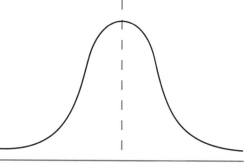

FIGURE 5.7 | Unimodal Distribution

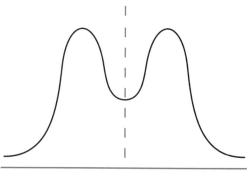

FIGURE 5.8 | Bimodal Distribution

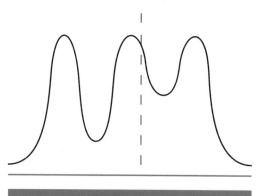

FIGURE 5.9 | Multimodal Distribution

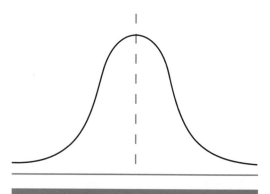

FIGURE 5.10 | The Bell Curve

GLOSSARY TERMS

Asymptotic (p. 41)

Bell curve (p. 38)

Bimodal (p. 43)

Central limit theorem (p. 38)

Distributions (p. 39)

Experiment (p. 38)

Gaussian curve (p. 38)

Kurtosis (p. 43)

Multimodal (p. 44)

Normal curve (p. 38)

Random process (p. 37)

Outliers (p. 41)

Skewness (p. 43)

Symmetrical (p. 42)

Unimodal (p. 43)

PRACTICE QUESTIONS

1. Dr. Knifewell performs pancreatic surgeries, and has found that although most patients get released quickly, sometimes infections occur, necessitating a longer stay. She wants to see this information graphically and asks you to plot the data. How would you describe the distribution of the data?

2. Describe the distribution below. Would you say that it is unimodal, bimodal, or multi-modal? Is it skewed to the left or the right?

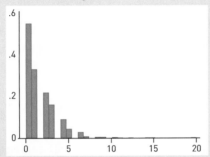

3. Look at the distribution of the variable below, with a super-imposed normal curve. What is the value for the largest outlier? What effect do you think it's having on the kurtosis value of the normal curve?

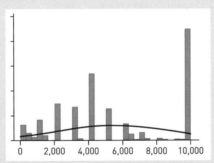

4. In recent years, the gap between rich and poor has been growing in Canada, suggesting that the middle class has been shrinking. Describe what impact this will have on a histogram of income in Canada.

5. Because of climate change, weather in Canada has become more volatile. What impact will this have on the tails of a histogram that plots daily temperatures? Will they get thicker or thinner?

6. A major cellular phone provider has been having problems with clients calling to complain that they're continually exceeding their monthly allotment of 500 airtime minutes, even

though the average usage is well below the allotment amount. They hire you to determine why they receive so many calls. As an adept statistician who sees merit in collecting data before making recommendations, you decide to run a small survey of usage among clients. These are the reported minutes used in a sample of 20 respondents:

| 50 | 124 | 130 | 23 | 77 | 1,012 | 102 | 1,750 | 900 | 499 |
| 998 | 890 | 12 | 42 | 35 | 223 | 399 | 239 | 1,200 | 0 |

What would you tell the cellular provider? How would you describe the distribution of data to them?

7. If you wrote a statistics exam, and found out that the distribution was skewed to the left, would you expect that there are outliers in the higher grade range or the lower?

8. Try to think of examples of data in your life that could be plotted as a histogram. Would you expect these data to be skewed, bimodal, etc.? Why?

Answers to the practice questions for Chapter 5 can be found on page 296.

NOTE

1. To experiment with coin-tossing, check out UBC economist Ken White's website: http://shazam.econ.ubc.ca/flip.

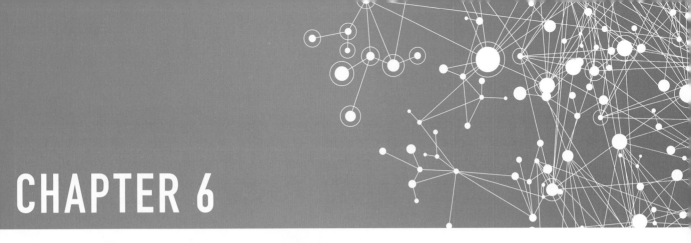

CHAPTER 6

Measures of Central Tendency and Dispersion

LEARNING OBJECTIVES

This chapter will examine the statistical measures used to understand the distribution of any variable. We'll be studying:

- measures of central tendency;
- measures of dispersion.

MEASURES OF CENTRAL TENDENCY

Depending on the nature of your inquiry, frequencies, percentages, rates, and/or ratios might not produce the information you want. For example, if you wanted to know how much most Canadians earn in a given year, it would be difficult to get that information by using any of the methods we've covered so far in this course. There would be too many categories for you to present in a table.

This is also true for the distribution of variables. To solve this problem you can use the **measures of central tendency** rather than the variables themselves. A common word for a measure of central tendency is an "average," which people often equate with the mean, even though the average is not limited to the mean (the mean is described as the arithmetic average). Rather, a measure of central tendency is a "typical" observation in your data set, which may be the value that falls in the middle of an ordered set, the average or the most frequently occurring. Which measure of central tendency you choose to report will depend on the level of measurement and, if your data are continuous, the distribution of your data.

Mode

One measure of central tendency is the **mode**, which is the most frequently occurring value in your data set, on a variable of interest. Suppose we are looking at ethnic origin in the 2006 Canadian census. The mode, or most frequently occurring answer among all ethnic-origin categories, would be Canadian (32.2 per cent of all respondents checked this box). More census respondents identified as Canadian than any other ethnic origin. Modes are most commonly used for nominal or ordinal data, although they can be used with any level of measurement.

Mean

The most commonly used measure of central tendency is the **mean**.

Suppose that you and nine of your classmates just received the grades from your first Intro to Stats exam. The grades were: 25 per cent, 35 per cent, 45 per cent, 47 per cent, 53 per cent, 64 per cent, 67 per cent, 75 per cent, 85 per cent, and 95 per cent (your grade is the 67 per cent). You want to know how you compare to your classmates. One way to do this would be to compare your grade to the arithmetic average, or mean, for the class. To do this, you need to add up all of the individual scores (25 + 35 + 45 + 47 + 53 + 64 + 67 + 75 + 85 + 95 = 591), and divide the sum by 10, the number of observations. This would yield 59.1 per cent (591 ÷ 10 = 59.1 per cent). The difference between your score and the average is 67 per cent − 59.1 per cent. So your score was almost 8 percentage points above the mean.

The mean can be expressed as the sum of all values of a particular variable, where the level of measurement is continuous, divided by the total number of observations used to calculate the sum. As you know from your past exam scores, the mean tells you the value of a "typical" person.

Let's put that information more formally. The equation for deriving the mean is as follows:

$$\overline{X} = \frac{X_1 + X_2 + X_3 + X_4 + \cdots + X_N}{N}$$

Or, more simply:

$$\overline{X} = \frac{\sum_{i=1}^{N} X_i}{N}$$

In these equations, $\overline{X}$ is equal to the mean of a variable (e.g., age).

X_1, X_2, X_3, etc., are equal to the individual values of X (e.g., person 1 is 20, person 2 is 40, person 3 is 19). X_i indicates the value for individual i (e.g., person 10,763 is 32).

N is equal to the total number of observations (e.g., N = 10,763). The second equation merely simplifies the first. Thus, ΣX = the sum (Σ) of the values for the sample (replacing the $X_1, X_2, X_3, \ldots, X_N$, etc.). The denominator does not change.

Here's another example of the mean. Let's suppose that we have five yearly income values: $5,000, $10,000, $15,000, $20,000, and $25,000. The mean is obtained by summing the five values ($5000 + $10,000 + $15,000 + $20,000 + $25,000 = $75,000) and dividing the sum by five, or the number of observations. This gives us $15,000, which is the income of the average person in the sample.

The average person is an abstraction. There does not need to be someone in your sample with the mean value. A test average could be 59 per cent, even if no one received that score. The average value is still useful because it tells you how you rank compared to the average.

Median

The third measure of central tendency is the **median**. Let's return to the five income values that we used to derive the mean. Sort the incomes by their value, and find the value that falls exactly in the middle; that's the median. In this example we have five observations, so the third individual is the person in the middle, and their income ($15,000), is the median of this sample. If there were an even number of observations (say, six instead of five), the calculation would be more complex. We would need to find the middle pair of numbers (the third and fourth observations), and then find the value that's halfway between them, by adding the values together and dividing by two.

In this example, the median and the mean are the same. This is often the case when data are normally distributed—something we'll cover in Chapter 7. In many cases there will be extreme values (very high or very low ones), which have a much stronger impact on the mean than the median. The total median income earned by everyone age 15 and over in the 2006 Canadian

EVERYDAY STATISTICS

Middle Matters

Every year, Statistics Canada releases an analytical report that summarizes the income dispersion of Canadians. In the analysis and the subsequent final report, the income information of Canadian families is reported on the basis of medians. The median is the point at which half of the families have a higher income and the other half have a lower income.

· ·

Q: Why do you think Statistics Canada releases income information using the median instead of the mean or the mode?

census was $25,615.00, but the individual values ranged from negative $50,000 to $200,000.[1] Why do we present the median instead of the mean? Because there is a substantial number of Canadians earning a large income, the mean will be affected by the extreme values. With variables that have extreme values, like income, the median is the preferred measure of central tendency, because it provides a truer picture of the average person. How typical is a person earning $200,000 or more? The answer is "not very typical," but these high earners have a huge impact on the calculation of the mean (imagine how many people it would take to remove the impact of 10 people earning $200,000!). When you have extremely high values, the median will be lower than the mean; when there are extremely low values, the median will exceed the mean. Since we have a cluster of people earning $200,000 or more, the median will be significantly lower than the mean.

MEASURES OF VARIABILITY

The normal curve doesn't just describe a **distribution**; it refers to assumptions about the data. Those assumptions grant statisticians access to a rich and diverse toolkit for data analysis.

BOX 6.1

Means and Medians: The History of Two Terms

Whose idea was it to compute summary statistics, and for what purpose? "Mean" is a very old term (Walker, 1929), sharing its roots with "median" from the Latin *mediānus*, for "middle." Although the concept of an average is quite common, the use of the mean has a long history. The mean is largely a descriptive and utilitarian measure (Stigler, 1986). In the eighteenth century, astronomers would average measurements, but only a small number and only if they were all taken under similar conditions. These measurements of celestial bodies were taken for the purposes of navigation. Pierre-Simon Laplace (1749–1827) worked on the mean in that context by comparing three observations, and published a paper on the subject in 1776.

Adolphe Quetelet (1796–1874) advanced the work of Laplace. Quetelet was an astronomer, statistician, and sociologist. He was interested in the mean as more than a descriptive measure. The stability of statistical aggregates, and hence of mean values, was the foundation of the science of social physics that Quetelet announced in 1831. Its key concept was *l'homme moyen*, the average man (Gigerenzer et al., 1991: 41). Quetelet measured physical characteristics to find their distribution and mean. From that he equated the normal with "the good," and deviation with deviance. Quetelet believed that if God produced man in His image, but in an imperfect way, some men would come closer to the perfect, or divine, image of man than others. The more a person deviated from the average, the less perfect Quetelet considered them to be.

But to get to that point, one must understand measures of variability. In its simplest terms, variability measures capture where individuals are positioned relative to one or more of the measures of central tendency. Some (like the range) are very simple to calculate, whereas others (like standard deviation) require more effort on your part.

The Range

Of all of the measures of variance, the range is the easiest to understand. Range is the lowest value subtracted from the highest value:

$$\text{Range} = H - L$$

where H is the highest value of your variable and L is the lowest.

For the example of the five yearly income values, the range would be $25,000 – $5000 = $20,000.

Mean Deviation

The range is useful for revealing how "wide," or spread out, the values are. What it cannot tell you is how far the "average" person is from the mean value. For example, it is possible that all values but two (one extremely high and one extremely low) are tightly clustered around the mean, but you would not know that by looking at the range.

The simplest method of determining how an observation ranks in the sample is the mean deviation. Defined as the average "distance" that each variable is from the class mean, the mean deviation is superior to the range because it reveals more than the difference between the highest and lowest scores (i.e., the most extreme values); it shows how far the average is from the mean. This shows how similar the individuals in your sample are, rather than just the highest or lowest-scoring person. The equation for the mean deviation is

$$\text{Mean Deviation} = \frac{\sum |X - \overline{X}|}{N}$$

The mean deviation is the sum of the **absolute values** of the distances from the mean, divided by the total number of observations. Continuing with our income example, we'd subtract the mean from every value (5000 – 15,000 = –10,000; 10,000 – 15,000 = –5000; 15,000 – 15,000 = 0; 20,000 – 15,000 = 5000; 25,000 – 15,000 = 10,000), sum the absolute values (10,000 + 5000 + 5000 + 10,000 = 30,000), and divide by the total number of observations to get $6,000 ($30,000/5 = $6000).

Although you've probably encountered absolute values already, it's good to be reminded that absolute value refers to the positive score of every value. The absolute values of –1, 2, –5, 11, and –100 would be 1, 2, 5, 11, and 100, respectively.

Variance and the Standard Deviation

The mean deviation is a useful measure of the **dispersion** of values for a variable, but since the absolute value has no straightforward mathematical relationship with the location of reported values, it is not usually used. Luckily, there are more desirable measures, and mean deviation is a useful foundation for understanding these measures.

Two alternatives to the mean deviation are **standard deviation** and **variance**. Both are closely related to the mean deviation, but neither uses absolute values.

The variance is the average *squared* distance (as opposed to absolute value) from the mean value. Squaring values eliminates negative values. Each observation contributes to the overall calculation of deviation. The equation is

$$s^2 = \frac{\sum (X - \overline{X})^2}{N}$$

In the equation, the numerator is also known as the **sum of squares**. It represents the sum of the squared deviations from the mean (note: we will use this frequently in the remainder of the text, so it's important to understand both this measure and standard deviation, below).

The standard deviation is the square root of the variance. Here's the equation:

$$s = \sqrt{\frac{\sum (X - \overline{X})^2}{N}}$$

Although there are similarities between the standard deviation, the mean deviation, and the variance, researchers most often use the standard deviation for dispersion because it can easily be related to the normal curve.

Since the standard deviation and the variance involve some arithmetic manipulation, it is easy to lose the meaning of the output. What, for example, does a standard deviation of 4 and a variance of 16 mean in everyday language? Like the mean deviation, variance

BOX 6.3

The Steps: Variance and The Standard Deviation

The variance for any sample can be obtained by

1. Subtracting the mean from each value;
2. Squaring the differences calculated in step 1;
3. Adding the squared deviations together;

4. Dividing the sum by the number of observations in your sample.

To get the sample standard deviation, take the square root of the variance.

and standard deviation are measures of the average distance a person is from the mean. In other words, it tells you how different, on average, an observation is from *l'homme moyen*, although it takes a few steps to get there. These steps are outlined in Box 6.3.

To understand what variance and standard deviation mean in everyday language, perhaps an example would be useful. Imagine that you were deciding between living in Toronto versus Calgary. Both locations have similar average high and low temperatures (although Calgary is a tad lower throughout the year), but does that mean that the two cities have the same climates? Not at all. Aside from differences in humidity, Calgary has a much higher probability of experiencing summer temperatures that dip below 5 degrees Celsius and winter temperatures that top 10 degrees Celsius. Toronto, by comparison, has a climate that's heavily moderated by its proximity to the Great Lakes. This means that these water masses bring an element of stability. If we were to compare the two cities statistically, we could say that the means are similar but that the standard deviation and variance are not, thereby resulting in climates that are quite different. In Toronto, you can safely put away your winter coat in one part of the year, and shorts in another, whereas in Calgary you'd be less likely to be able to do so.

BOX 6.4

Variance and Standard Deviation: History of Two Terms

The term "standard deviation" and the symbol σ (the Greek lower case sigma) were first used by Pearson in 1893 (Walker, 1929; Pearson, 1894). Variance was first employed by R.A. Fisher in 1918 (Walker, 1929).

Pearson developed standard deviation in the context of evolution, using the error curve, or *normal curve*. When discussing biological matters, specimens are not uniform and universal. To understand and describe genetic and population variations, not only is it important to recognize the measures of central tendency at work, but it's also important to have a formalized way of discussing the ends of the curve and the population described by the curve's extremities.

Since standard deviation and variance are so close to each other (the variance is just the standard deviation squared), it is somewhat redundant to talk about them both. For that reason, researchers will often talk about just the standard deviation. The other reason for focusing on standard deviation is that it connects directly to the normal curve. That is, the standard deviation describes how data are distributed about the mean in the normal curve. This forms one of the more important topics of the next chapter.

GLOSSARY TERMS

Absolute values (p. 51)	Median (p. 49)
Dispersion (p. 52)	Mode (p. 48)
Distribution (p. 50)	Standard deviation (p. 52)
Mean (p. 48)	Sum of squares (p. 52)
Measures of central tendency (p. 47)	Variance (p. 52)

PRACTICE QUESTIONS

1. Last year, a small statistical consulting company paid each of its five clerks $22,000, two statistical analysts $50,000 each, and the senior statistician/owner $270,000.
   a. How many employees earn less than the mean salary?
   b. What is the salary range?

2. The following 10 numbers represent the number of times a random sample of celebrities has signed autographs in the past month:

   46   57   68   2   4   14   0   0   2   101

   What is the mean, and mean deviation, for these numbers?

3. A sample of underweight babies was fed a special diet and the following weight gains (in lbs) were observed at the end of three months:

   6.7   2.7   2.5   3.6   3.4   4.1   4.8   5.9   8.3

   What are the mean, standard deviation, and variance of the weight gains?

4. If most of the measurements in a large data set are of approximately the same magnitude, except for a few measurements that are quite a bit larger, how would the mean and median of the data set compare, and what shape would a histogram of the data set be?

5. A sample of 99 distances has a mean of 24 metres and a median of 24.5 metres. Unfortunately, it has just been discovered that an observation erroneously recorded as "30" actually has a

value of "35." If we make this correction to the data, what would happen to the value of the mean? What about the median?

6. Whenever means and medians are compared for income in Canada, the mean is higher. Why do you think this is?

7. Over the past 100 to 200 years, several things have happened to the age distribution of Canadians. First, family sizes have been decreasing. Second, Canadians are living longer. Third, rates of premature death have declined. Discuss what you believe has happened to the mean, median, range, and standard deviation across this time period.

8. Given the discussion in this chapter on the relationship between standard deviation and the normal curve, do you think the tails would be longer or shorter for a distribution with a bigger standard deviation?

9. Jessica sends 55 text messages a day on average and has done so consistently since she got her phone 365 days ago. What is the mean deviation, standard deviation, and variance score for the number of text messages she sends every day?

10. When Helen becomes interested in something, she dedicates nearly all of her time to that activity. In the past, she's studied gardening, photography, sewing, scrapbooking, and crocheting. What usually happens, however, is that she eventually gets bored with the activity, and drastically reduces the amount of time she dedicates to that activity. Imagine that the number of hours per day that she spends on each activity follows a normal curve, except that she typically loses interest in an activity faster than she acquires it. Would you predict that the median number of hours she spends on each activity is higher or lower than the mean? Why?

Answers to the practice questions for Chapter 6 can be found on page S-4.

NOTE

1. Yes, some people in Canada have negative income! Can you think when this might occur? Hint: in some years, some businesses and investments lose money. Also, Statistics Canada recodes everyone earning more than $200,000 to prevent breaching confidentiality.

CHAPTER 7

Standard Deviations, Standard Scores, and the Normal Distribution

LEARNING OBJECTIVES

Chapter 7 will delve more deeply into the normal distribution. You will learn:

- more about the standard deviation;
- how to calculate, and use, the standard score.

INTRODUCTION

The crime rate in Prince Edward Island is 8,963 per 100,000 persons. That might seem high (or low), but how can you tell? How does PEI's crime rate compare to that of other provinces? What about US states? If the rate is high, how high is it relative to other places? If there's a difference between two places, is the difference meaningful? What if it's due to chance, or the way that you chose your sample? These questions form the focus of this chapter. How do we compare the values of different groups within a sample?

To answer those questions, beyond comparing the statistical means, we'll need to apply and expand on what was covered in the previous chapters. By the end of this chapter, you'll have enough statistical knowledge to place observations on a normal distribution and to rank values on a common metric by using the **standard score** (or **z-score**). Before we examine crime rates, you'll need to know how the mean and standard deviation relate to the normal curve.

HOW DOES THE STANDARD DEVIATION RELATE TO THE NORMAL CURVE?

First, let's discuss σ, the population standard deviation. Move beyond the detached calculations in the last chapter, and think of the standard deviation as a unit of measurement along an already-known continuum. The continuum is the **normal curve**. The standard deviation and standard score are used to determine the rank of an observation. Understanding these concepts will allow you to discuss your data with other people, even if they don't know the particulars of your study area.

For example, say you sell boats and need an accountant to increase your business's profitability. She wouldn't need to know anything about the boat business to help you (although it probably wouldn't hurt). She *does* need to know about money, and money remains the same across all businesses.

The standard deviation is like money; both are units of measurement. Although not as common as money, the standard deviation is used to describe characteristics of the normal distribution. In fact, the standard deviation is better than money for comparisons because it does not have specific currencies, and it is always possible (with some background information) to compare two observations to each other by using standard deviation scores.

Using the mean and standard deviation, the normal curve provides information about the characteristics of a variable. As in the example, it is not necessary to know anything about a variable or a study to see if its results show important differences between groups.

EVERYDAY STATISTICS

Standard Deviation and Your Local Weather

Standard deviation is often used in climatology to measure differences in temperature between two locations. For example, climatologists will compare two cities that have the same mean temperature and calculate the standard deviation for each city. This allows them to measure the difference in temperature variation between the two cities.

• •

Q: Considering the above application of the standard deviation, do you think that the standard deviation would be higher or lower for a coastal city compared to an inland city with the same mean temperature?

MORE ON THE NORMAL DISTRIBUTION

Most observations lie beneath the normal curve and are therefore subject to the rules of normal distributions. Because of that, there are standardized cut-points (standard deviations) that give a metric for determining the proportion of all observations that lie in six predetermined distances from the mean (usually denoted by μ, the Greek letter mu). There are usually three or four of these points above the mean and three or four below. To further illustrate this, consider Figure 7.1.

Figure 7.1 is a plot of the means of 10,000 samples of 200 observations, or the average of 200 observations on an interval/ratio variable (number of strikes at a plant, number of children, a heart rate, yield per hectare, or anything else), repeated 10,000 times. In the figure, each mean is treated like an observation. That might seem confusing, but don't worry about it too much at this point. We'll talk about it more when we get to **sampling distributions** in Chapter 9. At this point, think of each mean as an observation.

As we saw in the previous chapter, the mean is useful because it is a measure of central tendency, and we know that 50 per cent of all observations have values that exceed the mean, and 50 per cent have values that do not (assuming a perfectly normal distribution). By knowing the mean and the score on a particular variable, we can determine whether a person is in the top or bottom half of the sample. The mean provides a useful "cut-point" for assessing how an individual ranks. You likely already know this from exam scores in your previous courses, because it allows you to determine if you scored above or below the average.

Suppose you wanted to find cut-points other than the mean, because you require more information than the mean provides. You could use the standard deviation, which you learned about in the last chapter, or the standard score (also known as the z-score or **normal score**). The standard deviation allows more cut-points (usually six or eight) where the distribution of observations is known. The standard deviation is a coarser version of the standard score, so we'll talk about that first. The standard deviation shows what proportion of the sample, or population, lies on either side of certain key values. These values from a simulated normal distribution are denoted by vertical lines in Figure 7.1. The line in the centre of the histogram is μ (mu), the mean, and has a value of zero. The mean value of the raw scores is not necessarily zero (the mean age of the Canadian population, for example, is around 40), but when the values of a variable are standardized, zero is used for convenience. The vertical lines that move away from the mean are standard deviation markers. In the case of Figure 7.1, they are at ±1σ, ±2σ, and ±3σ (note: ± is shorthand for plus or minus, so ±1σ is "plus or minus one standard deviation from the mean").

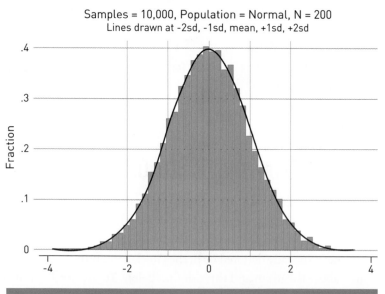

Samples = 10,000, Population = Normal, N = 200
Lines drawn at -2sd, -1sd, mean, +1sd, +2sd

FIGURE 7.1 | The Normal Distribution with Normal Curve and Standard Deviation Lines

Using the central limit theorem, we know that approximately 68.26 per cent of all observations lie between ±1 standard deviations from the mean, that about 95 per cent of all observations can be found between ±2 standard deviations from the mean (the more accurate figure is 95.44 per cent), and that almost all observations (about 99.74 per cent) lie between ±3 standard deviations from the mean. These values, often referred to in shorthand as 68-95-99, tell you what percentage of all observations lies between the positive and negative values of the standard deviation score and the mean. Remember that these values are hypothetical, and that to see exact percentages in your data, the sample size would have to be very large—larger than what's usually available. The data would also have to be *very* normally distributed.

Consider this scenario: suppose that you want to know the average number of people kayaking around the Champlain Bridge area of the Ottawa River per day. Since you want a good number of time points, you decide to use an hourly average for each experiment. You stretch your study out over the June–August period, yielding roughly 1,000 data points (you take a few vacation days off). Your sample mean is 32.3, and your standard deviation is 10.2. You could graph these data as a histogram like the one in Figure 7.2.

Following convention, the mean for Figure 7.2 is given a value of zero. Values higher than the mean are positioned to the right of zero, and negative values are to the left. This is done so that anyone can understand the data without knowing anything about the subject matter. The numbers across the horizontal axis don't refer to the number of kayakers per hour, but instead to the numbers of kayakers expressed in standard deviation units. Since the standard deviation is a commonly used measure, it is possible to use the information from other,

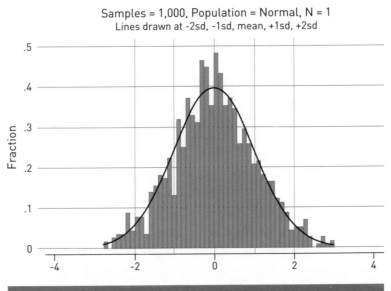

FIGURE 7.2 | Kayakers on the Ottawa River: A Hypothetical Example

unrelated data sets to study kayaking traffic on the Ottawa River. The *y*-axis is the fraction of experiments.

Even with 1,000 observations, the data for the number of kayakers approximate the normal curve fairly well, despite some gaps between the normal curve line and the bars representing the data. If we continued to stand on the Champlain Bridge and observe, the fit would improve. Since we know that as the number of observations increases so too does the improvement of the fit, we can assume without further observation that the normal curve is a fairly good approximation of the average number of kayakers on the Ottawa River. This allows us to apply what we know about the normal curve to our kayaking example.

Knowing the standard deviation allows us to estimate the proportion of all hours where mean values are above and/or below the grand sample mean and ±1, ±2, and ±3 standard deviations. Now, instead of only knowing whether any particular hour is above or below average, we can also begin to determine the *distance* a particular observation is from the mean. From this, we can determine where any particular hour is positioned relative to all other hours.

We know a lot about normal distributions. We know, for example, that about 99 per cent of all observations are between ±3 standard deviations from the mean. So approximately 1 per cent of all cases are outside of this range, because 100 per cent − 99 per cent = 1 per cent. We also know that roughly 68 per cent of all observations are within ±1 standard deviation from the mean, and that 32 per cent of all observations are likely to differ from the mean by at least 1 standard deviation (100 per cent − 68 per cent = 32 per cent). Finally, the same procedure applies for 2 standard deviations (100 per cent − 95 per cent = 5 per cent).

With the standard deviation, it is easy to determine the proportion of people above or below the standard deviation cut-points. This is done by subtracting the number of standard deviations of the cut-point you are interested in from 100.

In our kayaking example, we know that there will probably be between 22.1 and 42.5 kayakers for 68 per cent of all days in June through August (mean of 32.3±1, standard deviation of 10.2), between 11.9 and 52.7 kayakers on 95 per cent of all days (mean of 32.3±2, standard deviations of 10.2), and between 1.7 and 62.9 kayakers on just about any given day (mean of 32.3±3, standard deviations of 10.2).

This captures the observations that are on the centre portion of the normal distribution (it ignores the tails), but what if we're only interested in the left or right tail? This is a one-tailed assessment and can be found by dividing the values by two. For example, if we want to know the number of cases *below* −3 standard deviations, we divide 1 per cent by 2. We now know that roughly 1 per cent of all cases lie above or below 3 standard deviations from the mean, which means that half of 1 per cent, or 0.5 per cent, must lie below −3 standard deviations from the mean. Returning to our example, for 0.5 per cent of hours there are fewer than 1.7 kayakers on the river. We find this by using the "68-95-99 rule" mentioned above, which refers to the proportion of observations between 1, 2, and 3 standard deviations from the mean.

AN EXTENSION OF THE STANDARD DEVIATION: THE STANDARD SCORE

The standard deviation is a great way to determine how many observations are on either side of ±1σ, ±2σ, and ±3σ, but what if you want to set your own cut-point, such as the value that separates the bottom 10 per cent of your observations from the top 90 per cent? Suppose you wanted to study the characteristics of the lowest achievers in elementary school and decided to look at the lowest 10 per cent. Or that you wanted to study the world's most volatile nation-states, and you chose to identify them by how many years of peace they've had. Maybe you're interested in understanding the regularity of the gestation period of rabbits, using the number of days of pregnancy. Whether you're interested in low blood pressure, high earnings, large families, small insects, or high mortality rates, the standard score allows you to compare a single score with those of the population of interest.

The equation for the standard score is

$$z = \frac{X - \mu}{\sigma}$$

z = the z or standard score (expressed in standard deviations)
X = an individual's raw score
μ = the sample mean
σ = the sample standard deviation

The standard score, or z-score, is interpreted as a standard deviation that doesn't need to be stated as an integer. Since z-scores are standardized, the sum and mean are zero. The formula

---

BOX 7.1

It's Your Turn: Determining the Proportion of Observations at Various Standard Deviation Cut-Points

Now that you know the "68-95-99 rule," can you determine approximately what percentage of all observations lie at the following cut-points?

1. Below –2 standard deviations?
2. Below +3 standard deviations?
3. Above the mean?
4. Above +1 standard deviation?
5. Below +2 standard deviation?

The solutions for Box 7.1 can be found on page S-27.

for the z-score will convert the score of any individual observation into a z-value. This value is directly related to that of the standard deviation. A z-score of +1.0 is equivalent to 1 standard deviation above the mean. A z-score of −2.0 is the same as 2 standard deviations below the mean, etc. The difference is that it is possible to have a z-score of 1.5, but not a non-integer standard deviation.

Converting raw scores (test averages, heart beats per minute, etc.) to z-scores makes it possible to determine the rank of *any* score. This rank is expressed in **percentiles**. Like standard deviations, the standard score lets you place an observation on the normal curve so that you can express the proportion of the sample, or population, above or below a particular value. Unlike the standard deviation, there are more scores to remember than the 68-95-99 rule, so you might not remember all of the critical cut-point values. Appendix A has a table for converting z-scores to percentile ranks.

Table 7.1 is a primer, containing a few z-scores. The first column in Table 7.1 lists the z-score, followed by the proportion of all observations that lie between the mean and the z-score. The third column lists the proportion of observations that are beyond the calculated z-score (the percentage of all observations in a tail). Since the z-score is a standardized measure, these values remain true for any normally distributed variable.

There will be times when you will need to determine the area between two z-scores. Continuing the kayaking example, if you wanted to know how many days you might see between 20 and 40 kayakers, you would need to calculate two z-scores, one to establish a lower bound, and one for the upper bound. The mean number of kayakers is 32.3, and the standard deviation is 10.2. Calculate the lower bound first:

$$z = \frac{X - \mu}{\sigma}$$

$$= \frac{20 - 32.3}{10.2}$$

$$= -\frac{12.3}{10.2}$$

Next, the upper bound:

$$z = \frac{X - \mu}{\sigma}$$

$$= \frac{40 - 32.3}{10.2}$$

$$= \frac{7.7}{10.2}$$

$$= 0.75$$

Next, find these scores on the z-table. Usually, only positive values can be found on a z-table, so look for the nearest absolute value; −1.21 becomes 1.21. Now you simply need to add the values together from Column B in Table 7.1.

TABLE 7.1 | The z-Table (area under the normal curve)

A	B	C
z-score	Area between z and mean	Area beyond z
0.0	0.000	0.500
0.1	0.040	0.460
0.2	0.079	0.421
0.3	0.118	0.382
0.4	0.155	0.345
0.5	0.192	0.309
0.6	0.226	0.274
0.7	0.258	0.242
0.8	0.288	0.292
0.9	0.316	0.184
1.0	0.342	0.159
1.1	0.364	0.136
1.2	0.385	0.115
•	•	•
•	•	•
•	•	•
1.96	**0.475**	**0.025**
2.0	0.477	0.023
2.1	0.482	0.018
2.2	0.486	0.014
2.3	0.489	0.011
2.4	0.492	0.008
2.5	0.494	0.006

For 1.21, the closest z-value is 1.2, and for 0.75 the closest value is 0.8. Since we want to know the number of days *between* the two scores, we need to use information from column B. The value for 1.2 is 0.385, and for 0.8 it is 0.288. The first value tells us that there will be a z-score number of kayakers between 1.2 and 0 (the mean) for 38.5 per cent of all days. The value of 0.288 tells us that 28.8 per cent of all days will have a z-score of between 0 and 0.8. Adding these two values together yields 0.673, which means that roughly 67 per cent of days will have a z-score between −1.2 and 0.8, or between 20 and 40 kayakers, assuming that the number of kayakers on the Ottawa River follows a normal distribution.

A z-score can also be translated back into its actual value (such as the number of kayakers per hour). Suppose that we wanted to determine, with 95 per cent confidence, how many kayakers we would see in an hour. To determine this, work backwards from the formula. Instead of calculating z, which is unknown in the example above, we would calculate the upper and lower values of X, the cut-points that 95 per cent of observations are found in.

First, look at the z-table. Use the value where 47.5 per cent of all observations lie between z and the mean (column B). This table represents the absolute values of z. If you want to know the area both above and below the mean, you'll have to place a negative sign in front of the lower value. Since we want the z-value for the point where 47.5 per cent of all cases fall between z and the mean, we find it in column B: 1.96. We find the value for 47.5 per cent because it's half of 95 per cent, the number we want to capture. By ensuring that 47.5 per cent of our cases are above the mean, and that 47.5 per cent are below, we get a total of 95 per cent of all cases. We can insert the known values into our equation for the z-statistic, focusing first on the lower bound (where we assign a negative value to the z-statistic):

$$z = \frac{X - \mu}{\sigma}$$

$$-1.96 = \frac{X - 32.3}{10.2}$$

$$-1.96 * 10.2 = X - 32.3$$

$$-19.99 + 32.3 = X$$

$$12.31 = X$$

For the upper bound:

$$z = \frac{X - \mu}{\sigma}$$

$$1.96 = \frac{X - 32.3}{10.2}$$

$$1.96 * 10.2 = X - 32.3$$

$$19.99 + 32.3 = X$$

$$52.29 = X$$

We can be 95 per cent confident that in any given hour between June and August, we'll see between 12.31 and 52.29 kayakers on the Ottawa River from the Champlain Bridge.

It can be difficult at times to know what numbers you are interested in. You might be wondering why you should subtract a value from Column B from 1 at some times but not others. That is a good question, and there is no easy answer to it beyond simply understanding what each column represents. One strategy that I employed when first learning this stuff was to draw out normal distribution and figure out which part of the curve I was interested in. Ask anyone who has taken my statistics classes, and they'll confirm that this is advice I'm likely to give to those in doubt.

ONE-TAILED ASSESSMENTS

So far, we have been finding ranges where we know the upper and lower points ("How many observations lie beyond points 1 and 2?"). We've been looking at the proportion of observations *between* two known values, as in Figure 7.3. This may not always be the type of information we seek.

It is also useful to know the percentage of observations above or below a specified point, with no upper or lower limit imposed. To use our kayaking example, we might want to know the number of hours when we would see 20 or fewer kayakers. Or maybe we want to know when we'd see over 50 kayakers. In either case, we are interested only in observations above or below a specified point rather than between two values. The difference is shown in Figure 7.4.

When performing a one-tailed assessment, we must look at a different column on the z-table than for a two-tailed assessment. Instead of column B, we must now focus on column C. The change is very subtle, particularly since the number in column B plus the number in column C always captures exactly half of the normal distribution, and is always equal to 0.5, representing half of all observations.

To illustrate a one-tailed assessment, let's continue with our kayaking example. Suppose that we were starting a parasailing club and wanted to determine whether the Champlain Bridge area of the Ottawa River was sufficiently traffic-free (which we define as fewer than 10 kayakers per hour) to have our club there. What we need to know is what percentage of all summer hours have low kayaking traffic.

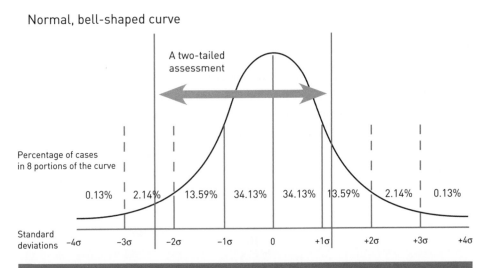

FIGURE 7.3 | A Two-Tailed Assessment

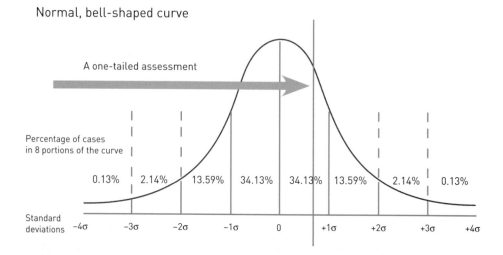

FIGURE 7.4 | A One-Tailed Assessment

We'd first need to calculate the z-statistic for 10 kayakers. We can use the same equation as before:

$$z = \frac{X - \mu}{\sigma}$$

$$= \frac{10 - 32.3}{10.2}$$

$$= \frac{-22.3}{10.2}$$

$$= -2.19$$

Now, however, instead of looking for how this corresponds with column B, which contains the area *between* the mean and z, we need to look at the area *beyond z*, found in column C (as always, treat the z-statistic as an absolute value). We see the number 0.0143, which is very low. This suggests that we're likely to see fewer than 10 kayakers per hour 1.4 per cent of the time. We may want to consider another location for our club.

What if we wanted to find a high-traffic area to discover how many hours we could expect to see more than 40 kayakers? The calculation would be the same:

$$z = \frac{X - \mu}{\sigma}$$

$$= \frac{40 - 32.3}{10.2}$$

$$= \frac{7.7}{10.2}$$

$$= 0.75$$

Looking at column C of the z-table for 0.75 gives us a value of 0.2266. We could expect to see at least 40 kayakers per hour, 22.7 per cent of the time.

So far, we have assumed that we are always looking for low values when the cut-off is below the mean, or high values when the cut-off is above the mean. The final scenario is one in which we want to know the percentage of all observations above a value when that value is below the mean, or the percentage of all observations below a value when that value is above the mean. To do that, we need to modify the values in the z-table slightly. Let's suppose that we want to know what percentage of all hours we would expect to see *fewer* than 40 kayakers. The z-value would remain the same, at 0.75, and we would still need to look at the value in column C, but we'd need to subtract that value from 100, yielding 77.3 per cent of all observations. The difference between this calculation and the previous one is that 22.7 per cent refers to all values above a z-value of 0.75, or 40 kayakers. There, we were interested in the information to the right of the cut-off point. Here, we are interested in the information to the left of the cut-off point, which is everything except 22.7 per cent. Since we begin with 100 per cent of all observations, we need only to subtract the portion we're not interested in.

Instead of subtracting the z-value from 100, you could get the same answer by taking the number in column B (0.2734) and adding 0.50. This is possible because 50 per cent of all observations lie on each side of the mean, so column B refers to the proportion of all observations between a specified value and the mean. If you are conducting a one-tailed assessment and will be dealing with more than half of all observations, this is the procedure that you'll have to use. If you are using less than half of all observations, the simple technique will work.

To help keep all of this straight, it is useful to draw a histogram like the one in Figure 7.5 (look ahead to Box 7.2).

PROBABILITIES AND THE NORMAL DISTRIBUTION

In the sections above, we used standard scores and the normal curve to help us identify numbers of occurrences, which is a measured outcome. The normal curve has many other uses, such as calculating probabilities. Think abstractly about the normal curve for a moment; **outliers** aside, every individual in a sample or population should be located somewhere along the normal curve. This means that there's a 100 per cent chance that we'll be able to locate someone, and once we know a little bit more about the person we can predict where they'll be on the normal curve. This links standard deviations, z-scores, and the normal curve to probabilities, and everything we learned up to now applies, except that we're dealing with probabilities instead of sample means, scattered across the normal distribution.

Suppose we want to know the probability of randomly selecting someone who earned between $23,000 and $50,000 from the population of Québec. According to the 2006 census, the mean income in Québec was $31,388, with a standard deviation of $39,396 (this number is probably low; public-use census data collapse extreme values). The first thing we need to do is calculate two z-statistics, one for $23,000:

$$z = \frac{X - \mu}{\sigma}$$

$$= \frac{23000 - 31388}{39396}$$

$$= -0.213$$

And one for $50,000:

$$z = \frac{X - \mu}{\sigma}$$

$$= \frac{50000 - 31388}{39396}$$

$$= 0.472$$

Next, we need to look up the values on the z-table (using column B because we're interested in a range). We find that the values are 0.0832 and 0.1808. Adding the scores together yields 0.264, so there's about a 26 per cent chance of randomly selecting someone who earns between $23,000 and $50,000 from the Québec population.

As with all of the other examples in this chapter, the calculated z-values can also tell us how many people are above or below a certain value. If, for example, we wanted to know the probability of selecting someone that earns above $50,000, that would be 31.92 per cent. This value corresponds with a z-value of 0.472 in column C of Appendix A.

That number probably seems a bit high because income is not a normally distributed variable. It is difficult to earn less than zero dollars, although some do (such as the self-employed). It is also difficult to earn a lot of money, although some do that too. Using techniques for normal distributions on income will probably introduce a lot of errors into our estimates.

Look at the comparison of the ways to describe scores on a normal distribution. To get a better sense of how the normal curve relates to standard deviation, cumulative percentages, and percentiles, consider Figure 7.6.

BOX 7.2

How to Convert the Standard Score to a Ranking: An Example

Between 1980 and 2004, Canada admitted over 4.5 million immigrants. The average years of schooling for this group is 11.42, with a standard deviation of 4.8 years. Suppose that a person has 10 years of education, and we want to know the proportion of people with more than 10 years of education.

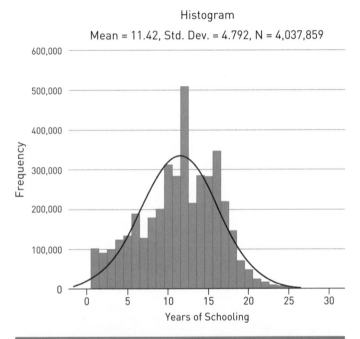

Histogram

Mean = 11.42, Std. Dev. = 4.792, N = 4,037,859

FIGURE 7.5 | Average Years of Schooling of Canadian Immigrants, 1980–2004

Source: Landed Immigrant Data Survey

Since the distance between our observed value and the mean is less than one standard deviation, we need to convert our score with the following equation:

$$z = \frac{X - \mu}{\sigma}, \text{ or } z = \frac{10 - 11.42}{4.8}, \text{ or roughly} - 0.296$$

Plunking this number into our table gives us the value 0.386, meaning that an impressive 61.4 per cent (100 – 38.6) of all immigrants to Canada have more than 10 years of education.

BOX 7.3

It's Your Turn: Converting Standard Scores to Percentile Ranks

Emily loved to eat out and go to movies with her friends, but her parents thought these activities were a waste of time and money. She was sure that everyone her age went out at least three times a week. Her parents did not agree—they were convinced that the majority of people only go out for special occasions, maybe once a month. Using the public-use micro data files collected as part of the 2004 General Social Survey, Emily looked for the number of evenings per month that Canadians between the ages of 18 and 29 reported they went to restaurants, movies, or theatres. She recoded people who went out "less than once a month" as going out once a month, because she did not want to exclude these people just because their response was not a whole number. She found the following:

The mean number of nights per month people went out was 5.7. The standard deviation was 5.1.

(Weighted n = 5,183,000 [rounded to thousands], excluding residents of Yukon, the Northwest Territories, and Nunavut, and full-time residents of institutions.)

Using the chart in Appendix A and the equation for the standard score, determine the following:

1. The range of values ±1 standard deviation from the mean.
2. The value that the lowest 10 per cent of all observations fall below.
3. The value that the highest 40 per cent of all observations are above.
4. The percentage of cases that fall between the values of 4 and 9.
5. The value that 75 per cent of all observations fall below.

The solutions for Box 7.3 can be found on page S-27.

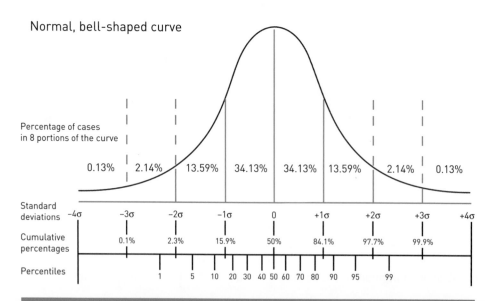

Normal, bell-shaped curve

Percentage of cases in 8 portions of the curve

0.13%   2.14%   13.59%   34.13%   34.13%   13.59%   2.14%   0.13%

Standard deviations   −4σ   −3σ   −2σ   −1σ   0   +1σ   +2σ   +3σ   +4σ

Cumulative percentages   0.1%   2.3%   15.9%   50%   84.1%   97.7%   99.9%

Percentiles   1   5   10   20 30 40 50 60 70 80   90   95   99

FIGURE 7.6 │ Standard Deviations, Cumulative Percentages, Percentiles, and the Normal Curve

GLOSSARY TERMS

Normal curve (p. 56)   Sampling distributions (p. 58)
Normal score (p. 58)   Standard score (p. 56)
Outliers (p. 67)   z-score (p. 56)
Percentiles (p. 62)

PRACTICE QUESTIONS

1. For the numbers below, find the area between the mean and the z:
    a. $z = -1.18$
    b. $z = 0.84$
    c. $z = -2.06$
    d. $z = 1.36$

2. For the numbers below, find the percentile rank (the percentage of individuals scoring below z).
    a. $z = 2.25$
    b. $z = -1.67$
    c. $z = 1.43$
    d. $z = -0.44$

3. For the numbers below, find the percentage of cases falling above z.
    a. $z = 0.25$
    b. $z = -1.21$
    c. $z = 1.21$
    d. $z = -2.01$

4. For the numbers below, find the percentages of cases falling between the two z-scores.
    a. $z = -0.38$ and $z = 1.63$
    b. $z = 0.88$ and $z = 1.55$
    c. $z = -1.93$ and $z = 1.09$
    d. $z = -2.22$ and $z = -1.34$

5. Sigmund wrote a statistics exam and scored 45 (mean = 52, standard deviation of 5). What is his percentile rank?

6. Lesley wrote the same test and scored 54. What percentage of individuals received a higher score?

7. You believe that your child is a genius and decide to have him write a standardized achievement test. To your delight, he scores a 148 (mean = 125, standard deviation = 15). What is your child's percentile rank?

8. Feng and Lucy both took a spatial abilities test (mean = 80, standard deviation = 8). Feng scored a 76 and Lucy scored a 94. What percentage of individuals would score between Feng and Lucy?

9. Evelyn typically brushes her teeth for two minutes (120 seconds). Her younger sister Abigail finds it annoying that she doesn't vary much in this regard. Evelyn decides to prove Abigail wrong, and determines that she spends either less than 88 seconds or more than 152 seconds roughly 5 percent of the time. Assuming a normal distribution, what is Evelyn's standard deviation?

10. Life in Ratroy is fairly boring, so much so that, out of boredom, Kody decides to spend every afternoon for a week counting how many crickets he hears chirping every hour in the field beside his house. Because he is statistically savvy, he knows that the week he chooses may not be representative, so he decides to compare his sample data to that of a normal population. Here are the sample data for the five afternoons.

	Monday	Tuesday	Wednesday	Thursday	Friday
1:00	53	34	65	54	47
2:00	44	23	55	33	54
3:00	32	27	47	45	53
4:00	66	19	59	39	45

a. Calculate the mean and standard deviation score for the numbers above.
b. How many hours fell beyond (or above and below) 1, 2, and 3 standard deviations from the mean?
c. This exercise has caused Kody to develop quite a passion for counting crickets—he is, after all, only human! At the same time, he wants to begin only counting crickets at "prime time," or when the chirps per hour are at their peak. Should he go for early afternoon (1:00–2:00) or late afternoon (3:00–4:00) counts?

Answers to the practice questions for Chapter 7 can be found on page S-5.

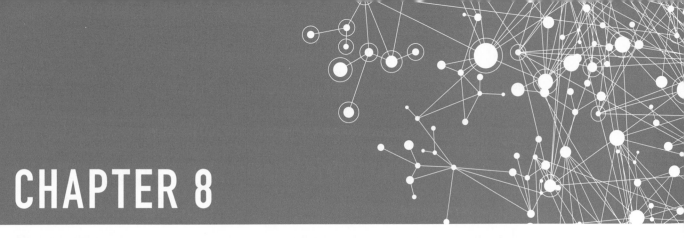

CHAPTER 8

Sampling

LEARNING OBJECTIVES

Up to this point, we've only worked with entire populations. Including all relevant observations is beneficial because it allows you to be certain that your results accurately describe your population. In reality, you are likely to be working with samples most of the time. That requires a few additional considerations. Consequently, in this chapter you will:

- learn how to identify a sample;
- examine the main sampling types of probability and non-probability samples.

INTRODUCTION

There are times when counting the entire **population** is costly, cumbersome, or otherwise problematic. For the 2011 census, the population of Canada was over 34 million. If the entire population had been included, the 2011 Census of Canada file would have over 30 million observations. Even with the speed of today's computers, it would take a long time to perform even basic analysis on such a large group. Using all of the data would also make it possible to identify persons, breaching Statistics Canada's assurance of **confidentiality**.

In these situations, it makes more sense to use a **sample**, or a fraction, of the entire population. Let's face it, we're more alike than we are different, so it's not necessary to include everyone every time we do analysis on the Canadian population. For example, if you wanted to know how much the average university student earns, you would not need to ask every single student because most students probably earn about the same amount of money. But since they're not identical, we can't reduce the sample size to one. In those circumstances, it is useful to look at a sample, or portion, of the population, because we can capture most of the information about the entire population without analyzing everyone. A sample that is accurately and carefully selected, without a lot of **sampling error**, allows a precise analysis without including the full population. The files that Statistics Canada releases for public use usually comprise 2.7 to 3 per cent of the entire Canadian population.

Sampling has a long history in Canada and was first used in the Canadian census in 1941. A 27-question questionnaire was completed for every tenth dwelling by an enumerator. Sampling was also used at the processing stage to obtain early estimates of earnings of wage-earners, of the distribution of the population of working age, and of the composition of families in Canada. In this case, a sample of every tenth enumeration area across Canada was selected and all population schedules in these areas were processed in advance. As with sampling house-holds, sampling at the processing stage was done to save time and money. Imagine analyzing all that data in 1941 without the help of computers!

Our discussion of standard deviations, standard scores, and normal distributions in the last chapter also applies here, although the topic is sufficiently complex to warrant its own chapter (Chapter 9). For now, as you read this chapter, think about how treating the mean of a sample as an observation allows you to plot a distribution of samples as though it were a sample of individuals. Furthermore, each of the sampling techniques described in this chapter will have a different level of sampling error, that is, the accuracy with which a sample resembles a population. We'll discuss sampling error more at the end of this chapter.

We're going to look at some of the challenges and potential pitfalls of using samples in quantitative research by examining methods for deriving samples and identifying the strengths and weaknesses of each method. Then we'll cover the sources and consequences of bias in the sample.

PROBABILITY SAMPLES

There are two types of sampling techniques: **probability** and **non-probability**. In a proba-bility sample, each unit has a known chance of being selected. In a random sample, we can select 10 observations out of a population of 100. Each observation has a 10 per cent chance of being included. If we wanted to sample 100 people on a university campus, 50 students and 50 professors, and there were 100 professors and 5,000 students, the probability of inclusion would be different for the two subpopulations. For professors, the selection probability would be 50/100, or 50 per cent, and for students the chance of being selected would only be 50/5000, or 1 per cent.

Probability samples have several desirable qualities. They are representative, allowing for generalization from sample to population. This means that

1. Sample means can be used to estimate population means.
2. If the population is normally distributed, the sample will be normally distributed too.
3. It is possible to estimate the discrepancy between sample mean and population mean. This measurement is the sampling error.
4. It is possible to test how well our results resemble what we could expect to see in the population by using **inferential statistical tests**.

5. Once a sample is selected, a variety of methods may be used to contact respondents, including mail, telephone, and Internet surveys.

In the next section, the four most popular types of probability samples are described. Keep in mind that each of the examples below is an ideal type. Any sample used by a statistical agency, such as Statistics Canada, is likely a combination of these types.

Simple Random Sample

Simple random samples are probably the most basic probability samples. To select one, list all possible units, number them consecutively, and then use a random number chart (like the one in Appendix F) to select a certain number, or percentage, of units. In a simple random sample, every unit has an equal probability of selection. The probability of selection is n/N, where n = sample size and N = population size.

Suppose that we have a population of 100 and we want to derive a sample of 10 observations. Each observation in a random sample would have a 10/100, or 1 in 10, chance of being selected in the sample. This means that the probability of selection is 10 per cent.

Simple random samples are easy to grasp, and they are the only sampling technique that give a *truly* random sample (all others include some other source of bias). The downside of simple random samples is that they can be cumbersome to generate, since they require you to assign a random number to every individual in a population, which can be time consuming (at least without the help of a computer).

Systematic Random Sample

Instead of choosing units by using a random number chart, for a **systematic random sample**, units are chosen from a **sampling frame**. The person deriving the sample can use a chart to select a random starting point or choose their own. Then they consistently choose every nth unit (such as every 10th observation). As long as there is no inherent ordering in the data set, a systematic random sample will represent the population fairly accurately, though not as well as a simple random sample, since it is not quite as random. Imagine that you were selecting every third person for your sample and for some reason they were more likely to be female. Your sample would have a disproportionate number of females and not be truly random. However, systematic random samples are a quick and accurate approximation of a simple random sample.

The defining characteristic of a systematic random sample is that it relies on a system of selection. One of the benefits of this is that it is possible for others to replicate your sample as long as they have the same sampling frame you used. The downside is that breaching confidentiality can become a concern. If an individual is able to identify your system of selection, they can then identify all individuals in the sample.

Stratified/Hierarchical Random Sample

A stratified sample can best be described as a series of two or more simple random samples operating within the same population. If you wanted to compile a representative sample of the population of Montréal by age, you would need to ensure that your sample contained a representative ratio of people within each predefined age grouping (0 to 15, 16 to 30, 31 to 45, 46 to 60, etc.). To do this, find the proportionate number of people in each age stratum, then stratify (categorize into different levels) the population by appropriate criteria (age), and randomly select the appropriate number of people from each category. Suppose you had six age groupings and wanted to ensure that you had a good number of people from each. With a stratified sample you would take a simple random sample of people *within* each age group, instead of taking one simple random sample and hoping that each age group was equally represented.

The key benefit of stratified sampling is that each population subgroup of interest is adequately represented in a sample. The disadvantage is that, like simple random sampling, generating a sample can be a lot of work.

In the 2006 census, Statistics Canada administered a long-form and a short-form questionnaire. The short-form questionnaire, administered to 80 per cent of Canadians, contained only eight questions, collecting data on age, sex, marital status, and mother tongue. The other 20 per cent of the population received a *much* longer questionnaire: the same eight questions on the short form plus another 53 unique questions.

The agency used stratified sampling to decide whom to choose for its long-form questionnaire sample. In all self-enumeration areas (defined as those where the majority were able to complete the questionnaire themselves), a one-in-five random sample of occupied private dwellings was selected to receive a long questionnaire. The non-sampled occupied private dwellings received a short questionnaire.

Recognizing that certain portions of the population would have to be "over-sampled" to achieve representativity, Statistics Canada decided to stratify or divide its sample into specific sub-populations. Most persons in collective dwellings received a long-form census, where a collective dwelling:

> Refers to a dwelling of a commercial, institutional or communal nature. It may be identified by a sign on the premises or by a census representative speaking with the person in charge, a resident, a neighbour, etc. Included are lodging or rooming houses, hotels, motels, tourist homes, nursing homes, hospitals, staff residences, communal quarters (military bases), work camps, jails, missions, group homes, and so on. Collective dwellings may be occupied by usual residents or solely by foreign and/or temporary residents.

> Source: http://www12.statcan.ca/census-recensement/2006/ref/dict/dwelling-logements002-eng.cfm

Cluster Sample

Cluster sampling is an easy way of gathering a large sample. It is used when researchers cannot get a complete list of the population they wish to study, but can get a complete list of groups, or "clusters," of the population. Rather than select individuals at random, this technique randomly chooses clusters. Usually, everyone in a cluster is included in the sample.

Suppose you wanted to investigate the use of lawn pesticides by the residents of Kelowna, but didn't have the resources to randomly sample the entire city. A cluster sample could be taken by identifying every street as a cluster. A random sampling of streets could be taken, and all residents of each chosen street could be included in the sample. It is easier to visit several streets in Kelowna than it is to bounce around the city in a random sample, observing the use of pesticides.

The main advantage of cluster sampling is that it is cost-effective. As long as the samples were chosen at random, researchers don't have to travel all over to get a representative sample. The disadvantage is that there is a higher, and more difficult to quantify, risk of sampling error.

NON-PROBABILITY/NON-RANDOM SAMPLING STRATEGIES

There is also a set of non-random techniques used to gather samples. They are less common in quantitative research, but you are still likely to encounter them, often when dealing with research done by polling firms or market research agencies.

Non-probability samples differ from probability samples in a few ways. They are not supposed to be representative of the population and are likely to somewhat biased. Non-probability samples are often used when researchers aren't concerned with representing an entire population. Here are some of the more common types of non-probability samples:

Convenience Sample

A **convenience sample** targets only individuals who possess characteristics that make them more accessible to the researcher. For example, if you live in Edmonton, it is easiest for you to derive a sample that contains only people living in Edmonton. Depending on the nature of your study, that might be okay, but you couldn't make generalizations about all of Canada by only researching in Edmonton. Convenience samples are useful for **pilot testing** a research instrument, like a questionnaire, when accuracy isn't a concern, but finding unclear questions and non-mutually exclusive response categories is.

Snowball Sample

Typically, **snowball sampling** techniques are used for populations that are not easily identified, resistant to being studied, or otherwise hard to reach. The term "snowball" is used because the sample increases in size as it rolls away from its source—just like a snowball. The sample will grow in size until it reaches the researcher's ideal. Researchers will make contact with a small group, asking members of that group to identify others who might be interested in participating in the study. Initial group members become informants, leading to others in their network.

Quota Sample

Quota samples are the non-probability counterpart to stratified samples. Often used in market research and opinion polls, they are a relatively cheap and quick way to get an adequate sample. As with a stratified sample, researchers decide on strata (such as levels of income), and then try to ensure that the sample is proportionately representative of the population in the categories of interest. Unlike a stratified sample, there is non-random sampling of each stratum's units. Since this is essentially a convenience sample, under-representation of less accessible groups is still a problem.

SAMPLING ERROR

Population samples rarely match the population perfectly. No matter how carefully a probability or non-probability sample is selected, there will be some degree of "mismatch" between the sample and the population. This is called sampling error. To differentiate between samples and population, different symbols are used to represent mean and standard deviation for a sample, versus mean and standard deviation for the population. The text will continue to use μ and σ to describe the mean and the standard deviation of the population. $\overline{X}$ and s will be used to describe the mean and the standard deviation of a sample.

EVERYDAY STATISTICS

The Right Sample for the Right Task

Each month, Statistics Canada conducts a survey called the Labour Force Survey, which estimates unemployment and the employment in the Canadian population. To collect its data, Statistics Canada divides each province into layers and selects small geographical areas from within each one. Each of the selected dwellings remains in the sample for six months and 1/6 is randomly sampled each month.

· ·

Q: What type of sampling method do you think Statistics Canada uses to conduct the Labour Force Survey?

TIPS FOR REDUCING SAMPLING ERROR

Sampling error and standard error are tied to each other. Reducing sampling error will usually reduce standard error too, so every good social statistician who collects his or her own samples aims to reduce sampling error, thereby reducing standard error.

Some error is to be expected in any sample that is smaller than the population. This bias may not be problematic for your research, as long as it is random. Non-random sources of bias are more serious, but there are some ways to avoid them when you are trying to derive a representative sample. Remember that probability samples are more representative than non-probability samples. When samples are not randomly selected, certain types of people are selected more often—the most agreeable, available, or even attractive—which affects the accuracy of your results.

An inadequate sampling frame is another potential problem. If certain members of your population are forgotten or excluded when the sampling frame is calculated, bias will be introduced in your research. Statistics Canada encounters difficulties when it is trying to enumerate Aboriginal and homeless populations. Not including these people will result in a misrepresentation of the Canadian population, biasing any results that come from these data. Statistics Canada tries to make its sampling frames as complete as possible in an effort to represent the entire population.

Finally, there is the problem of non-response. Potential respondents will sometimes refuse to answer questions, either because they don't want to or because they fear the consequences. If the non-response is random (e.g., if respondents were all equally unlikely to answer a question) this would not be much of a problem. Unfortunately, most studies find regularities in non-response, suggesting that certain people (men, those who are single, those with low education, etc.) are more likely to non-respond than are others.

GLOSSARY TERMS

Confidentiality (p. 73)

Convenience sample (p. 77)

Inferential statistical tests (p. 74)

Non-probability (p. 74)

Pilot testing (p. 77)

Population (p. 73)

Probability samples (p. 74)

Quota samples (p. 78)

Sample (p. 73)

Sampling error (p. 73)

Sampling frame (p. 75)

Simple random samples (p. 75)

Snowball sampling (p. 77)

Systematic random samples (p. 75)

PRACTICE QUESTIONS

1. You need to derive a sample of writing samples from a collection of grade six grammar classes. You have a list of all the children in the population, and your primary concern is with representativeness. Which sampling strategy would you use? Why?

2. The University of Alberta has 21 faculties, schools, and colleges. If you wanted to draw a representative sample of the entire student body, but wanted to be sure that you had a sufficient number of observations from each faculty, school, and college, which sampling strategy would you use? Why?

3. You're working with a vulnerable, hard-to-reach population, and would like to administer a questionnaire. Your primary concern is obtaining a sufficient sample size, even if representativeness is limited. Which sampling technique would you use? Why?

4. Frieda is having trouble choosing people to join her new orchestra, not because of a lack of interest, but because she is getting too much interest. She decides that she'll sample her population to find suitable people. She feels that everyone has equal talent, but she needs to ensure that each instrument is adequately represented. She approaches you for advice on how to randomly select the right mix of musicians. Which sampling technique would you tell her to use? Why?

5. Draw a 10 per cent simple random sample (use the random numbers in Appendix F) and a 10 per cent stratified random sample from the numbers below. Think about the strengths and weaknesses of each approach.

37	93	43	35	77	99
55	52	12	86	32	12
43	16	57	3	95	52
39	99	24	17	36	36
34	65	28	72	48	33
66	82	60	50	57	2
66	78	8	35	53	44
61	62	93	35	6	83
63	36	28	42	3	26
81	3	92	99	17	64

6. The 2011 census did not have a long-form version of the questionnaire that was distributed to 20 per cent of the Canadian population. Instead, the government of the day decided to employ a national household survey (NHS) in place of the long-form questionnaire, and to administer it to 33 per cent of the Canadian population, hoping that increasing the sample size would offset the non-response rates of a voluntary survey. The NHS questionnaire was largely identical to the 2006 census long-form questionnaire, except that individuals could choose whether they wanted to complete it. The expected response rate for the NHS was 50 per cent, which means that only half of all people issued an NHS questionnaire would

complete and return it. For the long-form census in 2006, the comparable response rate was 94 per cent.

a. If response rates were the same as in 2006, what percentage of the population would have filled out the long-form questionnaire in 2011? With a population of 33.5 million in 2011, how many Canadians would have completed a long-form census in 2011?

b. What percentage of the Canadian population was expected to complete the 2011 NHS? How many people is this?

Answers to the practice questions for Chapter 8 can be found on page S-7.

CHAPTER 9

Generalizing from Samples to Populations

LEARNING OBJECTIVES

In this chapter, we'll continue to move from discussing populations to discussing samples, by studying:

- the central limit theorem;
- confidence intervals and how to calculate them;
- how *t*-distributions can be used for small samples;
- the sampling distribution of means and proportions.

INTRODUCTION

Using the insights that can be gained from the normal curve, it is possible to estimate how closely a sample approximates the population. To do this, we will use the sampling distribution of means, the sampling distribution of proportions, and the central limit theorem.

First, let's start with the sampling distribution of means, which is easiest to explain with an example. Suppose that you wanted to identify the average body mass index (BMI) of all Canadian adolescents. You could measure all of the roughly 4.2 million people between the ages of 10 and 19 and get an accurate measure of the average BMI, but it would be prohibitively expensive and time-consuming to do so. Instead, you can use what you know about probability sampling and the normal distribution and get the same results in a more cost-efficient way. Instead of taking 4.2 million measurements, you could take a random subset of that group, using one of the sampling techniques outlined in the previous chapter.

When choosing the subset, you will need to consider a few things:

- How many people will you want to measure?
- How many people do you need to measure to get an accurate depiction of the population?
- How many people can you afford to measure?

A bigger sample size will give a more accurate approximation, but too big a sample will be nearly as impractical to measure as the entire population, thereby defeating the purpose of sampling. You could take a series of samples and plot them to reveal the **sampling distribution of means**. Repeatedly resampling from the adolescent population and calculating the average BMI from each sample will provide you with a list of means, like the coin-tossing example in Chapter 4 (except that this yields a **sampling distribution of proportions**, which we'll discuss after we discuss means). On their own, each of these means will be close to the population mean for BMI, but if you were to present the means as a histogram, you would get—you guessed it—an approximation of the normal curve. The most noteworthy difference in this instance is that observations represent means instead of people.

It is the **central limit theorem** that allows us to assume that any sample statistic we generate from a known population (such as the mean) will lie somewhere along a normal (or nearly normal) distribution. To continue with our example above, if we were to repeatedly draw a 5 per cent sample from our 4.2 million 10–19 year olds, and if we then plotted the mean BMI that we generate from each of our samples, the central limit theorem states that we'd have a distribution that is "normal enough" that we can consider it to be normal. With this information, we can use many of the equations that we've covered in the text so far.

The sampling distribution of means has three other notable qualities: First, the mean of (sample) means will be equal to the population mean μ. So a mean BMI calculated using a series of population subset means (for example, five per cent random samples taken 1,000 times) will be equal to the mean BMI for the whole population. The mean of means will be very close to the population mean.

Second, the distribution of means will be quite tightly clustered around the true population mean (though still following a normal distribution). The variance and standard deviation of the sampling distribution of means is small, so we can be fairly confident that the mean of any random sample will be very close to the true population mean. As a result, instead of taking numerous samples to approximate the population, this characteristic of the

BOX 9.1

From Populations to Samples: Relevant Symbols for Describing Sample Characteristics

Luckily, moving from populations to samples usually doesn't result in substantial changes to any equations. But some of the symbols, listed at right, are different:

	Sample	Population
Mean	$\overline{X}$	μ
Standard deviation	s	σ
Variance	s^2	σ^2

sampling distribution of means ensures that one random sample should be close enough to the population sample.

Finally, since it's unusual to take more than one sample, it's unlikely that we will know much about the sampling distribution of means for our samples (we don't know the mean of means, or the standard deviation of means). If we assume that our population is normally distributed, we can estimate how closely the mean of our sample approximates the population mean by using the following equation:

$$\sigma_{\bar{X}} = \frac{\sigma_X}{\sqrt{N}}$$

This equation gives us the **standard error of the sample mean** ($\sigma_{\bar{X}}$) when the population standard deviation (σ_x) is known. The standard error is described as the standard deviation of the population divided by the square root of the sample size. As you can see by the denominator $\sqrt{N}$, the larger the sample size is, the smaller the standard error. This makes sense, because we expect the mean to become more accurate as the sample size approaches the population. As sample size increases, the standard error should approach—but, until the sample and population are one and the same, never reach—zero.

In reality, we will rarely have a sample that is close in size to our population (the 2006 census public-use sample, for example, is only 2.7 per cent of the population), so we need to attach a measure of how confident we are in our measurement of the mean. This is known as the **confidence interval**.

CONFIDENCE INTERVALS

Because it is difficult to be certain that the mean we draw from a sample is exactly the same as the mean of the population we're interested in, we need to acknowledge that there is a chance of error, called the **standard error**, in the estimate. Think of the standard error as a type of standard deviation, except that instead of measuring how far an observation is from a mean, it refers to the distance that a sample mean is from a population mean.

To indicate level of confidence, we need to employ the standard error. Because the standard error is derived from the standard deviation, it can be used in almost the same way as the standard deviation. Instead of determining what proportion of observations lie between one, two, and three deviations from the mean, we are determining how much confidence we have in the accuracy of the mean taken from the sample.

Think of the sample mean as one of many in the sampling distribution of means. Each mean can be treated as an observation. Just as we can be certain that 68 per cent of all observations lie between ±1 standard deviation from the mean in a normal distribution, we can also be certain that roughly 68 per cent of sample means lie between ±1 standard error from the population mean. Extending this, we can construct a "confidence interval" by providing the upper and lower ranges (or **confidence limits**) of the standard error calculations. We can also construct a 95 per cent confidence interval by postulating that our population mean is within ±2 standard error units of the sample mean, or a 99 per cent confidence interval by postulating that our population mean is within ±3 standard error units of the sample mean. This translates to $z_{critical}$ values of 1.96 and 2.58, respectively, from the sample mean. To understand where we got 1.96 and 2.58 from, we need to look at the z-distribution (see Box 9.2).

Looking at the equation for the standard error, notice that the standard error will differ, based on both sample size and the size of the standard deviation. If a standard deviation is large, the standard error is also likely to be large. Calculating confidence intervals requires multiplying the standard error by the appropriate z-value (1.96 for a 95 per cent confidence interval, and 2.58 for a 99 per cent confidence interval).

BOX 9.2

The Steps: Estimating a Population Mean with a Known Confidence Interval

1. Calculate the sample mean.
2. Assuming that the population standard deviation (σ_X) is known, calculate the standard error of the sample mean by using the following equation:

$$\sigma_{\bar{X}} = \frac{\sigma_X}{\sqrt{N}}$$

Otherwise, you'll need to rely on the sample standard deviation and this equation:

$$s_{\bar{X}} = \frac{s_X}{\sqrt{n-1}}$$

3. Find the relevant value of $z_{critical}$ in the z-table in column A of Appendix A that corresponds with a 95 per cent confidence interval (1.96 for 95 per cent, 2.57 for 99 per cent in a two-tailed test).

4. Insert the relevant values into the following equation:

$$\text{Confidence Interval} = \bar{X} \pm (z_{critical} * \sigma_{\bar{X}})$$

or

$$\text{Confidence Interval} = \bar{X} \pm (z_{critical} * s_{\bar{X}})$$

Note that it will be necessary to do this for both the upper and lower bounds, which means that you will need to solve the equation for a positive and negative value of $z_{critical}$.

EVERYDAY STATISTICS

Confidence Intervals and Opinion Polls

In Canada, opinion polls are often conducted to gain an understanding of the opinion of the public on a specific issue, using a sample of the population. Since the polls are based on a sample of the population, the results are subject to a sampling error. The margin of error in opinion polls is usually represented as a confidence interval.

. . . .

Q: Why do you think confidence intervals are used to represent the sampling error in opinion polls?

THE *t*-DISTRIBUTION

William Gosset was a mathematician and chemist who graduated from Oxford in 1899. Arthur Guinness Son & Co. Ltd. was looking for new ways to make a beer of consistent quality and decided that Gosset was the person to ask for help. There was considerable variability in brewing quality across batches, making it difficult for Guinness to establish regularity in taste and standards. Guinness wanted to improve its consistency, but didn't know how and had neither the budget nor the inclination to botch large batches of brew to attain consistency. Gosset was thus limited to working with a few small batches. At that time, most statistical work focused on very large samples, so Gosset had to forgo traditional methods and develop techniques for assessing small samples.

The histograms in Chapter 5 showed that small samples tend to produce distributions that deviate from the normal distribution. Most important, the tails in small samples are larger, and the kurtosis value is often lower, even though the variable might have a normal distribution. Gosset's problem—and, often, our problem—was that the sample size was too small to accommodate the normal curve, causing him to underestimate the standard error. This led Gosset to the **student's *t*-distribution**.

Before Gosset, statisticians knew that their standard error estimates were slightly too small, but they surmised (correctly) that the difference would be very slight in samples that were greater than 50. Gosset determined the exact relationship between small samples and the normal curve with his discovery of the *t*-distribution.

The *t*-distribution is actually an infinite number of curves, one for every sample size greater than or equal to two. As sample size increases, the *t*-distribution increasingly resembles the standard normal distribution. By the time sample size reaches 50, the differences between the two are difficult to detect.

Values for the *t*-distribution can be derived by using the following equation (when mean $= 0$ and the variance is greater than one)

$$t = \frac{\overline{X} - \mu}{s_x}$$

or

$$t = \frac{\overline{X} - \mu}{s_x / \sqrt{n - 1}}$$

or

$$t = \frac{\overline{X} - \mu}{\sigma_{\overline{X}}}$$

or

$$t = \frac{\overline{X} - \mu}{\sigma_X / \sqrt{N}}$$

The last two equations, though technically correct, are unlikely to be very helpful because they are used to calculate t when population characteristics are known, even though t is used for small samples.

In the numerator for each equation, we subtract the population mean from the sample mean and divide that number by the denominator, which is the standard error estimate of the sample mean. The second equation is the same, except that the denominator is expressed as the standard deviation of the sample, divided by the square root of the sample size minus one, instead of the standard error. If you recall the earlier equation for standard error, you will recognize that the four equations produce essentially the same result, and which we use depends on the information at our disposal.

However, the equations are often useless, because we don't know the population mean or standard deviation. In fact, we usually know very little about the population, which is what got us into this mess in the first place!

The best we can strive for is a range where we're fairly certain our population mean will fall. For example, if we derived a sample of 1,000 and determined that the average number of drinks that the average person in the sample has per day is 2.3, it would be helpful to know how confident we could be that the mean for the Canadian population is ±0.2 drinks; say, 90 per cent, 95 per cent, or 99 per cent confident. Even though we don't know the population mean, we could use the t-distribution and say that we are 95 per cent certain that the average Canadian has between 2.1 and 2.5 drinks per day. In the equations, it is the population mean that we are trying to estimate. To do this, we have to find the t-value. Finding the t-value requires an understanding of **degrees of freedom**.

BOX 9.3

Why Is It Called the Student's *t*-Distribution?

Before Gosset's arrival at the Guinness Brewery, a Guinness employee had published a paper revealing some of the company's brewing secrets. As a result, Guinness heavy-handedly forbade all of its employees from publishing articles of any kind!

When Gosset developed the *t*-distribution as an employee of Guinness, then, he couldn't share his discovery with the world (at least, not unless he wanted to lose his job), and selected the pseudonym "Student" to protect his anonymity. Since that time, the distribution that he discovered has been known as Student's *t*-distribution.

WHAT IS A DEGREE OF FREEDOM?

Imagine that you live with five roommates, and split the bills according to usage (don't worry about how we calculate who owes what for now). This month, the total is $500, and your room-mates claim $435 of the bill. You don't need to know what each of the others owes to know that your share is $65, because what you owe is constrained by the amount that your roommates owe. Any combination of values could be assigned to what your roommates owe. As long as the sum equals $435, the amount that you owe does not change. You have the freedom to assign values (within reason) to everyone in the sample *except* the last observation. This is the main principle behind degrees of freedom. In this instance, there are five minus one, or four, degrees of freedom.

Typically, when working with the mean, the degrees of freedom (*df*) are equal to the number of observations in a sample, minus one ($n - 1$).

$$df = n - 1$$

Using the *t*-statistic, instead of *z*, is suitable when sample sizes are small and you want to construct confidence intervals. When constructing intervals, knowing *t* and the degrees of freedom allows you to account for the slight differences between the distribution of a variable with small *n*, and a distribution taken from a larger sample. When should you use *t* instead of *z*? Look at the values in Appendix B (the *t*-table) and notice that *t*-values converge upon those for *z* as degrees of freedom increase. At *df* = 120 they are identical; *t* should only be used when the sample size is less than 120.

ONE-TAILED VERSUS TWO-TAILED ESTIMATES

Looking at Appendix B, you'll notice a distinction between one- and two-tailed tests. To correctly estimate the confidence intervals for the population mean, you'll have to know which chart to use.

One-tailed tests determine how likely it is that an observation is above or below a specific threshold value. For instance, if we used sample data to find the probability of someone living below the poverty line we would use a one-tailed test. Because we have a hypothesis about the direction of the relationship (that is, the person is expected to be toward the bottom of the income distribution), we can focus our attention on one end of the distribution.

To estimate a population mean from a sample mean, a two-tailed test is used. If the sample is a representative sample, there is no reason to hypothesize that the value of the sample mean should be above or below the population mean. If the sample is random, there is an equal likelihood of it being above or below the population mean. There is no way to specify which direction we expect the difference to fall in, so both ends of the distribution have to be included. Two-tailed tests are more common, so they are the only kind shown in the *z*-table in Appendix A. If you need to conduct a one-tailed test using *z*, use the *t*-table with $df = \infty$, which gives you a critical value of 1.645.

BOX 9.4

Equations for Moving from Populations to Samples

Luckily, moving from samples to populations doesn't usually result in substantial changes to the equations but there are some new symbols that you'll need to be familiar with, embedded in these familiar equations. These new symbols and the resulting equations are listed below:

	Sample	Population
Standard error	$s_{\bar{X}} = \dfrac{s_X}{\sqrt{n-1}}$	$\sigma_{\bar{X}} = \dfrac{\sigma_X}{\sqrt{N}}$
Standard deviation	$s = \sqrt{\dfrac{\sum(X-\bar{X})^2}{n-1}}$	$\sigma = \sqrt{\dfrac{\sum(X-\bar{X})^2}{N}}$
z-statistic	$z = \dfrac{\bar{X}-\mu}{s_{\bar{X}}}$	$z = \dfrac{\bar{X}-\mu}{\sigma_{\bar{X}}}$
t-statistic	$t = \dfrac{\bar{X}-\mu}{s_x/\sqrt{n-1}}$	$t = \dfrac{\bar{X}-\mu}{\sigma_x/\sqrt{N}}$

(Although you shouldn't ever need to calculate a t-statistic for a population)

THE SAMPLING DISTRIBUTION OF PROPORTIONS

Much as we are able to make sense of sample means by relating them to the normal curve, we are also able to make sense of proportions the same way, thanks to the central limit theorem, the idea that the distribution will increasingly resemble a normal distribution as the number of trials increases.

To keep things simple, we'll look at proportions with only two categories here. If you were interested in proportions with more than two categories, however (such as modelling voter distribution in a national election), the logic would need only to be straightforwardly extended. Imagine that you wanted to identify the proportion of the population of Quebec that supported the 2012 student strikes. As you would expect, there is a "real" answer out there, and the only way to find this out would be to ask every single resident of Quebec—unlikely to happen. A second possibility would be to take several samples from the population and use the sample proportions to estimate the proportion within the population. Although more likely (you could choose to take random samples of people within certain communities), this would still be a lot of work. Furthermore, since the central limit theorem tells us that one well-chosen sample is all we really need, the easiest and most likely choice we'd make is to take just one sample from the whole population of Quebec. In the section below, we will discuss the techniques for doing this.

USING DEGREES OF FREEDOM AND THE *t*-DISTRIBUTION TO ESTIMATE POPULATION PROPORTIONS

To estimate population proportions, a measurement commonly used for opinion polls, we use a slightly different equation for the standard error:

$$s_p = \sqrt{\frac{p(1-p)}{n}}$$

The difference is in the numerator, where the proportion in a certain category is multiplied by one minus that proportion. The denominator includes only n, even though, technically, $n - 1$ would be appropriate, because the equation deals with a sample.

Once the standard error of the sample proportion has been calculated, the confidence interval remains the same, except that $\overline{X}$ is replaced by P:

$$\text{Confidence Interval} = P \pm (z_{critical} * s_{\overline{X}})$$

Everything else is the same, but let's look at an example anyway. Suppose that you wanted to gauge Canadian Aboriginal opinion about the 2006 protests in Caledonia, in southwestern Ontario, over land issues. You polled 500 Aboriginal people (composed of First Nations, Métis, and Inuit peoples). In your sample, you found that 62 per cent of all respondents believed that the protests were warranted. As interesting as this percentage is, what you really want to know is the attitude of the *entire* Aboriginal population of Canada, not just the sample. Since there are roughly one million Aboriginal people living in Canada, any claim you make from only 500 respondents will be suspect. Researchers try to put these kinds of doubts to rest by reporting confidence intervals. Using the information we have, let's construct a confidence interval.

First, we need to estimate the standard error of the sample proportion, using the following equation:

$$s_p = \sqrt{\frac{P(1-p)}{n}}$$
$$= \sqrt{\frac{0.62(1-0.62)}{500}}$$
$$= \sqrt{\frac{0.236}{500}}$$
$$= 0.022$$

To find the 95 per cent confidence interval for the population, we need to know the margin of error (z times the standard error). To find it, we need to find the value of 1.96 from the z chart. Why 1.96? Because it is the cut-point (in standard deviations) from which 95 per cent of all cases lie. We calculate the degrees of freedom to be n minus one, or 499. To be 95 per cent confident that our estimate is correct, we need to provide the range that 95 per cent of all observations fall into. If the sample were smaller, we would need to look up the value of t by using the degrees of freedom instead of z.

Second, multiply the standard error by 1.96 to find the margin of error.

$$\text{Margin of error} = 1.96 * S_p$$
$$= 1.96 * 0.022$$
$$= 0.043$$

Third, add and subtract the margin of error from the sample proportion, to find the values of the confidence interval.

$$95\% \text{ confidence interval} = \bar{X} \pm 1.96 S_{\bar{X}}$$
$$= 0.62 \pm 0.043$$
$$= 0.577 \text{ to } 0.663$$

Now we can say that we are 95 per cent confident that between 57.7 per cent and 66.3 per cent of Aboriginal peoples in Canada believe that the protests in Caledon were warranted.

BOX 9.5

The Steps: How to Estimate Population Proportions by Using Only Sample Characteristics

1. Estimate the standard error of the sample mean: $s_p = \sqrt{\dfrac{p(1-p)}{n}}$

2. Use $df = n - 1$ to calculate the degrees of freedom to find the critical value of z, or t, to find the desired confidence interval: $= p \pm z_{critical} * S_p$

3. It will be necessary to do this for both the upper and lower bounds (which explains why ± appears in the equation), meaning that you will have to solve the equation for a positive and negative value of $z_{critical}$.

THE BINOMIAL DISTRIBUTION

Technically speaking, the distribution of sample proportions is not a normal distribution. It is instead called the binomial distribution, and it differs from a normal distribution in that there are only two possible outcomes, the sum of which is always one. Furthermore, rather than modelling the dichotomy in a normal distribution, we are modelling the *probability* of the occurrence of an outcome in a binomial distribution.

To illustrate, let's look once again at coin-tossing. Tossing a coin in the air twice per trial will yield one of the following sequences:

TABLE 9.1 | Coin Toss: A Hypothetical Example with Two Tosses per Trial

Trial	First toss	Second toss
1	Heads	Heads
2	Heads	Tails
3	Tails	Heads
4	Tails	Tails

If you were to model the probability of one outcome, such as the number of heads, and used the data above, you'd have the following:

Probability of getting zero heads: ¼ (trial 4 had no heads).
Probability of getting heads once: ½ (trials 2 and 3 each had one head).
Probability of getting two heads: ¼ (trial 1 had 2 heads).

We now have four "observations" in the form of calculated probabilities from our four trials, which we can then plot:

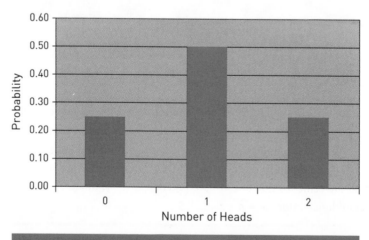

FIGURE 9.1 | Probability of the Number of Coin Tosses That Came Up Heads

We describe this distribution as "discrete" because there are only certain plausible probability calculations. For example, it would not be possible to have a probability of 0.4 in the exercise above, even though technically the value exists. Thus, the distribution cannot be considered a normal distribution. Instead, processes with only discrete probabilities are distinct, and the distribution for binary outcomes is the binomial distribution.

Don't fret about this too much, since we typically use the normal distribution to approximate the binomial. The normal distribution approximates the binomial when (a) sample size is sufficiency large, and (b) the probability of either outcome is not too close to 0 or 1. Since "sufficiently large" and "not too close" in the conditions above are both subjective, however, a fairly common rule of thumb is that sample size times probability of positive outcome is ≥ 10, as is the probability of a negative outcome.

$$n * p \geq 10$$

Applying this to our coin tossing example above, we have four observations (n) in our sample and the probability (p) of success in obtaining a head in a coin toss is 0.5. We would say then that our sample is too small to use the normal distribution as an approximation of the binomial, because n (4) times p (0.5) is less 2, much less than ten. Furthermore, the probability of getting tails ($1 - p$), the other outcome of interest, is also too small at

$$n * (1 - p) \geq 10$$
$$4 * 0.5 \geq 2$$

As you can see, this quick calculation penalizes heavily for binomial probabilities that stray from 0.5, which is something beyond your control. What you can often control, however, is sample size, so please always try to ensure that you have an adequate sample, which for $p = 0.5$ would be

$$n * p \geq 10$$
$$n * 0.5 \geq 10$$
$$n \geq 20$$

Consequently, in a situation like coin tossing, where $p = 0.5$, we should have a minimum of 20 observations to ensure that we can use the normal distribution to approximate the binomial.

Otherwise, one day you may face the proposition of learning about binomial distributions, something that is beyond the discussion in this text!

CONCLUSION

One of the bugbears of statistical analysis is trying to determine whether or not a certain relationship is real or due to sampling error. The short answer to this question is that as long as we are using samples, we *never* know conclusively that sampling error is not behind our results. The best we can do is to attach a high level of confidence to our results.

This concludes our discussion of univariate statistics. The coming chapters will explore methods of analysis using more than one variable. Most of what's been covered so far is foundational, but without that knowledge, performing any statistical analysis is nearly impossible. Now the focus will shift to analysis with more than one variable and how to measure and hypothesize about relationships between variables.

GLOSSARY TERMS

Central limit theorem (p. 83)
Confidence interval (p. 84)
Confidence limits (p. 84)
Degrees of freedom (p. 87)
Sampling distribution of means (p. 82)

Sampling distribution of proportions (p. 83)
Standard error (p. 84)
Standard error of the sample mean (p. 84)
Student's t-distribution (p. 86)

PRACTICE QUESTIONS

1. A research study was conducted, examining the differences between the perceived life satisfaction of men and women. Ten men and ten women were given a life satisfaction test (known to have high reliability and validity). Scores on the measure range from 0 to 60, with high scores indicating high life satisfaction and low scores implying the opposite. The data are presented below:

Men	Women
45	34
38	22
52	15
48	27
25	37
39	41
51	24
46	19
55	26
46	36

a. Calculate the mean, variance, and standard deviation for both men and women.
b. Calculate the standard errors for each mean estimate.
c. Estimate the 95 per cent confidence interval for each sample mean.

2. Professor Smart recently returned a lab assignment to his students. Before doing this, he polled them on the number of hours they spent on the assignments. There were

24 individuals in the lab, and the data were used to make inferences about subsequent classes. The data are presented below:

4.5	20	19	9
22	8	7	8.5
7.5	2.5	14.5	3.5
9	5	9	8
11	10.5	9	18
7.5	15	14	20

Compute and interpret the 95 per cent confidence interval. What does the interval mean?

3. In a sample of 50 individuals, 34 per cent prefer soft drink A to soft drink B. In the population, we could be 99 per cent confident that the real proportion lies between _____ per cent and _____ per cent.

4. What do you think happens to the standard error of a sample mean as the number of observations increases? What about confidence intervals?

5. You are taking a class with 12 other students, and you recently wrote an exam that yields an average score of exactly 78 per cent. When returning your exams, your professor informs you that she is unable to find your exam (all other students receive theirs).

75	44	89	92
92	55	66	86
97	76	83	88

What is your exam score?

6. Suppose that you have 10 pet cats, and that you know their average weight is four kilograms (all 10 cats weigh 40 kilograms), with a standard deviation of one kilogram. Recently, two of your cats escaped. Determined to find them, you decide to put posters around your neighbourhood. You record the weights of your remaining eight cats, calculate the standard deviation, and find it to be 0.8. Thinking about the weight of your cats in terms of degrees of freedom, would you be able to identify the weight of the remaining lost cat if you located and weighed the ninth one?

7. Suppose that in a sample of 121 students you find that 40 per cent of students in York Lanes purchase at least one food item per day. What is the 95 per cent confidence interval of the amount in the population?

8. Your friend Clara is very proud of her dog, and over the years she has compared her dog to yours. If you were the type of person who used statistics to assess her various claims, would you use a one-tailed or two-tailed assessment to verify the following statements?

    a. "My dog is bigger than your dog."
    b. "My dog is different from your dog."
    c. "My dog has more hair than your dog."
    d. "My dog wouldn't act like your dog does in public."
    e. "My dog weighs less than your dog."

9. Throughout most of 2011, software designer Rovio sold an average of 40,000 copies of its popular game *Angry Birds* every day, with a standard deviation of 1,000 copies. Now, on a random day in early 2012, Rovio has sold 38,000 copies. Can you be 95 per cent confident that this was a regular day?

10. How many texts does the average teen send in a day? Rogers Communications Inc. has asked you to answer this question. They provide you with a random (and anonymous) sample of their client base, yielding the following numbers:

47	11	66	94	77
99	50	10	57	2
100	13	37	93	37
97	79	81	36	78

What range could you give them with a 95 per cent confidence interval?

Answers to the practice questions for Chapter 9 can be found on page S-7.

PART II | BIVARIATE STATISTICS

CHAPTER 10

Testing Hypotheses between a Sample and a Population

LEARNING OBJECTIVES

This chapter will introduce ways to build and test hypotheses. Topics will include:

- null and research hypotheses;
- hypothesis testing with one large sample and a population;
- hypothesis testing with one small sample and a population.

INTRODUCTION

So far in this book, we've looked at the gap between sample means and population means as being the sole sources of sampling error. That is, we've assumed that the primary source of discrepancy between a sample and a population is that the sample does not perfectly represent the population. This is why it is so important to assess the amount of error when attempting to generalize from samples to populations, because that is believed to be the sole source of the gap. If a sample is not representative, how can we be certain that the observed trends we see in this sample also exist in the population?

There's another reason to compare the mean of a sample to a population: hypothesis testing. Here, rather than assume that sampling error is the source of difference, the difference could now stem from some other, systematic, factors; what that factor is becomes the matter under investigation. Whether test scores from McGill University differ from the national or provincial average, whether the summer of 2011 was significantly warmer than average, whether Saskatoon has a significantly higher quality of life than the rest of Canada—these are the types of issues that can be solved by comparing a sample mean to a population mean. Furthermore, the difference (if one is found and our sampling techniques are sound) doesn't stem from just sampling error (although it's likely that some of the gap can and will be attributed to sampling error).

This represents quite a departure from what we've discussed so far in the text. Up to this point we have been thinking of the gap between a population and a sample as sampling error, as something we wanted to get rid of. Now, the gap is what we use to identify whether a sample mean differs from a population mean in a *systematic* way.

For now, let's assume we have a sample that is sufficiently large (>120 observations), and that we're interested only in making comparisons to a population. Also assume that we know the population mean and standard deviation. Doing this means that we get to use the z-distribution, rather than the t-distribution. We'll look at how to handle a small sample and a population by using the t-distribution afterwards. But first, let's look at hypotheses.

WHAT'S A HYPOTHESIS?

You've probably heard people talk about hypotheses before. Perhaps you've even learned about them in your research methods course, but in case you haven't, a brief reminder might help.

In essence, a hypothesis is a tentative statement about the relationship between two variables (or potentially more, but we are only looking at two here). A hypothesis is a specific, testable prediction about a relationship that you expect to emerge from your analysis. For example, a study designed to look at the relationship between not studying for an exam and studying for an exam might have a hypothesis that states, "This study will test the hypothesis that people who study for statistics exams will have significantly higher scores than average."

A hypothesis like the one above (called a **research** or **alternative hypothesis** and denoted by H_a or H_1, H_2, H_3, etc.) is always accompanied by a **null hypothesis**. When casting hypotheses, it's important to remember that they must be *mutually exclusive and exhaustive*. A null hypothesis (usually denoted by H_0) is typically a statement of no relationship, that is, the sample mean will not be significantly different from a population mean. There are also instances where a null hypothesis indicates a direction, but these are less common. For example, the research hypothesis about the relationship between studying and statistics grades points to a significantly higher average grade for those who study. The null hypothesis could either be that there is no significant difference between those who study and the average, or that those who study have average grades that are equal to or less than the overall average. This requires you to make the ridiculous assumption that the average person probably doesn't study for their statistics exam, but let's suspend this dark prospect temporarily. The first null hypothesis does not imply a direction whereas the second does. Either is acceptable and should be driven by the research question you are asking.

Typically, a null hypothesis will be directional when the research hypothesis is. So, if our research hypothesis is that the average for those who study will surpass the overall average ($\overline{X} > \mu$), we are implying a direction to the relationship (recall that $\overline{X}$ refers to a sample mean and μ is the population mean). Our null hypothesis should also reflect that directionality. For this, we might formulate a null hypothesis that those who study will have an average that is equal to or less than those who don't study ($\overline{X} \leq \mu$). If we cared only about difference, not directionality, our research hypothesis would need only to state the existence of difference between the sample mean (those who study) and the overall average gained from your many years as a stats prof

($\overline{X} \neq \mu$), and the null hypothesis would assert no significant differences between the two ($\overline{X} = \mu$). As you can see, these are very different sets of hypotheses, geared to answer different questions. Which of these you choose depends on the information you're interested in obtaining.

Statistically, as you might have gleaned from the discussion above, choosing between null and research hypotheses is often done by comparing a sample mean to a population mean with the help of the normal distribution. Failing to find a significant gap between the sample mean and the population mean implies that there isn't sufficient cause to believe that a sample is significantly different from a population. But if you find a gap, it means one of two things: (1) a gap exists, and the sample of interest differs from the population, or (2) a gap exists, and it is due to sampling error. It is impossible to know with 100 per cent certainty which of the two possibilities is true. That is why we must settle for a confidence interval. Similarly, if no gap is found, it could be because there actually isn't a gap or because there's sampling error. This uncertainty is why we *never* say in the social sciences that we've proven either the null or the research hypothesis to be correct. Instead, the best we can say is that we have rejected or failed to reject the null hypothesis. Notice that we are discussing the null, rather than research, hypothesis; although there is no statistical reason to look at the null hypothesis, out of convention we typically discuss the null hypothesis when we are rejecting or failing to reject hypotheses. Research hypotheses often don't get much mention.

Although there is no statistical reason to focus on null hypotheses, it does make good sense to do so in terms of inferential logic. Imagine that you were visiting Earth from another planet, and you land in a maternity ward in a hospital in Waterloo, Ontario. Every person you see is much smaller than you—they are babies, after all! This leads you to hypothesize that all people from Waterloo weigh five kilograms or less. If everyone in your sample in the maternity ward satisfies the weight condition, would you say that you've proven this statement? Inferentially, this logic is flawed because you haven't measured everyone in Waterloo, so it's impossible to know with absolute certainty that this statement is true. But if you find someone in Waterloo who weighs *more* than five kilograms, you have reason to fail to reject the null hypothesis, because you've found an observation in your sample that contradicts the research hypothesis.

This is also why we cannot reject, or fail to reject, the null hypothesis with 100 per cent certainty. It is possible, for example, that the observer above was visiting Waterloo from another city. The best we can do is reject or fail to reject the null hypothesis with a high level of confidence (usually 95 per cent). This means that 95 times out of 100, or 19 times out of 20 (95/100 = 19/20), our conclusions would be the same as the one we just made if we drew a different sample from the population of interest.

What this means is that in the social sciences—indeed, in all sciences—hypothesis testing carries with it the possibility of making the wrong decision about rejecting or failing to reject the null hypothesis. If we use a 95 per cent confidence interval, there's a 5 per cent (or 1 in 20) chance that we've made the wrong choice. If we choose to reject the null hypothesis when it is actually true, we've made a **type one error**; if we fail to reject the null hypothesis when it is not true, we've made a **type two error**.

Which of the two error types do you think is more serious? Well, that depends on what you are doing. If, for example, you are looking at the effect of an experimental drug on a serious illness, failing to find an effect when in fact there is one, which would be a type two error, can result in a lost opportunity to develop a potentially life-saving drug. On the other hand, type one errors can be equally problematic, because they would lead you to conclude that a treatment or intervention has an effect on an outcome when in fact it doesn't. Can you imagine committing a type one error when you are studying the effect of prison sentences as a deterrent for certain types of crime? The implications of a mistake here can also be serious, underscoring the importance of doing everything possible to minimize both types of errors.

ONE-TAILED AND TWO-TAILED HYPOTHESIS TESTS

The type of difference you are looking for between your sample and your population will guide you when choosing between a one-tailed or two-tailed test. If your goal is simply to identify difference without direction (are Maritimers different from other Canadians?), then you are interested in a two-tailed test. If you believe that there is a direction to the difference (are Maritimers friendlier than other Canadians?), then you're interested in a one-tailed test. In other words, if you are hypothesizing directionality, then you're likely looking at a one-tailed test; if you're not interested in directionality, then it's probably a two-tailed test that you're after.

Appendix A contains both sets of values of interest. Generally, in the social sciences, we attribute any difference beyond the 95 per cent confidence interval to be statistically significant. In other words, if a sample mean is more than 1.96 standard deviations from the population mean, then we can say with confidence that the difference likely exists in the real world instead of just in the data. As this relates to your null and research hypothesis, you would *reject* the null hypothesis.

Let's further our understanding of hypothesis testing with an example. Every three years the Organisation for Economic Co-operation and Development (OECD) conducts tests of the reading ability of 15-year-olds in many of its member states. Each time, students are shown different kinds of written text, ranging from prose to lists, graphs, and diagrams. They are set a series of tasks, requiring them to retrieve specific information, to interpret the text, and to reflect on and evaluate what they have read. These texts are from a variety of reading situations, including reading for private use, occupational purposes, education, and public use. In 2009 (the most recent year for which data are available at time of writing), Canadian youth achieved a mean score of 524 ($s = 90$), compared to 493 ($\sigma = 93$) for OECD nations overall. The Canadian data were calculated from 22,383 students, and the overall scores came from roughly 470,000 respondents. Are Canadian students significantly different from the OECD average?

To answer this question, we first need to generate a null (H_0) and a research hypothesis (H_1). The hypotheses can be stated in words:

H_0: On average, there is no significant difference between the reading scores of Canadian 15-year-olds and 15-year-olds in other OECD countries.

H₁: On average, Canadian 15-year-olds differ significantly from 15-year-olds in other OECD countries.

Or, we can articulate our hypotheses with numbers:

$H_0: \overline{X} = 493$

$H_1: \overline{X} \neq 493$

In this example, we have an abundance of information to compare Canadian 15 year olds to those in the other OECD countries. We have the following pieces of information:

- sample size for Canada and all OECD countries;
- standard deviation for Canada and all OECD countries;
- mean for Canada and all OECD countries.

We are lucky to have this much information, because it allows us to compare the Canadian sample to the OECD sample quite easily. At the same time, despite having 470,000 OECD respondents, it is important to note that this is a sample, and that, technically, we do not have any population information. This serves as a good illustration of how rare population data are. For the purposes of illustration, and so that we can use real data rather than something synthetic, imagine that the OECD data come from a population, and that it is only the Canadian data that comprise a sample. Table 10.1 shows the symbols that we can attach to each number:

TABLE 10.1 | The PISA Scores for the Canadian Sample of the OECD, "Population," OECD Pisa Scores 2009

The PISA Canadian sample	The PISA OECD "population"
N = 22,383	
$\overline{X}$ = 524	μ = 493
s = 90	σ = 93

Source: OECD PISA Scores 2009

Let's ignore the size of the OECD sampled population since, although it's 470,000, we're assuming that it represents everyone. Since we are dealing with a sample size that exceeds 120, we can use the z-statistic.

Recall that the equation for the z-statistic with a sample is

$$z = \frac{X - \mu}{\sigma_{\overline{X}}}$$

where

> z = the z-score
> $\overline{X}$ = the mean of individual scores X
> μ = the sample mean
> $\sigma_{\overline{x}}$ = the sample standard error

Recall also that to get the standard error, you need to use the following equation:

$$\sigma_{\overline{x}} = \frac{\sigma_X}{\sqrt{N}}$$

which gives us

$$\sigma_{\overline{x}} = \frac{93}{\sqrt{22{,}383}}$$
$$= \frac{93}{149.61}$$
$$= 0.62$$

Returning to our main equation, we get

$$z = \frac{524 - 493}{0.62}$$
$$= 50$$

We're fortunate to have the population standard deviation (remember that we only have this information because we pretended the OECD sample was the population). It's more common to have only the s_x, the sample standard deviation, which means that we would have to estimate the standard error of the sample while building in some extra uncertainty for using s_x instead of σ_x.

For comparison purposes, let's quickly calculate t:

$$t = \frac{\overline{X} - \mu}{s_x/\sqrt{n-1}}$$
$$= \frac{524 - 493}{90/\sqrt{22383 - 1}}$$
$$= \frac{31}{0.589}$$
$$= 52.67$$

Where

> t = **the *t*-score**
> $\overline{X}$ = **the mean of individual scores *X***
> μ = **the sample mean**
> s_x = **the sample standard deviation**

Note how close the *t*-value of 52.67 is to the *z*-value of 50. This is because our sample size is so large. As mentioned in Chapter 9, it is only necessary to calculate the *t*-statistic when the sample size is less than 120. Looking at Appendix A, we see that the $z_{critical}$ for a 95 per cent confidence interval is 1.96, whereas $t_{critical}$ from Appendix B when $df = \infty$ is, you guessed it, 1.96. Our $t_{observed}$ and $z_{observed}$ values both greatly exceed this figure, so we can be 95 per cent confident that Canada's reading ability scores are significantly different from the OECD average. This means that we reject H$_0$, the null hypothesis.

In this example, we hypothesized the existence of a significant difference between our sample and the population, without making a statement about what that difference would be. This requires a two-tailed test. If we instead hypothesized that Canada's score is significantly *higher* than the OECD average, then we would conduct a one-tailed test. Our hypotheses, stated in words, would be the following:

> **H$_0$: On average, the reading scores of Canadian 15-year-olds are equal to or lower than the scores of 15-year-olds in other OECD countries.**
> **H$_1$: On average, the reading scores of Canadian 15-year-olds are significantly higher than the scores of 15-year-olds in other OECD countries.**

Notice that both hypotheses are changed to reflect directionality. Furthermore, we'll only use $z_{observed}$, given our sample size of 22,383.

Similarly, stated in numbers we have the following:

> **H$_0$: $\overline{X} \leq 493$**
> **H$_1$: $\overline{X} > 493$**

Statistically, the only difference lies in the value of $z_{critical}$. Rather than 1.96, $z_{critical}$ is now 1.65. The reason for the change is that we no longer need to determine whether or not $z_{observed}$ lies either + or − two standard deviations from the mean. We only need to see if it is beyond one tail, so the 95 per cent confidence *z*-statistic value is 1.65. Our $z_{observed}$ is also well beyond 1.65, so we can also reject the null hypothesis here. Looking at Appendix A, can you see why we use the value 1.65?

A 95 per cent level of confidence is a rather arbitrary level of certainty, and in certain circumstances it contains a higher level of error in judgment than we want. In this case, we could increase our level of confidence to, say, 99 per cent. For this, we would replace 1.96 and 1.65 with 2.57 and 2.33. Can you see why this is the case?

BOX 10.1

The Steps: Hypothesis Testing with a Large Sample and a Population

1. State the null and the alternative or research hypotheses. Typically, the research postulates that there is a significant difference between the sample mean and the population mean, whereas the null hypothesizes that there is no relationship. Differences that exist because of sampling error support the null hypothesis because they don't reflect actual difference.

2. Decide whether a one-tailed or two-tailed test is more appropriate, and locate the appropriate z-statistic values from Appendix A.

3. Compute $z_{observed}$ with the following equations

$$z = \frac{\overline{X} - \mu}{\sigma_X / \sqrt{N}}$$

or

$$\sigma_{\overline{X}} = \frac{\sigma_X}{\sqrt{N}} \text{ then } z = \frac{\overline{X} - \mu}{\sigma_{\overline{X}}}$$

if you prefer to calculate the standard error of the mean before calculating z.

4. Compare $z_{observed}$ with the $z_{critical}$ values of 1.96 (for a two-tailed test) or 1.65 (for a one-tailed test). If $z_{observed}$ exceeds $z_{critical}$, then you must reject H_0; if it does not, then you fail to reject the null hypothesis.

THE RETURN OF GOSSETT: STUDENT'S *t*-DISTRIBUTION

In the OECD example, we used a combination of sample and population characteristics to determine whether the differences witnessed in a sample were likely to exist in the population. This exercise is of little use in the real world, because there isn't usually that much information available, or that large a sample. There are rarely values for either σ, the population standard deviation, or μ, the population mean. A value for s and $\overline{X}$, the sample standard deviation, will always be available, or can be calculated. Unfortunately s is a biased estimator of σ; and there's no way to tell how big the difference is. We do know that the difference between s and σ shrinks as sample size increases. The closer the sample size comes to the population size, the more acceptable it is to use s as a "stand-in" for σ when calculating z-values.

Once a sample size of about 120 is reached, the differences are negligible (see for yourself: look at how minimal the differences between z-values and *t*-values are when $df = 120$ in the z- and *t*-distributions in Appendices A and B), and we can consider s to be a decent approximation of σ. Substitute the sample standard deviation for the population standard deviation, and use the techniques above, to get the equation:

$$t = \frac{\overline{X} - \mu}{s_X / \sqrt{n - 1}}$$

or, since,

$$s_{\bar{X}} = \frac{s_X}{\sqrt{n-1}} \text{ then } t = \frac{\bar{X} - \mu}{s_{\bar{X}}}$$

This looks a lot like the equation for z, except that s replaces σ in the denominator. Like z, t is a standardized unit that tells us how far $\bar{X}$ is from μ in standard deviations. Unlike z, which has only one distribution (the normal distribution), remember that t is a family of distributions, each differing slightly based on sample size. For smaller samples (<120), the t-distribution can differ substantially from the z-distribution.

Since we need to calculate degrees of freedom to use the t-distribution, it would be helpful to once again briefly review the concept. Recall that the degrees of freedom are the number of values in a set of scores that are free to vary. Using the example of determining how much money each of your five roommates has contributed to the household expenses, the degrees of freedom would be equal to the number of values you don't know minus one. Suppose that instead of calculating bills, you're going to dinner with four friends. The meal costs $100, and you and your friend Marcie each contribute $20. This would leave you with two degrees of freedom, because you know that there is $60 unaccounted for. Once you know how much two of your three friends who have not yet paid need to contribute, the final contribution will also be determined. Only two of the values are uncertain, or free, because the final value is always known by subtracting the cumulative total of contributions from the total bill.

In the current example, when we are trying to calculate the sample mean $\bar{X}$, and don't know any of the individual scores, the degrees of freedom will be equal to the number of observations minus one, reflecting that the final score will be determined by the score of other individuals.

To learn about what to do in the absence of information on the population, we'll first look at an example where only the population mean is known in addition to sample characteristics, then in Chapter 11 we'll look at instances where we have information only on samples.

EVERYDAY STATISTICS

Using the t-Distribution

In health research, the t-distribution is often used to determine whether there is a difference between the birth weights of babies who are born to women who live in poverty and women in the overall population.

. . . .

Q: Why do you think the t-distribution would be useful for comparing the birth weights of babies in a sample of the population?

HYPOTHESIS TESTING WITH ONE SMALL SAMPLE AND A POPULATION

As we saw in Chapter 7, working with means and standard deviations derived from small samples (<120) requires an additional measure of uncertainty, since it is likely that both the $\overline{X}$ and s parameters contain some error.

More often than not, we do not know anything about our population of interest and are working with samples that have smaller (<120) observations. What this means is that we must often resort to comparing two or more samples to get a sense of trends in the population (men and women; left-handed, right-handed, and ambidextrous people; immigrants and non-immigrants; university graduates and non-university graduates, etc.) to determine whether the differences we observe in the sample exist in the population. It is possible to do that using the t-distribution, which, it turns out, is not just useful for comparing small samples to populations but also for looking at just samples.

This part of Chapter 10 will primarily focus on the t-test to test hypotheses with information from small samples, one of the common applications of the t-distribution.[1] The t-test is used to compare the value of an interval/ratio variable across two values of another variable. For example, a t-test could be used to look at differences in the income of males and females.

The solution requires you to assume that the sample is fairly (but not perfectly) representative of the population, and build the uncertainty into our estimates. We acknowledge that our sample is not a perfect representation of our population, and that there's a possibility that any differences we observe are due to chance. However, if there are clear trends in the sample, they probably exist in the population. To present the differences between sample and population, acknowledge the uncertainty by reporting the values (e.g., means) for the sample as a range, or confidence interval.

Let's try using the following for a sample mean. Engineering students at Queen's University have been accused of consuming too much alcohol. Their average number of drinks per week is 12, with a standard deviation of 4.6 (taken from a random sample of 100 engineers), compared to 8 for the entire university population. Obviously, there is a difference between the sample and the population, but is it significant? There are two possibilities:

1. The mean of 12 taken from the sample of engineers is the same as the university mean (8), and the difference is caused by random chance or sampling error (H_0).
2. The difference is real (significant), and engineers drink more than other students (H_1).

What we've done here is cast the possibilities as a set of competing hypotheses. The first (labelled H_0) states that there is no true relationship between being an engineer and alcohol consumption. This is known as the null hypothesis, because it predicts that the relationship between two variables is null. The second (labelled H_1) is our research hypothesis, and it asserts that a connection does indeed exist between the two variables. Also note that we are hypothesizing a directional relationship (engineers generally outdrink other students).

Although it would be ideal to be able to prove that the research hypothesis is true, remember that in scientific research the best that we can do is reject or fail to reject the null hypothesis. This is because we can never be sure whether our relationships are actually causal, or if they are instead "merely" correlative. Imagine that males tend to drink more than females and that males are more likely to be engineers. The differences above would be significant, but it wouldn't be because engineers outdrink others. It would instead be because males outdrink females. By rejecting the null hypothesis instead of accepting the research hypothesis, we give ourselves room for such possibilities.

To choose between these possibilities, identify the probability of getting a sample mean of 12 for the engineers with a sample size of 100 when the engineers' true mean is 8. The convention dictates that a probability of less than 5 per cent indicates that the differences between the sample means will represent an actual difference.

If we treat the entire university as our population, and engineering students as our sample, we get values of 8 for μ, 12 for $\overline{X}$, 100 for n, and 4.6 for s_x. To calculate t, we use the following equation:

$$t = \frac{\overline{X} - \mu}{s_x/\sqrt{n-1}}$$
$$= \frac{12 - 8}{4.6/\sqrt{100 - 1}}$$
$$= \frac{4}{0.462}$$
$$= 8.66$$

The next step is to figure out how big the difference between the mean of the sample and the mean of the population is, using what we know about the normal distribution—particularly the **central limit theorem**. The normal distribution also tells us the probability of finding differences between samples and populations. We want to know if the probability of finding a difference of 4 drinks per week is less than 0.05 (or 5 per cent).

The equation places the difference between the population mean and sample mean into a common metric (that's why the standard deviation appears in the denominator), so that the value can be assessed with the normal distribution, like any other variable. If we multiply the population mean, sample mean, and standard deviation by 100, 1,000, or even 100,000, we could use the same table (z or t) to assess the significance of the differences. It's often useful to think of z- or t-statistics as techniques for translating values measured in different units—be they drinks, dollars, or donkey rides—into a common unit of measurement, or standard score, as discussed in Chapter 7.

One characteristic of the equation is that there is a term in the denominator ($\sqrt{n-1}$) that "penalizes" t if it's calculated using a small sample. The reason is that sampling error tends to *decrease* as sample size *increases* (and vice versa), so there is less certainty about the representativeness of a sample when it contains a smaller proportion of the population. However, representativeness does not increase proportionally with sample size, which is why the square root of $n - 1$ is used.

BOX 10.2

The Steps: Hypothesis Testing with a Small Sample and a Population

1. State the null and the alternative or research hypotheses. Typically, the research postulates that there is a significant difference between the sample mean and the population mean, whereas the null hypothesizes that there is no relationship. Differences that exist because of sampling error support the null hypothesis because they don't reflect actual differences.

2. Decide whether a one-tailed or two-tailed test is more appropriate, and locate the appropriate t-statistic values from Appendix B.

3. Compute $t_{observed}$ with the following equations

$$t = \frac{\bar{X} - \mu}{s_X / \sqrt{n - 1}}$$

or

$$s_{\bar{X}} = \frac{s_X}{\sqrt{n - 1}} \text{ then } t = \frac{\bar{X} - \mu}{s_{\bar{X}}}$$

if you prefer to calculate the standard error of the mean before calculating z.

4. Compare $t_{observed}$ with the $t_{critical}$ values taken from Appendix B at $df = n - 1$. If $t_{observed}$ exceeds $t_{critical}$, then you must reject H_0; if it does not, then you fail to reject the null hypothesis.

Look at Appendix B to get the critical t-value of 1.66 ($df = 99$ for a one-tailed test), which our observed value of 8.66 greatly exceeds. This tells us that there is less than a 5 per cent chance (actually less than 0.1 per cent chance) that the value we obtained from the sample of engineers is a fluke. Since we set a threshold of 5 per cent, we can be confident (though not completely certain) that overall differences between our samples of engineers and university students exist. In fact, for the differences to be significant, our t-value only needed to exceed ±1.66.

CALCULATING CONFIDENCE INTERVALS IN THE ONE-SAMPLE CASE

The variables t and z are also important for approximating the mean for a population when there is only one sample available. Because of sampling error, samples do not perfectly represent populations, so we can *never* be 100 per cent sure that any sample statistic equals the true population parameter. As a partial solution, we express uncertainty about estimates by lowering the confidence interval from 100 per cent and providing a range of values for the mean.

To analyze samples of normal populations with an unknown mean (μ), attach a range of plausible values to the sample mean ($\overline{X}$), using the following equation:

$$CI = \overline{X} \pm t * \frac{s}{\sqrt{n}}$$

The appropriate value of t can be found in the t-distribution at the back of the book, at $n - 1$ degrees of freedom.

Suppose that we have a sample of 15 refugees to Canada, and we want to look at the civic participation rates of refugees after one year in Canada. We ask respondents how many social organizations they belong to. Below are the data:

3	7	4	0	2
1	4	4	5	2
7	6	3	5	7

From these data it is possible to estimate the average number of organizations that members of the entire refugee population belong to. First, calculate the mean:

$$\overline{X} = \frac{\sum X}{n}$$
$$= \frac{60}{15}$$
$$= 4$$

Next, calculate the sample standard deviation, using the following equation:

$$s = \sqrt{\frac{\sum (X - \overline{X})^2}{n - 1}}$$
$$= \sqrt{\frac{68}{14}}$$
$$= 2.20$$

Use these values for the mean and standard deviation, and the critical value of t, to find the interval where we can be 95 per cent confident the mean falls. To find the value of t, use the degrees of freedom ($n - 1 = 14$) and a 95 per cent confidence interval, to retrieve the critical value of t of 2.145 (this number is found in Appendix B), leaving us with the confidence interval:

$$CI = \overline{X} \pm t * \frac{s}{\sqrt{n}}$$
$$= 4 \pm 2.145 * \frac{2.20}{\sqrt{15}}$$
$$= 4 \pm 1.22$$
$$= 2.78, 5.22 \text{ organizations per individual}$$

We can be 95 per cent confident that the mean number of social organizations for all refugees to Canada is between 2.78 and 5.22. If you wanted to be more confident of the range, say 99 per cent, go back to the *t*-table and find the critical value for a *df* of 14 and the 0.01 column. Now the critical value is 2.98, yielding a range of 2.31 to 5.69 social organizations. Now we're more confident, but the range is larger.

SINGLE SAMPLE PROPORTIONS

One requirement for generalizing from samples to populations is measuring variables at the interval/ratio level. However, it is possible to assess proportions instead of means in a single sample, using the normal distribution and applying most of the same logic and techniques. For example, you could determine if the same proportion of people with a certain characteristic in a sample is likely to exist in the population. The three things you need to calculate $z_{obtained}$ are sample proportions, population proportion, and sample size.

Let's illustrate $z_{obtained}$ with an example: A random sample of 120 individuals whose mothers put salt on their food during pregnancy reveals that 50 per cent of those people also put salt on their food. In the whole population, the proportion of people who salt their food is about 40 per cent. Are individuals with mothers who salted their food different from the rest of the population in this regard?

The proportion for the population is 40 per cent, or 0.4, and the sample proportion is 50 per cent, or 0.5. Using a 95 per cent confidence interval from the z table at the back of the book, we get a critical value of 1.96 (remember that 95 per cent is on both tails, so you will look for 95/2, or 47.5 per cent, or 0.475 on the table).

To calculate z with proportions, use the following equation:

$$z_{obtained} = \frac{P_{sample} - P_{population}}{\sqrt{P_{population}(1 - P_{population})/n}}$$

This is essentially the same equation as the one we used before, except that the population standard deviation in the denominator (which can't exist with nominal data) is replaced by the population probability of eating salt, multiplied by the probability of not eating salt. Otherwise, the equations are the same.

Inserting our values gives us the following:

$$z_{obtained} = \frac{P_{sample} - P_{population}}{\sqrt{P_{population}(1 - P_{population})/n}}$$
$$= \frac{0.5 - 0.4}{\sqrt{0.4(1 - 0.4)/120}}$$
$$= \frac{0.1}{\sqrt{0.002}}$$
$$= 2.24$$

Since 2.24 exceeds 1.96 (the critical value of z at 95 per cent confidence interval), we can say that there are differences at the 0.05 level between people whose mothers put salt on their food and the overall population. This suggests that whether or not your mother salted her food during pregnancy is a significant predictor of whether you will put salt on your food.

MEASURING ASSOCIATION BETWEEN DUMMY AND INTERVAL/RATIO VARIABLES WITH THE SAME GROUP MEASURED TWICE

So far, the focus has been on comparing samples and the populations that they're drawn from. Recently, Canadian researchers have become more interested in following people over a longer period of time. Since the early 1990s, Statistics Canada has launched a series of **longitudinal surveys**. One of the challenges of using this type of data source is comparing the same sample at two points in time. The procedure for doing that has several names, **paired samples t-tests**, **repeated measures t-tests**, or **t-tests for dependent samples**.

To use the same sample at each point in time, we focus only on the *difference* between scores for the first and second times. As with sample means, assume that the difference between means is normally distributed and rely on the t-distribution to reflect the possibility of a small sample size.

Despite the introduction of several new equations, the process is almost identical to a one-sample t-test. The new equations use new symbols, since they deal with differences between dependent observations.

The first equation calculates the differences between observations:

$$d_i = x_{i1} - x_{i2}$$

Where x_{i1} is the score at time one, x_{i2} is the score at time two, and d_i is equal to the difference between them.

The next equation is for the mean of the differences between time points:

$$\bar{X}_d = \frac{\sum d_i}{n}$$

The standard deviation is defined as

$$s_d = \sqrt{\frac{\sum (d - \bar{x}_d)^2}{n - 1}}$$

Or, if you want to avoid calculating $\bar{x}_d$

$$s_d = \sqrt{\frac{\sum d^2}{n - 1} - (\bar{X}_1 - \bar{X}_2)^2}$$

BOX 10.3

It's Your Turn: t-Test for the Same Sample Measured Twice

Joshua surveyed a number of his friends and acquaintances about how many sexual partners they had during the year they were 18 and how many partners they had during the year they were 21. How can he use the data to calculate whether the number of partners people have per year is significantly different between the two time points?

Individual	# of partners per year at age 18	# of partners per year at age 21	$d_i = x_{i1} - x_{i2}$	d^2
1	2	1		
2	0	0		
3	3	2		
4	1	2		
5	8	1		
6	1	1		
7	2	1		
8	0	2		
9	0	4		
10	3	1		
	$\overline{X}_1$	$\overline{X}_2$	d_i	Σd^2

1. For each age (column), calculate the average $\overline{X}_1$ and $\overline{X}_2$.

2. For each individual, calculate the difference between the number of partners at ages 18 and 21 ($d_i = x_{i1} - x_{i2}$) then sum that value (Σd_i). Square the difference for each person and sum the values.

3. Use the formula $s_d = \sqrt{\dfrac{\Sigma d^2}{n-1} - (\overline{X}_1 - \overline{X}_2)^2}$ to calculate the standard deviation.

4. Use the standard deviation to calculate the standard error of difference between means

$$s_{\overline{d}} = \frac{s_d}{\sqrt{n-1}}$$

5. Use those values to calculate the t-value using

$$t = \frac{\overline{X}_1 - \overline{X}_2}{s_{\overline{d}}}$$

6. Compare the t-value to the critical value from the t-table for 9 degrees of freedom at a 95 per cent confidence level. Is there a significant difference in the number of sexual partners at the two ages?

The solution for Box 10.3 can be found on page S-30.

To calculate the standard error of the difference between means

$$s_{\bar{d}} = \frac{s_d}{\sqrt{n-1}}$$

Finally, the *t*-value for dependent samples is the difference between means, divided by the standard error of that difference:

$$t = \frac{X_1 - X_2}{s_{\bar{d}}}$$

The *t*-value is compared to the critical values, as with one-sample cases, to see if the change within individuals is statistically significant.

You should see some overlap with the material in the last chapter. The difference is that Chapter 9 was about determining how closely a sample resembles a population while taking sampling error into account and this chapter was about whether certain segments of a population *actually* differ significantly from the entire population.

GLOSSARY TERMS

Alternative hypothesis (p. 99)
Central limit theorem (p. 108)
Longitudinal survey (p. 112)
Null hypothesis (p. 99)
Paired samples *t*-test (p. 112)

Repeated measures *t*-test (p. 112)
Research hypothesis (p. 99)
t-test for dependent samples (p. 112)
Type one error (p. 100)
Type two error (p. 100)

PRACTICE QUESTIONS

1. The students of the University of New Brunswick have begun a fundraising initiative to reduce the prevalence of diabetes in the province. Last year, they raised $43,000, and this year the chief fundraiser expects the amount to be higher.
    a. Generate a null and research hypothesis that would allow you to test for a difference without saying anything about the direction of the difference.
    b. Now, do the same thing, except hypothesize a direction in the relationship.

2. For the past few years, Amber's drive to work has taken an average of 75 minutes ($\sigma = 8$ minutes). She thinks she's found a shorter way and wants to see if the average time for the new route is significantly different from that of the old route. Last week she tried the new route 5 times, and got an average of 73 minutes. Help her determine whether or not the new way is significantly faster.

    a. Calculate $z_{obtained}$.

    b. Compare this value to $z_{critical}$, using a 95 per cent level of confidence.

3. From 1990 to 2005 (inclusive), Jasper earned approximately \$31,000 per year ($\sigma = 27,000$). He wants to know if his earnings were significantly different from the Canadian population. Across this period, the average wage was roughly \$29,000/year. Help Jasper determine whether or not his income was significantly different from that of the Canadian population.

4. In a recent Ipsos-Reid poll (http://www.ipsos-na.com/news/pressrelease.cfm?id =3809), of a random sample of 3,219 Canadian adults, 52 per cent thought that the price of food is too high. The 95 per cent confidence interval that Ipsos-Reid provides is 1.7 percentage points. What range is the population average 95 per cent likely to lie between?

5. Ted loves his basil plants and believes that he has a special relationship with them. In his mind, this causes them to grow more leaves than his neighbour's plants. Ted is a good statistician, and feels confident that he can prove his claim statistically. His neighbour is rather indifferent to the entire exercise, but he wants to be a good neighbour, so he lets Ted come over and count the leaves on his 10 plants. Ted counts an average of 57 leaves on his neighbour's plants, with a standard deviation of 8 leaves. On his own 12 plants, he finds 61 leaves, with a standard deviation of 9 leaves. Help Ted determine whether there is any statistical evidence to support his belief in his basil superiority.

6. Scout and Lily are both avid highland dancers, and they compete annually in the Antigonish Highland Games. Their parents have consistently told the girls that their scores are likely to be significantly higher than average, because they've gone to so many competitions already, and are therefore much better practised than everyone else. Develop a set of null and research hypotheses that would allow you to test

    a. If Scout and Lily's parents are right, and the girls are significantly better than their competition.

    b. If Scout and Lily's parents are wrong, and the girls are no different from the other competitors.

7. Roughly 32 per cent of a random sample of 172 individuals in the city of Edmonton feel that the Eskimos are likely to win the next Grey Cup. In the entire Alberta population, the comparable figure is about 27 per cent. Are Edmontonians significantly different from Albertans overall in their love for their home team? Use a 95 per cent confidence interval to draw your conclusion.

8. Sneha has recently become interested in the differences in the amount of personal space required by people of different ethnic groups. Based on her experience, people who were born and raised in Canada require approximately an arm's length of distance between themselves and the people they're talking to. She drafts a set of hypotheses about whether there are differences by group, and after her study she fails to reject the null hypothesis when she should have. Has she committed a type 1 or type 2 error?

9. Looking at the z-table in Appendix 1, what happens to the probability that you'll reject the null hypothesis as values of $z_{critical}$ increase? Does the probability of rejecting the null hypothesis increase or decrease?

10. If you reject the null hypothesis, are you saying that the sample does or does not differ from the population on your outcome of interest?

Answers to the practice questions for Chapter 10 can be found on page S-8.

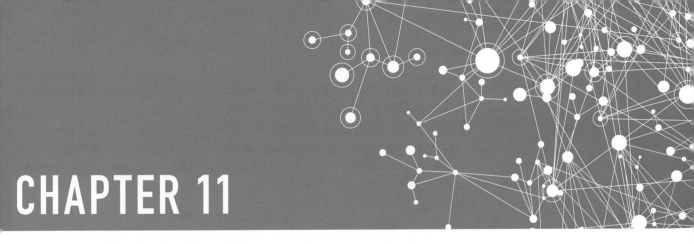

CHAPTER 11

Measuring Association between Dummy and Interval/Ratio Variables: *t*–Tests with Two Samples

LEARNING OBJECTIVES

Now that we're working with two samples, there are two sources of sampling error we need to account for when testing hypotheses. This chapter will introduce several ways of dealing with two samples:

- standard error of the difference between means;
- two-sample *t*-tests;
- one- and two-tailed tests;
- comparing proportions with two samples.

INTRODUCTION

In Chapter 10, we looked at simple random population samples, either comparing each sample to its population or itself at different points in time. So far, we've assumed that our samples and/or populations had roughly equal variances, thereby requiring information about the population. To use the *z*-distribution for one-sample cases, you need to have both the population mean and the standard deviation. To use the *t*-distribution, the only population characteristic you need is the mean. However, both cases require at least some population information. Although *t*-tests for dependent samples don't require population characteristics, we have to assume that the samples contain the same sampling error.

It is common to find variances in what's being compared. For example, if we wanted to compare men and women, Hondas and Toyotas, or even dogs and cats, it wouldn't be surprising to discover that the sample or population variances between the groups are different for most characteristics. Why would they be the same?

This chapter will focus on comparing the means of two distinct groups, or *independent samples*. When comparing two values, what we're typically looking for is the central tendency (usually the mean) and the variation (the standard deviation) of the population. The mean for group one would be calculated as

$$\bar{X}_1 = \frac{\sum X_1}{n_1}$$

For group two

$$\bar{X}_2 = \frac{\sum X_2}{n_2}$$

Similarly, the sample standard deviation can be calculated as

$$s_1 = \sqrt{\frac{\sum (X_1 - \bar{X}_1)^2}{n_1}}$$

For group two

$$s_2 = \sqrt{\frac{\sum (X_2 - \bar{X}_2)^2}{n_2}}$$

To calculate the distance between a sample mean and a population mean (when we know μ and σ), calculate the z-value for the difference between sample means as:

$$z = \frac{\bar{X}_1 - \bar{X}_2}{s_{\bar{X}_1 - \bar{X}_2}}$$

The z-test is used because it's assumed that we have big enough (≥ 120) samples (we'll discuss small samples momentarily). The symbols should be familiar now, except for the denominator term

$$s_{\bar{X}_1 - \bar{X}_2}$$

This term is the standard error of the difference between means. It is also referred to as the anticipated level of error between the measurements of the two-sample means and can be found by using the following equation:

$$s_{\bar{X}_1 - \bar{X}_2} = \sqrt{\left(\frac{s_1^2}{n_1 - 1} + \frac{s_2^2}{n^2 - 1}\right)}$$

The standard error is the degree of certainty about how closely our calculated means (calculated from two samples) resemble the means of the two respective populations. A wider variance (the s^2 values in the numerator) results in higher calculations, as does a reduction in sample size (seen in the denominator).

Once the standard error is determined, the z-value can be calculated:

$$z = \frac{\overline{X}_1 - \overline{X}_2}{s_{\overline{X}_1 - \overline{X}_2}}$$

A larger standard error value (the denominator), or a smaller difference between means, will result in a lower z figure. This reflects waning confidence in whether the observed differences would also be found in the population.

Using small samples (<120) complicates things further: doing so relies on the t-distribution instead of the z-distribution (because of the differences in distributions) and involves a more complicated calculation of the standard error of the difference between means:

$$s_{\overline{X}_1 - \overline{X}_2} = \sqrt{\left(\frac{n_1 s_1^2 + n_2 s_2^2}{n_1 + n_2 - 2}\right)\left(\frac{n_1 + n_2}{n_1 n_2}\right)}$$

Substituting t for z requires the following equation:

$$t = \frac{\overline{X}_1 - \overline{X}_2}{s_{\overline{X}_1 - \overline{X}_2}}$$

This should look familiar, as it is the same equation that you use for calculating z for two samples. The big difference lies in the calculation of the standard error of the difference between means. If you think about this for a moment, it shouldn't surprise you, because it is the level of certainty that we attach to our estimates of the means that differs, not the actual estimates of the means. Thus, we need to alter only one component of our calculation, albeit in a much more complicated way.

As we saw earlier, the t-distribution is actually a family of distributions, making it necessary to identify which distribution to use by calculating the degrees of freedom. The calculation for degrees of freedom is slightly more complicated than in the one-sample case, and can be found by entering the two sample sizes in the following equation:

$$df = (n_1 + n_2 - 2)$$

If the calculated z- or t-statistics exceed the critical value (1.96 for z, approaching 1.96 for t) for both the z- and t-distributions, you can be 95 per cent confident that differences exist. Since the null hypothesis is *always* to assume that groups are the same, reject the null whenever z exceeds $z_{critical}$ or t exceeds $t_{critical}$. Once again, as sample size increases, the t-statistics and the t-distribution increasingly resemble the z-statistic and the z-distribution.

Let's illustrate with an example. Suppose that we were interested in studying the effects of class size on university learning, and that we hypothesized that students in universities with large classes (>75) have lower standardized test scores than students in small-class universities. After completing a first-year course, you get a score of 81 from 100 large-class students (s = 11) and 83 from 92 small-class students (s = 10) on a standardized test. You want to know if the differences you observe in your two samples are statistically significant, or if you can be 95 per cent confident that similar differences exist in the two populations. Let's call the large-class students group 1 and the small-class students group 2. For illustration purposes, let's assess the difference by using both z and t.

Our hypotheses would be as follows:

H_1 = Students from universities with large class sizes (>75) will score lower on the standardized test than students from universities with smaller class sizes (≤75). Or, $\mu_1 < \mu_2$.

Note that even though we're dealing with two samples, we use μ, the symbol for a population mean, because that is what we're ultimately interested in.

H_0 = Students from universities with large class sizes (>75) will not score lower on the standardized test than students from universities with smaller class sizes (≤75). Or, $\mu_1 \geq \mu_2$.

Note that these are directional hypotheses, which point us to a one-tailed test. If we were hypothesizing non-directionality, H_1 would be $\mu_1 \neq \mu_2$ and H_1 would be $\mu_1 = \mu_2$.

Let's put our values above in the appropriate equations. First, z. Let's calculate the standard error of the difference between means:

$$s_{\overline{X}_1 - \overline{X}_2} = \sqrt{\left(\frac{s_1^2}{n_1 - 1} + \frac{s_2^2}{n_2 - 1}\right)}$$

$$= \sqrt{\left(\frac{11^2}{100 - 1} + \frac{10^2}{92 - 1}\right)}$$

$$= \sqrt{\left(\frac{11^2}{100 - 1} + \frac{10^2}{92 - 1}\right)}$$

$$= \sqrt{\left(\frac{121}{99} + \frac{100}{91}\right)}$$

$$= \sqrt{(1.222 + 1.099)}$$

$$= 1.523$$

Now, we simply put this information into our equation for z:

$$z = \frac{\overline{X}_1 - \overline{X}_2}{s_{\overline{X}_1 - \overline{X}_2}}$$

$$= \frac{81 - 83}{1.523}$$

$$= -1.313$$

So, we get a $z_{observed}$ value of -1.313. Now let's calculate t, remembering that our value for the numerator remains the same. This leaves us with the more complicated version of the equation for calculating the standard error of the difference between means.

$$s_{\bar{X}_1 - \bar{X}_2} = \sqrt{\left(\frac{n_1 s_1^2 + n_2 s_2^2}{n_1 + n_2 - 2}\right)\left(\frac{n_1 + n_2}{n_1 n_2}\right)}$$

$$= \sqrt{\left(\frac{100 * 11^2 + 92 * 10^2}{100 + 92 - 2}\right)\left(\frac{100 + 92}{100 * 92}\right)}$$

$$= \sqrt{\left(\frac{12100 + 9200}{190}\right)\left(\frac{192}{9200}\right)}$$

$$= \sqrt{112.1 * 0.02}$$

$$= \sqrt{2.242}$$

$$= 1.50$$

Now, we can calculate t:

$$t = \frac{\bar{X}_1 - \bar{X}_2}{s_{\bar{X}_1 - \bar{X}_2}}$$

$$= \frac{81 - 83}{1.50}$$

$$= -1.333$$

which gives us a $t_{observed}$ value of -1.333. Note how close this number is to $z_{observed}$ above.

Returning to our hypotheses, how do we use these numbers to test our hypothesis? First, let's look at the z-table in Appendix A. For a 95 per cent confidence interval with a one-tailed test, we get a $z_{critical}$ value of 1.65, which is greater than our observed value of 1.313 (remember that we can drop the negative sign).

To obtain $t_{critical}$ for a 95 per cent confidence interval, we need to calculate our degrees of freedom for t as $df = (n_1 + n_2 - 2)$, or 190. Since our highest value is for 120, we will use the value for ∞, which is 1.645. Once again, this is greater than our $t_{observed}$ value of 1.336. Regardless of which statistic you calculate, we must draw the same conclusion and fail to reject the null hypothesis.

In the example above, we calculated both t- and z-statistics for illustration purposes, even though we really only needed one. When should you use t versus z? There is no broad consensus on this, but a good rule of thumb would be to use the z-statistic when (a) the sum of the two sample sizes is greater than 120, and (b) when both samples have at least 30 observations. Otherwise, opt for the t-statistic. In any instance, you should have at least 10 observations in each group to make meaningful comparisons.

COMPARING PROPORTIONS WITH TWO SAMPLES

As with the one-sample case, you can compare proportions of a dichotomous nominal variable across samples. To find the value of $z_{obtained}$ or $t_{obtained}$, several equations, again, are needed. Take a closer look and you'll see that most of these resemble the one-sample case.

Let's revisit the equation for $z_{obtained}$ in the one-sample case:

$$z_{obtained} = \frac{P_{sample} - P_{population}}{\sqrt{P_{population}(1 - P_{population})/n}}$$

BOX 11.1

It's Your Turn: The Two-Sample *t*-Test

Sophia is enrolled in a sociology course examining ethnicity in Canada. For her term paper she is interested in the extent to which people who grew up in Canada feel that they "fit into" Canadian society. Using data collected in 2002 for the Ethnic Diversity Survey (Public Use Micro-data File), she selected people who were either second generation (they were born in Canada, but one or both parents were not) or third generation or more (both the respondent and their parents were born in Canada). The dependent variable was a response to the question "Up until you were age 15, how often did you feel uncomfortable or out of place because of your ethnicity, culture, race, skin colour, language, accent, or religion?" and the responses ranged from 1 (all of the time) to 5 (never). Although the responses were ordinal, she treated them as interval responses.

Sophia found the following:

	Generation status—2nd or 3rd	N	Mean	Standard deviation	Standard error mean
Felt uncomfortable before age 15	2nd—parents born outside Canada	6,799	4.59	.776	.009
	3rd or more—respondent and parents born in Canada	23,237	4.78	.593	.004

Source: Ethnic Diversity Survey Public Microdata File, 2002
Note: Rescaled weights for data have been used (weight/average weight for sample selected). Target population was people aged 15 and older living in private dwellings in the 10 Canadian provinces. Sample excludes those under age 15, people living in collective dwellings, Indian Reserves, people who declared an Aboriginal ethnic origin or identity on the 2001 census, and people living in the territories and remote areas (Statistics Canada User's Guide, p. 4, Catalogue no.89M0019GPE).

1. What would Sophia's null hypothesis be?
2. Use the information in the table to calculate the *z*-score (this will require you to calculate the standard error of the difference between means).
3. Comparing the *z*-score to the critical value for 95 per cent confidence, would you reject or fail to reject the null hypothesis?

The solution for Box 11.1 can be found on page S-31.

Now, let's compare it to the formula for $z_{obtained}$ in the two-sample case:

$$z_{obtained} = \frac{P_{s_1} - P_{s_2}}{s_{\bar{X}_1 - \bar{X}_2}}$$

The similarities in the numerator are obvious: instead of $P_{population}$, which indicates the proportion of the population in a group or category, the proportion of respondents in the second sample, P_{s_2}, is used. So far, so good.

The denominator for a one-sample case can be expressed as $s_{\bar{X}_1 - \bar{X}_2}$, which is equivalent to

$$\sqrt{P_{population}(1 - P_{population})/n}$$

Consequently,

$$z_{obtained} = \frac{P_{sample} - P_{population}}{\sqrt{P_{population}(1 - P_{population})/n}}$$

So the formula for calculating z in a one-sample case can also be stated as

$$z_{obtained} = \frac{P_{sample} - P_{population}}{s_{\bar{X}_1 - \bar{X}_2}}$$

and looks like the previous equation for two-sample means.

Remember that one-sample and two-sample equations are not identical. Calculating the standard deviation of differences between a sample mean and a population mean is not the same as calculating the standard deviation between the means of two samples, because of differences in the source of error. When comparing a sample to a population, there will be error only in the sample mean (there cannot be error in the population parameters), so it is sufficient to include n in the denominator to acknowledge that the size of the error is partially a function of sample size.

With two samples, any errors are probably because there are two sources, so the calculation of

$$s_{\bar{X}_1 - \bar{X}_2}$$

is more complicated than

$$\sigma_{\bar{X}_1 - \bar{X}_2}$$

To calculate $s_{\bar{X}_1 - \bar{X}_2}$ we have to find P_u, an estimate of the proportion of the population in the category of interest (such as the proportion of men and women who smoke). In the social sciences, we always assume that the null hypothesis is true and that there are no differences between groups (we assume that the proportion of male and female smokers is the same in the population). P_u can be calculated as the average of the proportions in samples one *and* two, adjusting for sample size, using the equation

$$P_u = \frac{n_1 P_{s_1} + n_2 P_{s_2}}{n_1 + n_2}$$

where P_{s_1} is the proportion of people in a group in sample one, and P_{s_2} is the proportion of people in a group in sample two.

On its own, P_u is of little interest (it is basically a weighted average of the two samples), but it is useful for calculating $s_{\bar{X}_1 - \bar{X}_2}$:

$$s_{\bar{X}_1 - \bar{X}_2} = \sqrt{P_u * (1 - P_u)\frac{n_1 + n_2}{n_1 n_2}}$$

This number $(s_{\bar{X}_1 - \bar{X}_2})$ is known as the standard deviation of the difference between sample proportions. If we assume that both samples are drawn from normally distributed populations, we can assume that the difference of means is also normally distributed.

The value for $s_{\bar{X}_1 - \bar{X}_2}$ is used in the following equation to calculate the obtained value of z:

$$z_{obtained} = \frac{P_{s_1} - P_{s_2}}{s_{\bar{X}_1 - \bar{X}_2}}$$

ONE- AND TWO-TAILED TESTS, AGAIN

This chapter has only explained how to differentiate one group from another group, without considering the directionality of difference, using a **two-tailed test**. Often, you will be concerned with differences in one direction. For example, instead of studying whether men and women have significantly different numbers of friends, you might want to know if males have more friends than females, or vice versa.

Once again, this introduces the need for a **one-tailed test**, which measures the significance and direction of a relationship. There is no statistical reason for choosing a one-tailed test over a two-tailed test; the choice is theoretically driven. So if you are trying to determine whether or not groups are equal, use a two-tailed test. If you believe that a group has more, or less, of a quality than another group, use a one-tailed test.

To use a one-tailed test, a slight modification of the two-tailed case is needed. The modification is the use of a different value from the z- or t-table. Let's illustrate using the 95 per cent confidence interval from the z-table in Appendix A. As you know, $z_{critical}$ must exceed ± 1.96 to be considered significant. In column C of the table, the area beyond z is listed as 0.025, so when both tails are included we will have a 95 per cent confidence interval. However, the one-tailed case needs to have 5 per cent of all values falling in only one of the two tails, pointing to a $z_{critical}$ value of roughly 1.65. If we hypothesize that one group will have a higher score than another (i.e., that males have more friends than females), we use a value of +1.65. For a lower score (males have fewer friends), we use −1.65. Follow the same process for t-scores.

Look at the z-table and find the one-tailed values for 90 per cent and 99 per cent confidence intervals.

BOX 11.2

It's Your Turn: The Two-Sample Proportion

Using data from the Aboriginal Peoples Survey 2001 (Public Use Microdata File), you've decided to study whether women or men who consider themselves to be very, moderately, or not very religious or spiritual people are more likely to engage in prayer to maintain their religious/spiritual well-being. You've recoded the variable for prayer so that if a person responded yes, their value is one. If this was not a way they maintain their spirituality, they were coded zero (therefore the means reflect the proportion who do pray). You expect that the women will be significantly *more likely* to use prayer to maintain their spirituality than the men. You use a statistical software package like STATA or SPSS to find the weighted n (or the population frequencies), the mean, and the standard deviation:

Group Statistics

Male or female		N	Mean	Standard deviation	Standard error mean
Prayer	Male	114,734	0.381	0.486	0.001
	Female	143,013	0.516	0.500	0.001

Source: 2001 Aboriginal Peoples Survey, Public Use Microdata File
Note: APS is a post-censal survey, with selection based on responses to four questions examining aboriginal identity (e.g., self-report, list of Aboriginal groups in list of ethnic or cultural group(s) they belong to. Includes residents of 10 provinces and three territories. Only off-reserve adults are included in the PUMF. Individuals were excluded if they lived in a collective dwelling (Statistics Canada 2001, 6–9).

1. Calculate the estimate of the proportion of the population in the category of interest (the proportion of somewhat spiritual men and women who use prayer) by using the equation:

$$P_u = \frac{n_1 P_{s_1} + n_2 P_{s_2}}{n_1 + n_2}$$

2. Use this value to calculate the standard deviation of the difference between sample proportions:

$$S_{\bar{X}_1 \bar{X}_2} = \sqrt{P_u * (1 - P_u) \frac{n_1 + n_2}{n_1 n_2}}$$

3. Calculate the value of $z_{obtained}$ using $z_{obtained} = \dfrac{P_{s_1} - P_{s_2}}{S_{\bar{X}_1 - \bar{X}_2}}$

4. Compare the value of $z_{obtained}$ to the critical value (Hint: Remember that your hypothesis had direction).

The solution for Box 11.2 can be found on page S-32.

EVERYDAY STATISTICS

A Closer Look at the *t*-Test

T-tests often provide a quick and easy way to compare two independent samples, for example comparing the life satisfaction levels of those who are married with those who are not. Using the Aging and Social Support Survey (GSS16), we see that men have a slightly higher but significant score on life satisfaction. When we divide the sample into married and non-married portions of the population, however, we see that *both* married and unmarried women are slightly happier than men, even though in the aggregate we see the opposite.

• •

Q: How do you explain this strange result?

GLOSSARY TERMS

One-tailed test (p.124)   Two-tailed test (p. 124)

PRACTICE QUESTIONS

Leslie wants to write her doctoral dissertation in a year; Dayle wants to do it 350 days. Each dissertation will be 175,000 words. In their first 10 days of writing, these are the word counts:

Leslie	Dayle
530	340
650	750
720	210
380	200
370	905
510	1,015
520	600
580	400
440	300
490	200

1. Write a set of null and research hypotheses that allows you to test the significance of the difference. Is this a one-tailed or two-tailed test?

2. Who has a higher average daily word count? What are their standard deviations? What about the standard error of the difference between means?

3. Will there be a 95 per cent significant difference in time to completion? Should you use a *t*-test or a *z*-test to determine this? Why?

4. A research study was conducted to examine the differences between men and women on perceived life satisfaction. In total, 200 men and 200 women were given life satisfaction tests. Scores on the measure range from 0 to 60, with high scores indicating high life satisfaction. Men scored an average of 48 ($s = 7$), and women scored 45 ($s = 5$). Recalling our discussion of hypotheses from Chapter 10, draft a set of non-directional null and research hypotheses that will allow you to identify whether a significant difference exists in the population.

5. From these data, can you conclude that there is a significant difference between the means of these two groups? What is the implication of this for your decision to reject or fail to reject the null hypothesis?

6. In a recent Genworth Financial survey of the housing experiences of recent immigrants to Canada (www.genworth.com), 76 per cent of recent immigrant non-homeowners ($n = 201$) said that distance to work was very important for them, compared with 68 per cent of homeowners ($n = 218$). Generate a set of non-directional null and research hypotheses that will allow you to identify whether a significant difference exists in the population.

7. Are the differences in the proportion of these groups significant at the 95 per cent confidence level?

8. Tess believes that dogs are more intelligent than cats, and she has developed an intelligence test that can be validly administered to both animals. For some reason, she had considerable success convincing dogs to take the exam, and administered 93 tests. She had less luck with cats, however, and could only administer 28 exams so she is unsure about how to proceed. She approaches you and asks for assistance. What would you tell her regarding
   a. whether a *z*-test or *t*-test is more appropriate, and why.
   b. whether a one-tailed or two-tailed test is more appropriate, and why.

9. Assuming that for dogs the mean was 75 and the standard deviation was 12, and for cats the mean was 79 and the standard deviation was 12, what does Tess's test tell you about the comparative intelligence of cats versus dogs?

Answers to the practice questions for Chapter 11 can be found on page S-10.

CHAPTER 12

Bivariate Statistics for Nominal Data

LEARNING OBJECTIVES

Although what's been covered so far in this text is useful, it is foundational information—you need to know these things to do statistics in the social sciences, but what you've learned so far probably won't form the analytical centrepiece of any research project. For that, we usually conduct more sophisticated bivariate (analysis of two variables) or multivariate analysis (more than two variables). This chapter will continue to focus on bivariate analysis by:

- examining some of the reasons that it is useful to study more than one variable at a time;
- learning what independent and dependent variables are;
- studying chi-square tests of independence;
- learning some popular techniques for measuring the association between two nominal variables.

INTRODUCTION

Typically, social scientists are interested in uncovering the **associations** or **relationships** between several variables. Some examples of relationships that social scientists might be interested in are

- how the introduction of a child into a household affects the number of hours worked by members of that household (particularly whether it differs for men and women);
- differences in budgetary spending between majority and minority governments;
- differences in family size, by religion;
- whether members of particular visible minority groups are more susceptible to certain diseases;
- whether marital status affects the number of hours spent at clubs, discos, malls, churches, synagogues, etc.

In each example, there are two variables of interest. Although we might be interested in the characteristics of each particular variable, what is central for the investigation is identifying the relationship *between* the two. Nothing that's been covered so far helps with this; we need to learn new methods.

To simultaneously analyze two variables that cannot be ranked or ordered, you'll need to learn **bivariate analysis** for nominal variables. You'll learn to deal with ordinal and interval/ratio variables by using contingency tables, which help researchers "visualize" the relationship between two variables; how to measure the existence and strength of two nominal variables; and how to identify some techniques for assessing the relationship between two continuous variables.

ANALYSIS WITH TWO NOMINAL VARIABLES

The first step for performing bivariate analysis is organizing the data so that patterns can be easily discerned. Suppose a researcher wants to identify connections between exposure to television commercials for a pizza restaurant and the behaviour of 1,000 people watching television. What would be a useful way of identifying and assessing the nature of this relationship?

For nominal data like these, it is useful to create a frequency table, like the one in Table 12.1. In the table, the information is organized into two columns. The left column shows the possibilities or response categories; the right shows the number of people in each category and the total number of people in the study (the cell in the bottom right corner).

Using Table 12.1, it is possible to draw some conclusions from the sample: The overwhelming majority of the people in the study had no reaction to the pizza commercial. The next two most popular alternatives are "Grab food from the refrigerator" and "Change channels." A minority (40 people) actually engaged in the behaviour that the pizza companies sought—they ordered a pizza (let's assume that they called the company advertised). It is difficult to determine whether 40 people in 1,000 is a sufficient number to warrant the huge advertising costs—that is a decision that only the pizza company can make—but we can see that for most people the advertisement had very little effect.

TABLE 12.1 | Response of 1,000 Television Viewers to a Pizza Commercial

Response of respondent to television commercial	F
Order a pizza	40
Grab food from the refrigerator	100
Change channels	110
No reaction	750
Total	1,000

The relationship could be expanded by comparing the responses of any two population subgroups—say, men and women. This is done by subdividing the column on the right by the sex of the respondent, then determining which of the variables is affecting the value of the other. This is often referred to as "determining the order of causality." The variable that we think is modifying the outcome is an **independent variable**, and the outcome of interest is the **dependent variable**. Note: These two terms are important, because they apply to all relationships and are used often.

In the example, we hypothesize that the sex of the respondent will relate to the reaction to the commercial. To determine if this hypothesis is correct, the first task is to determine how the data can be best presented.

Adding the sex of the respondent to the table (see Table 12.2) makes interpretation more difficult, but also more interesting. Independent variables are conventionally shown as columns and dependent variables as rows. These tables are called **contingency tables**, or cross-tabulations. Obviously, most people had no reaction to the pizza commercial, but that was true for women more often than men. This is determined by looking at the ratio of total women in the study to the number of women who had no reaction to the pizza commercial (490 out of 620, or roughly 79 per cent). On the other hand, of the 380 men in the study, only 260, or 68 per cent, of them did not react to the commercial (260/380 = 68 per cent).

What is more interesting (at least to the pizza company) is not who does *not* respond to the pizza commercial, but who actually does. Only 10 women out of 620 ordered a pizza after viewing the commercial, compared with 30 out of 380 men. There are several ways to explain these results (1) men like pizza more than women do; (2) men and women like pizza equally, but the pizza commercial resonates with men more than women; or (3) women like pizza more than men do, but TV is not an effective way to target women.

We don't know if any of these explanations is true. Before we can explore the alternatives, we need to determine whether the results, which are based on a sample of 1,000 men and women, can be generalized for the population. This brings us back to our recurring question about the degree to which we can be certain that our sample accurately reflects the population. To assess for any bivariate association, we need to learn about the chi-square test of significance.

TABLE 12.2 | Response of 1,000 Television Viewers to a Pizza Commercial by Sex

Response of respondent to television commercial	Sex of respondent	
	Female	Male
Order a pizza	10	30
Grab food from the refrigerator	60	40
Change channels	60	50
No reaction	490	260
Total	620	380

BOX 12.1

Cross Tabulations: History of a Term

In the second half of the seventeenth century, the German empire was fractured, suffering from balkanization and the resulting social ills of poverty and civil disruption. In response, the state bureaucracies started defining and cataloguing the micro-states, seeking not only to describe, but to organize, hierarchize, and classify them. Though bureaucrats called this a "statistical" analysis, they were not using the quantitative method used today but an early version of a cross-table. The countries constituting the empire were put into the rows of a cross-table, and state characteristics were used as columns. In this way, rulers could compare states based on the presence of a particular characteristic, from art and culture to agriculture, and the total character of any state could be read across the rows. Using the table, it was possible to sum up a state, and compare it to other states by using nominal features.

This new method of comparative taxonomy was met with resistance. Critics saw the tables as "vulgar" statistics that allowed qualitative equivalence and conceptual reduction. This was at odds with what the critics valued as "subtle and distinguished" statistical analysis—an analysis that did not employ tables at all. Neither form of schematic qualitative analysis is used any longer, having been replaced by quantitative analysis, which has historically also been driven by nations' desires to organize and understand their populations (Desrosiers, 1998).

Statistician Karl Pearson (1857–1936), following in the footsteps of Francis Galton (1822–1911), argued that contingency tables allow one to schematize "the *partial relationship* between two phenomena, midway between two limits—absolute independence and absolute dependence—or *correlation*, synonymous with association" (Desrosiers, 1998: 110). The emphasis on "contingence" is important. Pearson believed absolute unilinear causation to be rare to non-existent. Philosophical understandings of the nature of what was being described lie behind the table's schematization. Pearson described them as contingency tables because he considered each event in the observable world to be unique; the human process of observation and classification is what allows for predictability. Regularity is a consequence of human conceptualization and abstraction, not an inherent feature of an external world.

EVERYDAY STATISTICS

The Utility of Contingency Tables

During an election period, news stations will often report the percentage of the population that is planning on voting for a particular political party. This information is collected from a sample of the population and is sometimes presented with data on the age or sex composition of those surveyed. A contingency table is often presented to give the public an overall picture of the expected outcome of the election.

. . . .

Q: Why is a contingency table a good way to represent the information collected during an election period?

The Chi-Square Test of Significance

The chi-square, introduced by Karl Pearson in 1900, is a widely used method for determining the level of agreement between the frequencies in a distribution of observed data and the frequencies calculated on the assumption of a normal distribution. Pearson wanted to determine the frequency with which trends derived from a sample would also be seen in the population. He developed the chi-square to serve that purpose. Since then, it has become an important part of statistical theory and practice.

The chi-square can be used for all levels of measurement, not just nominal data, and for combinations of levels—nominal/ordinal, ordinal/interval, nominal/ratio, etc.—making it extremely useful. It is **non-parametric**, so you don't have to make assumptions about the shape or distribution of a sample and/or population (it doesn't need to be normally distributed, for example). Using the chi-square makes it easy to identify statistically significant relationships between characteristics without worrying about whether the variables are normally distributed until after a relationship has been identified.

Perhaps the most compelling aspect of the chi-square is that it can be directly calculated from bivariate tables, such as Table 12.2, by comparing the discrepancies between observed values and expected values. It determines whether the observed differences in data come from random sampling error, or if they exist in the data.

To calculate the chi-square, you need to

1. Compute row and column totals, or **marginals**.
2. Divide the marginals by the total number of possible variable values to determine the distribution of highest probability. These are the expected values.

For example, there are 400 students and 20 classes at a high school. With no other information about the distribution of students (that is, there are no independent variables predicting allocation across classes), we would expect each class to have 20 students. If there were discrepancies between the expected class sizes and the observed class sizes, we might suspect that there are factors other than random allocation (popularity of teachers, subject matter, location of friends, etc.) behind classroom designation. Chi-square measures the magnitude of that discrepancy and tells us whether we should pursue further analysis.

To further illustrate the calculation of chi-square, let's imagine that there are two soccer teams, A and B, each made up of 11 people (there are 22 people in total). Of these, 12 are female, and 10 are male. If we guessed at the distribution of men and women across teams A and B, assuming that there were no factors influencing their distribution, we would guess that each team would be expected to have 6 females and 5 males.

To calculate the expected numbers, we must derive the expected frequencies for *each cell*. The expected frequencies are shown in parentheses in Table 12.3; the numbers not in parentheses are the actual (observed) frequencies, surrounded by row and column totals. The expected

TABLE 12.3 | Sex Composition of Two Hypothetical Soccer Teams

	Female	Male	Total
A	7(6)	4(5)	11
B	5(6)	6(5)	11
Total	12	10	22

frequency is the number of observations in each cell, if the independent variable has no impact on them. It can be calculated using the equation:

$$f_e = \frac{\sum column * \sum row}{n}$$

The expected frequency f_e is equal to the column marginal, multiplied by the row marginal, divided by the total number of observations. There are a total of 12 women and 10 men, with 11 people on each soccer team. Let's calculate the expected frequency for each of the four cells:

Upper left

$$f_e = \frac{\sum column * \sum row}{n} = \frac{12 * 11}{22} = \frac{132}{22} = 6$$

Upper right

$$f_e = \frac{10 * 11}{22} = 5$$

Lower left

$$f_e = \frac{12 * 11}{22} = 6$$

Lower right

$$f_e = \frac{10 * 11}{22} = 5$$

These numbers are the most likely distribution of men and women across the two teams, assuming a random distribution with no other explanatory factors or independent variables. In the event of a non-integer, it is acceptable to have an expected frequency that is not a whole number (e.g., 5.3) even though it is not likely to occur in reality (it is not possible to have part-persons on soccer teams).

The numbers that represent the expected distribution (typically expressed as f_e for expected frequencies) are used with the numbers you have observed (f_o for observed frequencies) to calculate chi-square X^2 by using the following formula:

$$\chi^2 = \sum \frac{(f_o - f_e)^2}{f_e}$$

				$\dfrac{(f_o - f_e)^2}{f_e}$
Group	f_o	f_e	$(f_o - f_e)^2$	
AF	7	6	1	0.17
AM	4	5	1	0.20
BF	5	6	1	0.17
BM	6	5	1	0.20
Total	22	22		$X^2 = 0.74$

TABLE 12.4 | Sex Composition of Two Hypothetical Soccer Teams

To reduce the possibility of calculation errors, it is useful to organize the data in a table like Table 12.4. In the far left column, each of the four cells is identified by its team name (A or B), and whether the cell refers to females or males (F or M). "AF" refers to the cell containing the frequency of females on team A. The observed frequencies, f_o, appear in the second column, followed by expected frequencies, f_e, in column three. Column four is $(f_o - f_e)^2$, the solution for the numerator of the chi-square equation, and column five solves the equation for each row. The summation of values appears in the bottom right cell, and represents the value of chi-square in this example.

Now that we have the chi-square value, we need to assess it by using a chi-square table. Like other distributions (normal distribution, t-distribution, etc.), chi-square has a known distribution (the table is shown in Appendix C), which means that we can determine if there are significant differences between observed and expected values. To do this, we need to revisit **degrees of freedom**, but with a slightly different calculation to reflect that two variables are being used.

When we looked at the t-distribution to assess sample means, we calculated the degrees of freedom to be equal to sample size minus one. We subtracted one from the sample size because the individual values of any particular set of numbers can be determined using $n - 1$ values. Since there was one variable, only one value was determined by the others.

Now we are looking at two variables, but the same logic applies. Remember that it is possible to determine the value of any cell by knowing the table total and the value of all other cells. Now there are two values that are determined entirely by other values. In this case, degrees of freedom can be defined as the number of rows, minus one, times the number of columns, minus one:

$$\text{degrees of freedom} = (r - 1)(c - 1)$$

In the example, there are two rows and two columns in Table 12.3 (we never count the totals columns), so the degrees of freedom are $(2 - 1)(2 - 1) = (1)(1) = 1$. Using Appendix C, we can choose a level of significance (also often called σ or p-value) of either 0.05 or 0.01. Next, find the correct number for the degrees of freedom that we calculated (1). For our example, with a level of significance of 0.05, the critical chi-square value is 3.841. To determine whether our observed values differ significantly from the expected values, we need to compare the calculated chi-square value of 0.74 to 3.841. If the calculated value exceeds the critical value, we can conclude that the observed values differ significantly from expected values.

BOX 12.2

Chi-Square: The Steps

1. Compute row and column totals, or marginals.
2. Divide marginals by the total number of possible variable values to determine the distribution of highest probability. These are the expected values.
3. Subtract expected cell frequencies from observed cell frequencies.
4. Square that number and divide it by the expected frequency.
5. Sum the product of these calculations. This is your observed chi-square value.
6. Assess the statistical significance of this number using the chi-square chart in Appendix C; $df = (r-1)(c-1)$.

Our calculated value is well *below* the critical value, suggesting that a respondent's sex is not a significant factor in determining which team they will be on.

Further analysis of this association is probably unnecessary, since chi-square suggests that the observed trends could have easily appeared at random. An important point to make about the chi-square is that it depends on both the strength of the relationship *and* the sample size. The difference in sex composition across teams may be too slight for us to be certain about its existence. It is also possible that the relationship is not significant because our sample of 22 is too small to determine if a significant association exists. With our pizza commercial example, we could express the same doubts. Sample size is not as important for the measures that we'll discuss in the next section.

MEASURES OF ASSOCIATION FOR NOMINAL DATA

As you know by now, researchers are interested in identifying not only the significance of relationships between variables, but also the strength of those relationships. Before the pizza company revamps its advertising strategy to more effectively target women, it would be useful to know if sex is associated with women's reaction to television commercials, or if the study was a fluke. For various reasons (perhaps a non-probability sample was used), it is possible that the 1,000 people in the study do not accurately reflect the pizza company's target audience. If that was the case, the patterns in Tables 12.1 and 12.2 would not be an accurate representation of the pizza company's customer base.

To solve this problem, a measure of **statistical significance** between sex and the reactions of the study members is needed. This measure will allow us to determine whether the observed patterns actually exist, or if they were due to chance or bias. This we have with chi-square. What we don't have, but need, is a measure of the strength of the association.

The level of measurement of a particular variable determines which measures of association are suitable. For nominal data, we'll learn about phi, Cramer's V, and lambda.

Phi

Phi is a chi-square-based measure of association used only for tables where both the independent variable and the dependent variable can have two response categories (2 by 2 tables). The chi-square coefficient depends on the strength of the relationship and sample size, but phi eliminates the influence of sample size by dividing chi-square by the sample size, n, and taking the square root.

$$\phi = \sqrt{\frac{\chi^2}{n}}$$

Since phi is a **symmetrical** measure, it doesn't matter which of the two variables you believe is the independent variable (although it's good practice to keep them straight). Phi is the percentage of difference between a product of the diagonal cells and the product of the non-diagonal cells. It is the magnitude of difference between observed and expected values, adjusting for sample size. Phi defines a perfect association as one with complete statistical dependence, for example, if all members of a certain category of the independent variable (e.g., all women) are also all members of one response of the dependent variable (e.g., all grabbed food from the fridge). Phi defines a null relationship as statistical independence (e.g., there is no difference between what men and women did after seeing the pizza ad).

Let's suppose that you were interested in the relationship between owning a gun to protect personal property and being a victim of a crime. You want to determine if people who are victims of crime are more likely to take extreme measures to protect themselves and their property. Since both gun ownership and victim data are nominal variables, with only two possible categories (yes/no), using phi is a good way of determining whether an association exists. Let's use the 2004 Victimization Survey (GSS cycle 18) as a data source (see Table 12.5).

TABLE 12.5 | Gun Ownership and Victims of Crimes

Owns gun	Have you been a victim of a crime in the past 12 months?		Total
	Yes	No	
Yes	21,400	234,900	256,300
	(17,994)	(238,306)	
No	1,793,400	23,799,000	25,592,400
	(1,796,806)	(23,795,594)	
Total	1,814,800	24,033,900	25,848,700

Source: 2004 Victimization Survey (GSS cycle 18)

TABLE 12.6 | Computing Chi-Square for Gun Ownership and Victims of Crimes

Group	f_o	f_e	$(f_o - f_e)^2$	$\dfrac{(f_o - f_e)^2}{f_e}$
YY	21,400	17,994	11,600,836	644.71
YN	234,900	238,306	11,600,836	48.68
NY	1,793,400	1,796,806	11,600,836	6.46
NN	23,799,000	23,795,594	11,600,836	0.49
Total	25,848,700	25,848,700		$x^2 = 700.34$

Source: 2001 Census of Canada

The first thing we need to do is create a table to calculate chi-square, as we did in Table 12.4 (see Table 12.6).

Looking at Appendix C, we can see that chi-square is significant. Now that we have chi-square, the calculation of phi is relatively straightforward:

$$\phi = \sqrt{\frac{x^2}{n}} = \sqrt{\frac{700.34}{25848700}} = 0.005$$

The interpretation of 0.005 is complicated and beyond the scope of this text, but suffice it to say, there is a significant association between gun ownership and victimization (700.34 is much higher than the critical value of 3.841 found in Appendix C). Turning to the phi value of 0.005, researchers typically regard values between zero and 0.10 as a weak association, 0.10 and 0.30 as a moderate association, and values between 0.30 and 1.0 as a strong association. Since phi is a symmetrical measure, no distinction is made between independent and dependent variables, so we don't know if victimization results in gun ownership, or vice versa. When two values are completely dependent on each other, phi will take the value of one. When there is no dependence, phi will take the value of zero. Each observation has a specific value for one variable (for example, a respondent reports owning a gun) whenever they report a value on the other variable (that they've been a victim of a crime in the past 12 months). The results point to a weak association.

Despite having some undesirable qualities, phi is a popular measure for 2 by 2 tables. It is not possible to analyze the pattern of the relationship without looking at the contingency table, so trends in the data cannot be determined from the measure of association alone. Phi is only useful for measuring the existence and strength of the relationship, but there is no easy way to measure the direction of that relationship.

BOX 12.3

It's Your Turn: Phi—Drinking and Daily Exercise

A student was thinking about the different men she knows: the men who were always exercising and the men who were always drinking. It seemed that none of them liked to both exercise and drink, but she thought that maybe this just happened among her friends. Using data from the Canadian Community Health Survey (CCHS, wave 2.1), she randomly selected 20 cases to test her null hypothesis that men who exercise at least 15 minutes a day are as likely as those who exercise less to regularly consume 12 or more drinks in a week (these cases were selected only from male respondents who provided an answer for both questions). If the student rejects her null hypothesis, she'll be able to conclude that there is a significant relationship between exercise and drinking for males.

TABLE 12.7 | Drinking and Exercise, 20 Cases from the Canadian Community Health Survey, Wave 2.1

Case	Regularly has more than 12 drinks a week (1 = yes, 0 = no)	Participates in at least 15 minutes of exercise daily (1 = yes, 0 = no)	Case	Regularly has more than 12 drinks a week (1 = yes, 0 = no)	Participates in at least 15 minutes of exercise daily (1 = yes, 0 = no)
1	1	0	11	0	1
2	0	0	12	0	0
3	1	0	13	0	0
4	1	1	14	1	1
5	0	1	15	0	0
6	0	0	16	1	0
7	1	1	17	0	0
8	1	0	18	0	0
9	0	0	19	1	0
10	0	0	20	1	1

1. Create a table (like Table 12.6) that compares your dependent (as rows) and independent (as columns) variables. Include column and row totals. (In this example, because we are not testing a causal relationship, either variable can be the independent or dependent variable).

2. Compute the expected values for each cell and add values to the table in question 1.

$$f_e = \frac{\Sigma_{column} * \Sigma_{row}}{N}$$

3. Create a chi-square table (like Table 12.6). To do this, you will (1) subtract the expected from the observed value in each cell, and square the number, and (2) divide it by the expected value $\frac{(f_o - f_e)^2}{f_e}$. Once that is done for each cell, compute the totals to find the X^2 value.

4. Calculate phi $\phi = \sqrt{\dfrac{X^2}{N}}$. Is there a strong or weak association between the variables?

The solution for Box 12.3 can be found on page 324.

Another limitation of phi is that it is sensitive to shifts in marginal distributions. Phi does not necessarily vary from zero to one. For tables larger than 2 by 2, the maximum value of phi is the square root of $k - 1$, where k is the number of response categories in the variable with a smaller number of categories. Phi can be greater than 1.0 for larger tables, with a theoretical maximum of infinity, differing depending on table size. Because of this, phi is typically only used with 2 by 2 tables. For tables larger than 2 by 2, the appropriate chi-square-based measure is **Cramer's V**.

Cramer's V

Cramer's V is an elaboration of phi, except that it always assumes a value between zero and one. Calculating Cramer's V is simple, using the following equation:

$$V = \sqrt{\frac{x^2}{(n)(\min(r - 1)|(c - 1))}}$$

Although the equation seems more daunting than the one for phi, they are actually similar. The difference is in the denominator, which is the number of observations multiplied by the lesser of the number of rows – 1, or the number of columns – 1.

If we calculated Cramer's V for city of residence and favourite Canadian NHL hockey team from a sample of 1,000 people, we would have 26 different cities and 6 hockey teams. The denominator for the Cramer's V equation would be 1000 * (6 – 1), or 5000, because the hockey teams variable has 6 values, considerably fewer than the 26 values for city of residence. For a 2 by 2 table, the denominator would be n (2 – 1), which equals n, and reduces the equation for Cramer's V to that of phi.

Since Cramer's V is so similar to phi, they share almost all of the same properties and weaknesses.

BOX 12.4

Phi and Cramer's V: The Steps

1. Calculate the observed chi-square value (Box 12.2).
2. For phi, divide chi-square by the number of observations, then take the square root.
3. For Cramer's V, divide chi-square by the number of observations, multiplied *either* by the number of rows minus 1 *or* by the number of columns minus 1 (use the smaller of the two values), then take the square root.

BOX 12.5

It's Your Turn: Cramer's V

Based on readings that Jeff had done for his sociology of the family course, he wondered if women were more or less likely to have worked full-time rather than part-time in the last year if they were married, divorced, or single. Using data from the 2001 Census of Canada, he selected only women who answered both the questions on full- vs part-time work and marital status, and recoded marital status to combine divorced and separated (people who were widowed were excluded). He found the following observed and expected (in brackets) values for the Canadian population:

TABLE 12.8 | Chi-Square for Women's Relationship between Work Status and Marital Status in 2000

Work status in 2000	Marital status			Total
	Married	Divorced/separated	Single	
Worked mainly full-time weeks	3,485,748(3,321,615.99)	604,011(525,916.09)	1,193,175(1,435,401.92)	2,582,934
Worked mainly part-time weeks	1,291,201(1,455,333.0)	152,330(230,424.9)	871,134(628,907.1)	2,314,665
Total	4,776,949	756,341	2,064,309	7,597,599

Source: 2001 Census of Canada

1. Using the observed and expected frequencies for each cell, compute chi-square.
2. Instead of computing phi, compute Cramer's V (because there is more than one degree of freedom) using this equation:

$$V = \sqrt{\frac{\chi^2}{(n)(\min(r-1)|(c-1))}}$$

The solution for Box 12.5 can be found on page 326.

THE PROPORTIONAL REDUCTION OF ERROR: LAMBDA

The final measure of association for nominal data that we will study is lambda. Like phi and Cramer's V, lambda is used to measure the strength of a relationship between two nominal variables. It is non-directional, and since it relies on a **proportional reduction of error**, its numbers are interpreted more straightforwardly than either phi or Cramer's V. Lambda allows us to answer the following question: How much is our ability to predict one variable improved by taking another variable into account?

To get lambda, calculate the extreme possibilities, then calculate the total classification error by comparing the extreme predictions with the actual distribution of observations across response categories.

Like the other measures, the mechanics of calculating lambda are better illustrated with an example. Suppose we wanted to determine if there is a relationship between smoking and the sex of the respondent, and saw the trends found in Table 12.9 in our hypothetical data.

From Table 12.9, we see that a higher proportion of females in our sample are smoking. From this, we might conclude that knowing the sex of a respondent increases the accuracy of our prediction about whether or not they are a smoker. However, what we don't know yet is whether the difference is big enough that we would see a similar trend in the population. To determine if that is the case, we need to make two predictions and ignore the influence of the independent variable (sex). The first prediction is that everyone is a smoker (S = 103, NS = 0), and the second is that nobody smokes (S = 0, NS = 103). Then we calculate the classification error in both cases, which is the number of observations minus the number of misclassified cases.

For smokers, it would be equal to

103 (the total number of observations) − 63 (the number of correctly classified cases) = a total of 40 misclassifications

For non-smokers, the misclassification would be equal to 103 − 40 = 63.

To calculate lambda, we keep the lower of the two misclassifications (40). This is because we are interested in making the best possible prediction with no additional information from any independent variable. We will call this number E_1. For this example, E_1 = 40.

TABLE 12.9 | Smoking and Sex of Respondent (fictional data)

	Female	Male	Row total
Smokes	42	21	63
Does not smoke	10	30	40
Column total	52	51	103

BOX 12.6

Why Does Non-Directionality Matter?

Because variables that are measured at the nominal level cannot be ranked or ordered, it's not surprising that these measures are non-directional. A non-directional measure is the best we can hope for.

BOX 12.7

Calculating Lambda: The Steps

1. What are the extreme possibilities? Make two predictions, ignoring the independent variable for now:
   a. Everyone is in one category of the dependent variable.
   b. Everyone is in the other category of the dependent variable.
2. Calculate classification errors (total minus number in one category, total minus number in the other category).
3. Keep the smaller of the two classification errors. This is the best possible prediction that can be made without information from an explanatory (independent) variable. Call it E_1.
4. What are the extreme possibilities for each value of the independent variable?
   a. Repeat step two for each category of the independent variable.
   b. Sum the lowest classification errors of each category of the independent variable. This is E_2.
5. Calculate lambda as $\lambda = \dfrac{E_1 - E_2}{E_1}$

The next step is to determine how much better we can do by using the values of our independent variable, sex of respondent. As you did last time, calculate the extreme possibilities for each value of the independent variable first, except that now we predict, first, that all females smoke, and second, do not smoke, and then do the same for males, calculating the classification error each time.

Predicting that all females smoke yields a classification error of 10 (52 – 42 = 10), and predicting that they do not smoke misclassifies 42 people (52 – 10 = 42). Predicting that all males smoke yields a classification error of 30 (51 – 21 = 30). Predicting that they do not smoke misclassifies 21 people (51 – 30 = 21).

Choose the lowest classification error for each sex, and sum those numbers to produce E_2, which is the total classification error that can be made with the information provided for the independent variable. Since the fewest errors come from guessing that all women smoke (10), and that all men do not (21), we sum those numbers to get a classification error of 31. This is the second error, and it represents the best possible prediction that can be made by including the independent variable, sex.

Finally, we define lambda (λ) as the percentage improvement from knowing a person's sex, using the following equation:

$$\lambda = \frac{E_1 - E_2}{E_1}$$
$$= \frac{40 - 31}{40}$$
$$= 0.225$$

The number tells us the change in the number of correct predictions between knowing the value for the independent variable and not knowing that value. The accuracy of the smoking prediction improves by 22.5 per cent when the value of the independent variable (sex of respondent) is known.

BOX 12.8

It's Your Turn: Lambda

Jose and his friend Vanessa have been arguing about whether women are more safety-conscious than men when they play sports. Vanessa is sure that they are, but Jose is sure they are just as likely as men to take risks. To test whether there is any difference between the two, Vanessa and Jose randomly select 100 individuals from the second wave of the CCHS who had gone in-line skating during the previous three months, and had responded to a question about whether they use protective gear when skating. They found the following:

Wears all protective equipment for in-line skating	Female	Male	Row total
Yes	9	2	11
No	42	47	89
Column total	51	49	100

1. Make the two extreme predictions for the dependent variable. The lower prediction will be E_1.
2. Calculate the extreme predictions by using the independent variable to determine E_2.
3. Calculate lambda (or the percentage increase in predictive accuracy): $\lambda = \dfrac{E_1 - E_2}{E_1}$

The solution for Box 12.8 can be found on page 326.

GLOSSARY TERMS

PRACTICE QUESTIONS

We're interested in the relationship between religion and city of choice. Questions 1–5 refer to the results of the data from a selected sample from the 1901 census:

Religion	City		
	Saint John	**Toronto**	**Quebec City**
Roman Catholic	98	329	641
Church of England	73	552	30
Methodist	26	414	8
Presbyterian	55	403	5

1. Why are these variables nominal?

2. Calculate chi-square for each of the cells.

3. How many degrees of freedom are there in the table?

4. Calculate phi and Cramer's V. Which of the two measures would you use? Why?

5. Imagine that we had only data for Roman Catholics and the Church of England for Saint John and Quebec City. Choose the appropriate statistic to measure the association and calculate it.
    a. Looking back at our discussion of hypotheses in Chapter 10, draft a set of directional null and alternative hypotheses about a potential difference between Saint John and Quebec City (for example, is one city significantly more Roman Catholic than the other?).

On July 25, 2011, *The Globe and Mail* polled its viewers to gauge their opinion on whether facial-recognition technology constituted an infringement of privacy. Questions 6–8 refer to the results of this poll (modified to include males and females), listed below:

Does facial-recognition technology constitute an infringement of privacy?	Female	Male	Row total
Yes	699	376	1,075
No	1,000	842	1,842
Column total	1,699	1,218	2,917

6. Draft non-directional null and research hypotheses for the table above.

7. Calculate lambda for the table above.

8. Based on your results in Question 7, do you find any reason to reject or fail to reject the null hypothesis you postulated in Question 6?

9. Bo and Jonah both like to study how people behave in society. One day, they decide to observe people in the public library for a morning, to see how many people could work in a public space without communicating with anyone. They hypothesize that those over the age of 30 will have different patterns of communication than those 30 and under. Here are the data they generate:

	Doesn't speak to anyone	Speaks with at least one person
Age 30 and under	17	15
Over age 30	12	22

Calculate chi-square for the above table (since we are only interested in significance of differences, we can use chi-square even though other measures like lambda would give us more information). Then, identify whether you have amassed any support for Bo and Jonah's hypothesis.

Answers to the practice questions for Chapter 12 can be found on page 305.

CHAPTER 13

Bivariate Statistics for Ordinal Data

LEARNING OBJECTIVES

This chapter will continue our overview of the various measures of association for the different levels of measurement. We'll cover several measures for ordinal data, specifically:

- Kruskal's gamma (γ);
- Spearman's *rho* (ρ_s);
- Somers' *d*;
- Kendall's tau-*b*.

INTRODUCTION

In Chapter 12, we looked at some of the tests of significance and measures of association frequently used for nominal variables. Some of the measures (phi, Cramer's V) are based on the chi-square, whereas the others (lambda) rely on a "proportional reduction in error." Since nominal data cannot be ranked or ordered, we did not discuss any statistics that assess the *direction* of a relationship between two variables. So, we cannot determine what happens to the value of the dependent variable as the value of the independent variable changes. The best we can do with these data is to figure out how knowing the value of one nominal variable (the independent variable) will help us to accurately predict the value of another nominal variable (the dependent variable).

In this chapter, we will look at tests of significance and measures of association for ordinal variables. Since ordinal variables have more desirable statistical properties than nominal variables (notably, the ability to rank response categories), after completing Chapter 13, not only will you be able to assess the significance of difference and the proportional reduction of errors, you will also be able to measure the **direction** of any relationship. You will thus also be able to generate directional hypotheses.

There are at least four popular measures of association for variables measured at the ordinal level: Kruskal's gamma (γ), Spearman's *rho* (ρ_s), Somers' *d*, and Kendall's tau-*b*. As with nominal variables, one of the most useful ways to understand the relationships between ordinal variables is to look at a contingency table.

CONTINGENCY TABLES/CROSS-TABULATIONS

To illustrate measures of association between ordinal variables, consider an example from mental health research. Suppose you want to determine if there are differences in self-perceived mental health by level of education. You hypothesize that people with higher education levels are likely to report higher mental health levels, because you believe that a critical component of mental health is self-fulfillment and life satisfaction, two things that you think are related to education. What would you need to determine whether that relationship actually exists? In Canada, this inquiry can be made using the Canadian Community Health Survey, a longitudinal survey conducted by Statistics Canada. We'll use wave 2.1 of the Canadian Community Health Survey, which provides data from 2003 on a broad range of health topics.

The first thing to do is some univariate analysis: look at the distribution of each of the variables and identify **outliers** and/or **missing data**, etc. We want to make sure that there are enough observations in each possible category (you'll see why this is important in a minute), and that there are no outliers, that is, observations with scores that lie far outside the area under the normal curve. Once that is done, we can look at the relationship with more confidence.

First, let's look at education, which we hypothesize to be the independent variable. Using Table 13.1, we can see that approximately one-quarter of the total population has less than a secondary school education. Another 17.8 per cent have achieved a secondary school diploma,

| TABLE 13.1 | Educational Attainment Levels of the Canadian Population, Canadian Community Health Survey, Wave 2.1, All Observations |

		Highest level - respond. 4 levels (D)			
		Frequency	Per cent	Valid per cent	Cumulative per cent
Valid	‹ than secondary	6,923,116	26.1	26.6	26.6
	Secondary grad.	4,726,816	17.8	18.2	44.8
	Other post sec.	1,996,934	7.5	7.7	52.5
	Post-sec. grad.	12,333,484	46.4	47.5	100.0
	Total	25,980,349	97.8	100.0	
Missing	Not stated	575,081	2.2		
Total		26,555,430	100.0		

Source: Canadian Community Health Survey Public Use Data, Wave 2.1

7.5 per cent of all respondents have attained at least some post-secondary training, and the remaining 46.4 per cent claim to have successfully completed post-secondary training. Although the accuracy of these results can't be assessed without comparing them with results from another data set (such as the census), it is not unreasonable to believe that approximately half of all Canadians have completed post-secondary training. Similarly, that 26.1 per cent of all Canadians have less than a secondary school education probably fits with what we would see in the census data. If we saw that 80 per cent of all people in Canada didn't have post-secondary training, that should raise a red flag for us!

Since these values make sense to us, we can say that they appear to have **face validity**. Therefore, we can be fairly confident about using them in our analysis. Note that there are a number of people who, for whatever reason, did not answer the question. Treat these instances as missing data, meaning that they will not add any useful information to the analysis. In fact, they might obscure our investigation of the relationship between education and mental health, because most software packages will treat the missing cases as another response category (unless we tell the software to do otherwise, or the data have already been defined as missing).

Now, let's look at Table 13.2. Again, we see that there are several missing responses in our mental health measure. Before we perform any bivariate analyses, we want to eliminate these cases from our investigation. More important, since we are analyzing two variables at a time, we want all observations to have available data for both variables.

For now, we'll skip over how to select or exclude cases (please consult your lab manual to learn how to exclude cases in the package that you are using for your course), since it is done

TABLE 13.2 | Self-perceived Mental Health of the Canadian Population, Canadian Community Health Survey, Wave 2.1, All Observations

Self-perceived mental health		Frequency	Per cent	Valid per cent	Cumulative per cent
Valid	Excellent	9,941,583	38.4	38.4	38.4
	Very good	9,068,745	34.2	35.0	73.4
	Good	5,666,929	21.3	21.9	95.3
	Fair	997,559	3.8	3.9	99.2
	Poor	210,984	0.8	0.8	100.0
	Total	25,885,801	98.5	100.0	
Missing	Don't know	35,749	0.1		
	Refusal	8,105	0.0		
	Not stated	625,774	2.4		
	Total	669,629	2.5		
Total		26,555,430	100.0		

Source: Canadian Community Health Survey Public Use Data, Wave 2.1

differently in each statistical package. The 575,081 cases that were missing in Table 13.1 have been excluded from Table 13.3, leaving only observations with valid values for each variable.

All of the "don't know," "refusal," and "not stated" responses have been eliminated in all of the tables that follow. Now that the data are in shape, we can look at **contingency tables**. First, educational attainment

TABLE 13.3 | Educational Attainment Levels of the Canadian Population, Canadian Community Health Survey, Wave 2.1, Valid Observations Only

Highest level – respond. 4 levels (D)		Frequency	Per cent	Valid per cent	Cumulative per cent
Valid	‹ than secondary	6,923,116	26.6	26.6	26.6
	Secondary grad.	4,726,816	18.2	18.2	44.8
	Other post-sec.	1,996,934	7.7	7.7	52.5
	Post-sec. grad.	12,333,484	47.5	47.5	100.0
	Total	25,980,349	100.0	100.0	

Source: Canadian Community Health Survey Public Use Data, Wave 2.1

Then self-perceived mental health

TABLE 13.4 | Self-perceived Mental Health of the Canadian Population, Canadian Community Health Survey, Wave 2.1, Valid Observations Only

Self-perceived mental health		Frequency	Per cent	Valid per cent	Cumulative per cent
Valid	Excellent	9,923,648	38.4	38.4	38.4
	Very good	9,055,679	35.0	35.0	73.5
	Good	5,652,134	21.9	21.9	95.3
	Fair	994,779	3.9	3.9	99.2
	Poor	210,764	0.8	0.8	100.0
	Total	25,837,004	100.0	100.0	

Source: Canadian Community Health Survey Public Use Data, Wave 2.1

In Table 13.5, the distribution of self-rated mental health is presented, contingent on education, by the number of observations. In Table 13.6, the same information exists but is presented in percentages. Pay particular attention to how the data are "clustered" in certain cells. Note that in Table 13.5, every cell has a fairly high number of observations, so we needn't worry about **sparsity** affecting our results. Other than that, it is difficult to glean any

TABLE 13.5 | Observed Counts of Education by Self-perceived Mental Health Status, Canadian Community Health Survey, Wave 2.1, Valid Observations Only

Highest level - respond. 4 levels (D) * Self-perceived mental health cross-tabulation

Highest level - respond. 4 levels (D)	Self-perceived mental health					
	Excellent	Very good	Good	Fair	Poor	Total
‹ than secondary	2,158,456	2,237,899	1,789,087	331,363	70,770	6,587,575
Secondary grad.	1,725,723	1,639,759	1,028,018	181,424	41,202	4,616,126
Other post-sec.	768,166	685,646	413,825	87,898	18,494	1,974,029
Post-sec. grad.	5,103,471	4,327,080	2,299,402	373,042	76,288	12,179,283
Total	9,755,816	8,890,384	5,530,332	973,727	206,754	25,357,013

Source: Canadian Community Health Survey Public Use Data, Wave 2.1

useful information. For this reason, when working with large data sets it is easier to identify trends by looking at the percentages of observations in each cell, rather than the number of observations.

Looking at Table 13.6, we start to see that a relationship exists between education and perceived mental health. Taking a look at the entire table, note that the number of people reporting better perceived mental health gradually increases as education levels get higher. Similarly, poor mental health appears to be negatively related to education. Beyond identifying the direction of the relationship between the two variables, it is difficult to identify the strength of the relationship. We need to rely on measures of association partly for this reason. Some of the leading measures for ordinal data are discussed below.

TABLE 13.6 | Education by Self-perceived Mental Health Status Presented as Percentages, Canadian Community Health Survey, Wave 2.1, Valid Observations Only

Highest level respond. 4 levels (D) * Self-perceived mental health cross-tabulation

Highest level - respond. 4 levels (D)	Self-perceived mental health (per cent)					
	Excellent	Very good	Good	Fair	Poor	Total
‹ than secondary	32.8	34.0	27.2	5.0	1.1	100.0
Secondary grad.	37.4	35.5	22.3	3.9	0.9	100.0
Other post-sec	38.9	34.7	21.0	4.5	0.9	100.0
Post-sec. grad.	41.9	35.5	18.9	3.1	0.6	100.0
Total	38.5	35.1	21.8	3.8	0.8	100.0

Source: Canadian Community Health Survey Public Use Data, Wave 2.1

KRUSKAL'S GAMMA (γ)

Like lambda for nominal variables, gamma (γ) relies on a proportional reduction of error, meaning that using it describes the odds of correctly predicting a score. By calculating gamma, we can determine by how much our ability to predict the score of Y is improved if we take the score of X into account. However, unlike lambda, the values of gamma range between −1.00 and +1.00, because the measure is directional.

To compute gamma, two quantities are necessary:

1. N_{same} is the number of case pairs that are ranked in the *same* order on both variables, also known as concordant observations.
2. $N_{different}$ is the number of case pairs that are ranked in a *different* order on each variable, also known as discordant observations.

To understand what we mean by N_{same} and $N_{different}$, consider an example. Although we could continue with the mental health example above, it is a fairly large cross-tabulation for introducing gamma. So, let's look at something simpler.

Suppose that we are interested in the relationship between educational attainment and income for Aboriginal Canadians. To do this, we can use the 2001 Aboriginal Peoples Survey, which includes highly detailed information on this and many other contemporary characteristics of Canada's Aboriginal peoples. Although there is more detailed information in the survey, pretend for the purpose of this example that we only have two dichotomous, ordinal measures of income and education.

Looking at Table 13.7, it is easy to see that high school graduates are more likely to earn an income than people without a high school diploma. In the "Yes" column for "High school graduate?" there is a much larger proportion of individuals in the "Yes" row for income (roughly 84 per cent) than the "No" row (16 per cent). Compare this to those without a high school diploma (the column labelled "No"). Only 71 per cent of all people in that column are earning an income, and 29 per cent of people report having no income.

TABLE 13.7 | The Relationship between Graduation from High School and Income from Paid Employment or Self-employment

		High school graduate?		
		Yes	**No**	**Total**
Income from paid employment or self-employment	Yes	329,269	86,485	415,754
	No	62,278	35,285	97,563
Total		391,547	121,770	513,317

Source: 2001 Aboriginal Peoples Survey

Table 13.7 suggests that there is a relationship between having a high school diploma and earning some income from paid employment or self-employment. What we do not know at this point is whether the relationship is strong, moderate, or weak. Our first step is to generate a research and null hypothesis:

> **H_1: Those with a high school diploma are more likely to report earned income from paid employment or self-employment ($\mu_{hsdiploma} \leq \mu_{nohsdiploma}$)**
>
> **H_0: Those with a high school diploma are either not distinguishable from those without a high school diploma, or they are less likely to report earned income from paid employment or self-employment ($\mu_{hsdiploma} \leq \mu_{nohsdiploma}$)**

We can use gamma to test the hypotheses. To calculate gamma we need two numbers. The first, N_{same}, is calculated by multiplying the number of people who have positive values on both variables (high school graduate = yes, earning income = yes) by the number of people who have negative values on both variables (high school graduate = no, earning income = no). This gives us

$$329269 * 35285 = 11618256665$$

Next, calculate, $N_{different}$, which is equal to the number of observations with different values on each variable. In a 2 by 2 table, these are the two opposite cells of the ones used to calculate N_{same} yielding:

$$62278 * 86485 = 5386112830$$

Now that we have N_{same} and $N_{different}$, we calculate gamma by using the equation:

$$\gamma = \frac{N_{same} - N_{different}}{N_{same} + N_{different}}$$

Inserting our numbers of interest, then making the necessary calculations, yields:

$$\gamma = \frac{11618256665 - 5386112830}{11618256665 + 5386112830}$$

$$= \frac{6232143835}{17004369495}$$

$$= 0.367$$

The equation gives us a gamma value of 0.367. Now we know that if we guessed whether or not a person earns an income, we would make 36.7 per cent fewer errors than if we knew whether or not that person has a high school diploma.

The equation may look daunting, but that's only because of the big numbers. There are over 500,000 people in the study (actually, it is more accurate to say that there are over 500,000 *weighted* observations in the study (that is, the data from respondents have been adjusted to better represent the population). Using smaller samples would make these numbers less intimidating.

TABLE 13.8	Rough Guidelines for the Interpretation of Gamma Values	
Value	**Strength**
Between 0.0 and 0.10	Weak
Higher than 0.10 and less than 0.30	Moderate
Greater than 0.30	Strong

If you look at Table 13.8, you can see from the rough guidelines for interpreting gamma that this value counts as a strong relationship, so now we know that there is a strong relationship between education and income in the Aboriginal population, and strong support for rejecting the null hypothesis.

Gamma ranges in value from −1.00 to +1.00, and, like lambda, has a proportional reduction in error interpretation. A value of −1.00 indicates that all (untied) pairs are discordant, which implies a perfect negative relationship: that is, knowing a person's score on an independent variable improves your ability to predict the score on the dependent variable, but the relationship is negative. A value of +1.00 indicates the opposite; all untied pairs are concordant and the relationship between independent variable and dependent variable is perfect and positive. Knowing a person's score on an independent variable improves your ability to predict the score on the dependent variable, and the relationship is positive. A discordant pair is defined as any value where values on each variable run in a different "direction"— meaning that somebody who has a high score on the independent variable has a low score on the dependent variable, and vice versa. A concordant pair refers to any observation with scores that run in the same direction; here, a high score on the independent variable would be matched by a high score on the dependent variable. Let's use another example: the relationship between support for a smoking ban in the workplace and an individual's level of education (see Table 13.9).

In a 2 by 2 table like Table 13.9, calculating concordant and discordant pairs is easy. When your contingency table is arranged properly (so that values consistently go from high to low, or low to high, on both axes), concordant pairs in a 2 by 2 table are defined as those in the top left and bottom right cells, and discordant pairs are those in the top right and bottom left cells. The top left cell of frequencies (where individuals do not support smoking bans and hold less than a university degree), represents one of the two concordant cells; 18 people with both low support for smoking bans and lower levels of educational attainment are placed there. The other concordant table is the bottom right cell of frequencies; 14 people with high support for smoking bans and higher levels of education are found there.

In a table that is larger than 2 by 2, it is more difficult to calculate concordant and discordant pairs. This is because determining whether a pair is concordant or discordant depends on the location of a particular cell. Imagine Table 13.9 having three categories for each variable, instead of two.

TABLE 13.9 | How to Calculate Concordant and Discordant Pairs in a 2 × 2 Table

	No university training	At least some university training	Total
No support for ban	18	10	28
Full support for ban	10	14	24
Total	28	24	52

A concordant pair is defined as any positive diagonal of a particular cell. A positive cell is one where responses to one variable are in the same direction as responses to another variable (ties are ignored for gamma in a table larger than 2 by 2). For example, in Table 13.10 the cells concordant with the top left cell, *a* (less than high school diploma, no support for smoking ban), are cells *e, f, h,* and *i*. Each one is both below and to the right of cell *a*. Other concordant cells in Table 13.10 are *f* and *i* with *b*; *h* and *i* with *d*; and *i* with *e*. In a 3 by 3 table, these form the four concordant sets.

The next step is to sum the number of observations that are concordant to each cell, and multiply that sum by the cell frequency, giving us N_{same}. To help with that, it is useful to organize the information in the manner seen in Table 13.11.

Now that we have N_{same}, we must calculate the number of discordant cells and observations ($N_{different}$). The logic is the same as for calculating concordant cells, except that we tally the number of observations operating in the *opposite* direction (to the left and below). For cell *c*, the discordant cells would be *e, d, g,* and *h*; for cell *b* it is *d* and *g*; for *f* it is *g* and *h*; and for *e* it is *g*. Table 13.12 organizes information in the same way as Table 13.11, but this time for the discordant cells.

Tables 13.11 and 13.12 give us N_{same} and $N_{different}$, so we can calculate gamma using the same formula as before:

$$\gamma = \frac{N_{same} - N_{different}}{N_{same} + N_{different}}$$

$$= \frac{1728 - 1124}{1728 + 1124}$$

$$= 0.212$$

The value of 0.212 implies a moderately strong and positive relationship. If the number was negative, the relationship would be moderate but negative.

Although gamma is widely used, it has the limitation of ignoring tied pairs. A significant proportion of all observations are often not used in the calculation of a relationship, suggesting that gamma tends to overestimate the relationship between variables, especially when there are a lot of tied cases.

TABLE 13.10 | How to Calculate Concordant and Discordant Pairs in a Table Larger than 2 × 2

	Less than high school diploma	High school diploma, no university	At least some university training	Total
No support for ban	18(a)	10(b)	10(c)	38
Some support for ban	14(d)	12(e)	11(f)	37
Full support for ban	10(g)	14(h)	14(i)	38
Total	42	36	35	113

TABLE 13.11 | Concordant Cells of Table 13.10

Cell	# of concordant cells	# of concordant observations	Contribution to N_s
A	4 (e, f, h, i)	12 + 11 + 14 + 14 = 51	18 * 51 = 918
B	2 (f, l)	11 + 14 = 25	10 * 25 = 250
C	0		
D	2 (h, l)	14 + 14 = 28	14 * 28 = 392
E	1 (l)	14	12 * 14 = 168
F	0		
G	0		
H	0		
I	0		

$$N_s = 1{,}728$$

TABLE 13.12 | Discordant Cells of Table 13.10

Cell	# of discordant cells	# of discordant observations	Contribution to N_d
a	0		
b	2 (d, g)	14 + 10 = 24	10 * 24 = 240
c	4 (d, e, g, h)	14 + 12 + 10 + 14 = 50	10 * 50 = 500
d	0		
e	1 (g)	10	12 * 10 = 120
f	2 (g, h)	10 + 14 = 24	11 * 24 = 264
g	0		
h	0		
i	0		

$$N_d = 1{,}124$$

BOX 13.1

Gamma: The Steps

1. Calculate N_{same} (or the number of concordant pairs).
2. Calculate $N_{different}$ (or the number of discordant pairs).
3. Calculate gamma by using the following equation:

$$\gamma = \frac{N_{same} - N_{different}}{N_{same} + N_{different}}$$

4. As a rough guideline, consider values between 0 and 0.10 to be weak, between 0.10 and 0.30 to be moderate, and 0.30 or higher to be strong.

BOX 13.2

It's Your Turn: Calculating Gamma

Zane has recently noticed a lot of media attention about how people are afraid of walking alone in his city at night. He wonders if this fear stems from a belief that the Canadian justice system is not effective. To find out if this is true, he uses data from the 2004 General Social Survey (GSS18), which focused on victimization. Since the GSS is a very large survey and Zane knows he would have to compute gamma by hand (his computer is broken), he decides to select a sample of 500 people. Once the missing cases are removed, Zane has 413 observations. The contingency table is presented below.

Relationship Between Views of Justice and Frequency of Walking Alone at Night

| | Count | | | |
| | Courts do good job of quick justice | | | |
		Good	Average	Poor	Total
Walk alone at night	At least once a week	40	77	86	203
	Up to once a month	18	61	51	130
	Never	16	26	38	80
Total		74	164	175	413

Source: 2004 General Social Survey

1. Compute N_{same} and $N_{different}$ (Hint: use a table to make this easier.)
2. Calculate gamma: $\gamma = \dfrac{N_{same} - N_{different}}{N_{same} + N_{different}}$
3. Determine if there is a weak, moderate, or strong relationship between people's views on the efficiency of the courts and walking alone in neighbourhoods after dark.

The solution for Box 13.2 can be found on page S-35.

SPEARMAN'S *RHO*

As you can imagine, calculating gamma isn't easy using any table larger than 2 by 2. Although it is possible, and most software packages do it, my humble opinion is that it is much easier to use some of the other measures of association for ordinal variables whenever a table exceeds 2 by 2. Also, given the limitations of gamma, it is often useful to consider other options.

Spearman's *rho*, or Spearman's Rank Correlation Coefficient, is one such option. The traditional formula for calculating the *rho* is:

$$\rho_s = 1 - \frac{6 * \sum D^2}{N(N^2 - 1)}$$

Spearman's *rho* is a somewhat unique measure, because it relies exclusively on the *rank* of observations, rather than the value, making it a prime candidate for calculations using ordinal data. Since it is not possible to measure distances between values with ordinal data, Spearman's *rho* takes the approach of comparing the level of concordance between one variable and another.

To illustrate, consider an example. Suppose we suspect that there is a relationship between the number of races a cyclist wins, and the number of endorsements they receive. To keep it simple, let's look at five cyclists from different countries: Japan, US, Canada, Russia, and Venezuela. Each has won a number of races, and we believe that winning a race makes a particular candidate more attractive to sponsors, leading to an increase in the number of endorsements received.

Since *rho* is only concerned with ranks, it is necessary to sort and rank each of the variables.

The easiest way to calculate Spearman's *rho* is by organizing all of the information in a table, like Table 13.14. It is also helpful to have a null and research hypothesis:

> H_1: **As the number of races that a cyclist wins increases, so too does the number of endorsements he or she receives.**
> H_0: **There is no relationship between race wins and endorsements.**

Once we have the information organized, calculating *rho* is easy because we can straightforwardly measure the discrepancy between the rank of one variable and the rank of the other.

TABLE 13.14 | Spearman's *Rho* and the Relationship between Races Won and Endorsement Participation

	# of races won	Rank	# of endorsements	Rank	D (rank for wins – rank for endorsements)	D²
Japan	5	3	4	4	−1	1
US	2	5	3	5	0	0
Canada	3	4	5	3	1	1
Russia	6	2	7	1	1	1
Venezuela	7	1	6	2	−1	1
Totals					0	4

D is the difference between rankings on number of races won and number of endorsements, and D^2 is $D * D$. By summing D^2, we get one of the numbers that we need to calculate *rho*.

$$\rho_s = 1 - \frac{6 * \sum D^2}{N(N^2 - 1)}$$

$$= 1 - \frac{6 * 4}{5(25 - 1)}$$

$$= 1 - \frac{24}{120}$$

$$= 0.80$$

The sign of *rho* indicates the direction of the relationship. Our value here indicates that we have a strong and positive relationship and that we have found considerable reason to reject the null hypothesis.

Squaring *rho* allows for a PRE-type interpretation (Proportional Reduction in Error), which means that we can calculate the reduction in our errors by using the value of the independent variable. In this case it's $0.8^2 = 0.64$, so our errors of prediction will be reduced by 64 per cent.

BOX 13.3

Spearman's *Rho*

Psychologist Charles Spearman (1863–1945) first proposed the measure of correlation we call *rho* in a 1904 paper titled "The Proof and Measurement of Association between Two Things." In that paper, he did not call the value he arrived at *rho*, nor did he give it the Greek letter ρ, which is used today. In that early paper, the value was similar to, but not the same as *rho*, as we know it today. Calling it a "method of rank differences," Spearman listed some disadvantages:

1. It can be done with ranks only, not measurements.
2. The probable error we get tells us what correlation we could expect from independent variables. It doesn't tell us the error we can expect to attribute to measurement (as Pearson's probable error does).
3. Because the values of Somers' *d* do not follow a normal, or even symmetrical, distribution, there are problems when one takes negative values as inverse correlation.
4. This value ρ_s is not the same as the *rho* of other methods of correlation.

Spearman continued working and reflecting on formulae for assessing correlation, and took up *r* again in a 1906 paper titled "Foot Rule for Measuring Correlation," where he advocated it as a quick rule for determining correlation, while still being comparable to Pearson's *r*.

Spearman's motivation was apparently to establish a suitable rule for correlation in psychology that is both pragmatic and statistically meaningful. One of his supporting arguments for this measure of correlation is that it can be done in less than a minute by hand, in some cases entirely in one's head, and can provide a guideline (or foot rule, as Spearman calls it) for what sort of correlation, or lack thereof, one is looking at. It is up to the reader whether the standard formula for *rho* fulfills Spearman's desire for a foot rule requiring only a "trifling expenditure" on the part of the researcher. Perhaps, just as electronic calculation has supplanted the extensive need for logarithmic tables, the ease of use of statistical formulae is no longer a determining factor in their development.

BOX 13.4

It's Your Turn: Calculating Spearman's *Rho*

Andy feels that he's been doing pretty well in his statistics class. His friend Marianne is surprised—they always study together, but she doesn't do as well. What could be the difference? "Andy does go out drinking every weekend," she thinks to herself. To figure out if drinking more might improve her grades, Marianne conducts a small study. She asks Andy and seven other friends what grade they received on the midterm, and how many drinks they usually have in a week. These are the data she collects:

Case	Number of drinks a week	Grade
1	10	65
2	2	75
3	2	52
4	0	98
5	1	45
6	5	55
7	20	70
8	3	60

At first glance, there doesn't appear to be much of a pattern, but she realizes that a ranking table would be more thorough.

1. Complete the ranking table below.

   Note that there are two people who have the same number of drinks (two drinks per week). When this happens, the ranking is the average of the two ranks. If they take up the places for ranks three and four, they will each rank 3.5. When in doubt about how to handle ties, you'll know you've made the right choice when the sum of *D* equals zero.

Case	Number of drinks a week	Drinks rank	Grade	Grade rank	D	D²
1	10		65			
2	2		75			
3	2		52			
4	0		98			
5	1		45			
6	5		55			
7	20		70			
8	3		60			

2. Calculate *rho*: $\rho_s = 1 - \dfrac{6 * \sum D^2}{N(N^2 - 1)}$

3. Square the value of *rho*.

4. How much does knowing the number of drinks a person has in a week improve your ability to estimate how well Marianne and Andy will do in their statistics class?

The solution for Box 13.4 can be found on page S-36.

BOX 13.5

Spearman's *Rho*: The Steps

1. Organize the observations into a chart, with columns for score on each variable of interest, their respective ranks, the differences between the two (D), and the differences between the two squared (D^2). D^2 will be the most useful for calculating *rho*.

1	2	3	4	5	6	7
Case	Raw score of variable 1	Rank of variable 1 (1st, 2nd, etc.)	Raw score of variable 2	Rank of variable 2 (1st, 2nd, etc.)	D (column 3 – column 5)	D^2
n						

2. Calculate *rho* as

$$\rho_s = 1 - \frac{6 * \sum D^2}{N(N^2 - 1)}$$

SOMERS' *d*

Somers' *d* is one of several alternatives to gamma, and is quite similar to *rho* except that it adjusts for tied ranks on the dependent variable. Ties occur when two pairs of scores are both concordant for the independent variable—one ranks higher than the other—and discordant for the dependent variable—the same variable again ranks higher. This equation is used to calculate Somers' *d*:

$$d = \frac{N_{same} - N_{different}}{N_{same} + N_{different} + Ties_y}$$

As you can see, this equation is very similar to gamma except for the addition of a term in the denominator. Calculating the number of ties can be problematic; see Table 13.15 for help.

Let us go back to the example of levels of education and support for a smoking ban. Table 13.10 is repeated on the next page, renumbered a Table 13.15. In Table 13.15, cells *b* and

c are tied with a; c is tied with b; e and f are tied with d; f is tied with e; h and i are tied with g; and i is tied with h, yielding the following value for $Ties_y$:

$$Ties_y = 18(10 + 10) + 10(10) + 14(12 + 11) + 12(11) + 10(14 + 14) + 14(14)$$
$$= 360 + 100 + 322 + 132 + 280 + 196$$
$$= 1390$$

N_{same} is 1,728 and $N_{different}$ is 1,124, so we can find d:

$$d = \frac{N_{same} - N_{different}}{N_{same} + N_{different} + Ties_y} = \frac{1728 - 1124}{1728 + 1124 + 1390} = 0.142$$

This is a lot lower than the gamma value of 0.212, because there is an additional term in the denominator. Like gamma, values for Somers' d range between −1 and +1 with an approximately similar interpretation. Hypothesis testing and formulation is also similar, in that it is directional.

TABLE 13.15 | Levels of Education and Support for Smoking Ban

	Less than high school diploma	High school diploma, no university	At least some university training	Total
No support for ban	18(a)	10(b)	10(c)	38
Some support for ban	14(d)	12(e)	11(f)	37
Full support for ban	10(g)	14(h)	14(i)	38
Total	42	36	35	113

BOX 13.6

Somers' d : The Steps

1. Calculate N_{same}, or the number of concordant pairs.
2. Calculate $N_{different}$, or the number of discordant pairs.
3. Calculate $Ties_y$, or the number of ties.
4. Calculate Somers' d using the following equation:

$$d = \frac{N_{same} - N_{different}}{N_{same} + N_{different} + Ties}$$

Just as when you're using gamma, consider values between 0 and 0.10 to be weak, between and 0.30 to be moderate, and 0.30 or higher to be strong.

BOX 13.7

It's Your Turn: Calculating Somers' d

Isa is convinced that people who study full-time have dirty homes, but she wants to test her theory using Somers' d. Using data from the 2001 Census of Canada Individual File, Isa randomly selects 250 people who had answered questions about their educational status and the number of hours they spent on housework. She recodes educational status, going from not being a student to being in school full-time. She also recodes hours of unpaid housework into three categories.

The relationship between educational status and hours spent on unpaid labour per week

Hours on unpaid household labour/week	Educational status			Total
	Not studying	Part-time student	Full-time student	
Less than 5	52	1	20	73
5 to 14	59	2	5	66
15 or more	106	2	3	111
Total	217	5	28	250

Source: 2001 Census of Canada

1. Compute N_{same} and $N_{different}$ and $Ties_y$.

2. Calculate Somers' d: $d = \dfrac{N_{same} - N_{different}}{N_{same} + N_{different} + Ties_y}$

3. Based on your calculation, what can you say about the relationship between hours of unpaid household work and being a student, using Somers' d? Is Isa's theory correct?

The solution for Box 13.7 can be found on page S-37.

KENDALL'S TAU-B

Kendall's tau-b is conceptually similar to gamma and Somers' d, but it goes one step further than Somers' d and corrects for tied pairs on both the dependent variable and the independent variable. Its equation is

$$\text{tau-}b = \frac{N_{same} - N_{different}}{(N_{same} + N_{different} + Ties_y)(N_{same} + N_{different} + Ties_x)}$$

Calculating $Ties_x$ is similar to calculating $Ties_y$, except instead of looking for ties on the dependent variable, it also looks for ties on the independent variable. So, for Table 13.15

$$Ties_x = 18(14 + 10) + 14(10) + 10(12 + 14) + 12(14) + 10(11 + 14) + 11(14)$$
$$= 432 + 140 + 260 + 168 + 250 + 154$$
$$= 1404$$

And so the equation is:

$$\text{tau-}b = \frac{N_{same} - N_{different}}{\sqrt{(N_{same} + N_{different} + Ties_y)(N_{same} + N_{different} + Ties_x)}}$$

$$= \frac{1728 - 1124}{\sqrt{(1728 + 1124 + 1390)(1728 + 1124 + 1404)}}$$

$$= \frac{604}{\sqrt{(4242)(4256)}}$$

$$= 0.142$$

In our example, Somers' d and tau-b are identical, because 1,390 and 1,404 are so close that multiplying essentially equal numbers (4,242 and 4,256) and then taking the square root has almost no effect on the denominator.

WHAT ABOUT STATISTICAL SIGNIFICANCE?

You may have noticed that we haven't been discussing statistical significance a whole lot in this chapter. This exclusion was intentional, and although the considerations covered in earlier chapters also apply here, calculating significance statistics is the same process as that described in Box 12.2. Generally, however, ordinal data have three or more categories for each variable, making the calculation of chi-square cumbersome, though certainly possible.

It is often helpful to rely on chi-square to identify whether an association is statistically significant. Indeed, it can be quite difficult to test hypotheses without a measure of significance. However, chi-square treats both your independent and dependent variables as nominal, forcing you to disregard some of the information inherent to ordinal variables, such as the direction of the relationship. The upside of chi-square is that it can be calculated with relative ease with smaller tables. In larger tables, where the calculations become rather gruelling, it is still possible to understand the underlying principle even if you are relying on a computer for the calculations. For this reason, it is often used to test hypotheses with ordinal variables, even though, strictly speaking, it is a rather blunt instrument for doing so. As we discussed in Chapter 12, the degrees of freedom are equal to $df = (r - 1)(c - 1)$. When chi-square is below the critical value, we say that our variables of interest are independent, thereby lending no support for rejecting the null hypothesis. If the calculated value exceeds the critical value, the variables are likely not independent and you would fail to reject the null.

Thinking about this in terms of association, the null hypothesis would be that there is no association between the two variables, or that the value of gamma, tau-b, Somer's d, or Spearman's *rho* is 0. The test you are performing is to determine if the measure of association is significantly different from 0. You can determine this with chi-square, although you must implicitly treat the variables as nominal to do so.

A superior, though perhaps more complicated, method for identifying the statistical significance of a measure of association for gamma, tau-b, Somers' d can be taken from the normal curve values of z. To calculate $z_{obtained}$, use the following equation (shown using gamma, although also suitable for tau-*b* and Somers' *d*):

$$z_{obtained} = \sqrt{\frac{N_s + N_d}{N(1 - G^2)}}$$

You should have at least 120 observations to use this test. Otherwise, use the *t*-value and define the degrees of freedom as $df = n - 1$. In either instance, values that fall below the critical value are insufficient to reject the null; values that exceed the critical value lead you to fail to reject the null.

For Spearman's *rho*, use the following equation:

$$t_{obtained} = \sqrt{\frac{N - 2}{1 - r_s^2}}$$

Where degrees of freedom are defined as $df = n - 2$ (we subtract 2 because we can determine a person's rank on each variable once we know all the other values).

EVERYDAY STATISTICS

Choosing the Right Significance Test

In the early 1950s, Cyril Burt, a famous British psychologist, concluded that genetic factors are more important than environmental factors in determining IQ. Burt based this conclusion on a study that he conducted with 42 pairs of identical and non-identical twins who were reared apart. Burt then measured the difference in the IQ scores of the twins, and found that the IQ scores of identical twins were closer than those of the non-identical twins.

· ·

Q: What type of significance test do you think Burt conducted to obtain his findings?

CONCLUSION: WHICH ONE TO USE?

In this chapter, we have covered four different measures of association for ordinal data. How do you choose which of these measures to use? Unfortunately, that is a hard question to answer.

There are occasions when one measure is preferable to another. For example, if there are a lot of ties, it is desirable to use something other than gamma. Spearman's *rho* is often easiest to understand when you're more interested in ranks than scores. Some of the others can be computationally intense, and might be undesirable in certain situations, such as when you must calculate it by hand. It's important to remember that although they won't give you the same numbers, most measures will yield similar results in most circumstances.

BOX 13.8

Kendall's Tau-*b*: The Steps

1. Calculate N_{same}, or the number of concordant pairs.
2. Calculate $N_{different}$, or the number of discordant pairs.
3. Calculate $Ties_y$, or the number of ties in the dependent variable.
4. Calculate $Ties_x$, or the number of ties in the independent variable.
5. Calculate Kendall's tau-*b* by using the following equation:

$$tau-b = \frac{N_{same} - N_{different}}{\sqrt{(N_{same} + N_{different} + Ties_y)(N_{same} + N_{different} + Ties_x)}}$$

As with gamma and Somers' *d*, values between 0 and 0.10 are weak, higher than 0.10 and up to 0.30 are moderate, and 0.30 or higher are strong.

BOX 13.9

It's Your Turn: Kendall's Tau-*b*

Using the same data that Isa collected in Box 13.7, can you see any changes in the relationship when you calculate Kendall's tau-*b*?

1. Compute the value for $Ties_x$.
2. Calculate Kendall's tau-*b*:

$$tau-b = \frac{N_{same} - N_{different}}{\sqrt{(N_{same} + N_{different} + Ties_y)(N_{same} + N_{different} + Ties_x)}}$$

3. Does the inclusion of the ties on the independent variable change what Isa can say about the relationship between students and hours spent on housework?

The solution to Box 13.9 can be found on page S-38.

GLOSSARY TERMS

PRACTICE QUESTIONS

1. Jerry is interested in the relationship between exercising every week and improvements in health. He thinks it might be part of why older people care for themselves better than young people do. Here are the data he is working with:

	Changes in self-rated health	
Exercises every week	Poor	Good
No	13	11
Yes	17	25

Formulate a null and research hypothesis to test Jerry's hunch.

2. Calculate gamma for the table above, then determine its statistical significance by using the t-distribution. Does this support Jerry's hypothesis?

3. Universities across Canada are working hard to increase their research revenues. It may be difficult for some universities to increase their profiles, however, because funding agencies might be more likely to continue to give money to the universities that they have given to in the past, creating a pattern of path dependency. To test this prospect, you are hired by a consortium of universities.

Universities and Research Revenue in 2000 and 2009			
Case	University	2000 research revenue, $000	2009 research revenue, $000
1	University of Toronto	372,119	858,182
2	University of British Columbia	165,992	524,569
3	University of Alberta	206,667	507,613
4	Université de Montréal	253,099	486,179
5	McGill University	234,340	432,118
6	McMaster University	106,892	377,732
7	Université Laval	168,382	282,657
8	University of Calgary	134,507	264,358

Note: Figures not adjusted for inflation

Source: Research Infosource (http://www.researchinfosource.com/top50.shtml).

What null and research hypothesis would allow you to identify the presence of path dependence (assume that the funding comes from sources in the same ratios across years)?

4. Calculate Spearman's *rho* for the ranking of the eight universities above. Do you find support for path dependence? Is your value of *rho* statistically significant? How do you know?

5. Suppose you are interested in squirrels and nuts (who isn't??), and you hypothesize that the heavier a squirrel is, the more food that squirrel will hide away for the winter. Since the nuts vary dramatically in size, you can only treat the data as ordinal. Formulate a set of hypotheses to test whether this is true.

6. Calculate Somers' d to identify the relationship between squirrel mass and the number of stashed nuts. Do your results support or fail to support your null hypothesis from #7 above?

Number of nuts stored for winter	Weight of squirrel			
	‹ 0.5 kg	0.5 kg–1 kg	› 1 kg	Total
Fewer than 25	12	11	5	28
25 to 44	6	7	9	22
45 or more	3	2	12	17
Total	21	20	26	67

7. Now, calculate Kendall's tau-b for the same data. Does tau-b lead you to make a different decision regarding your hypotheses?

Answers to the practice questions for Chapter 13 can be found on page S-14.

CHAPTER 14

Bivariate Statistics for Interval/Ratio Data

LEARNING OBJECTIVES

Chapter 14 will continue to survey techniques for assessing associations between two variables. Now that we've moved through dichotomous–interval/ratio, nominal–nominal, and ordinal–ordinal relationships, we will look at measures of association between two interval/ratio variables. Specifically, this chapter will focus on:

- Pearson's r;
- what r tells us about explained variance;
- what to do when there are mixed levels of measurement in your independent and dependent variables.

INTRODUCTION

By now, you probably know that when we examine associations between variables, we are primarily interested in how much the categories of one variable relate to categories of another variable. Interval/ratio data, which is the focus of this chapter, are unique because not only can they be used to determine whether a relationship exists between two variables, they can also determine the *direction* and *strength* of that relationship, as well as the rate of change. Unlike the measures of association we learned for nominal and ordinal levels of measurement, interval/ratio variables can be used to represent relationships graphically, so we can determine the approximate *rate of change* in the dependent variable across the values of the independent variable.

PEARSON'S r: THE CORRELATION COEFFICIENT

The primary measure of association used for interval/ratio variables is another contribution of statistician Karl Pearson. Pearson's r measures the amount of change in Y produced by a unit change in X, where the units are expressed as standard deviations. Like some of the ordinal measures covered in the last chapter, r ranges between -1 and $+1$, with zero representing no relationship between variables. A value of -1 denotes a perfectly negative relationship: as X rises/declines in value, Y always moves by the same amount (as measured in standard deviations) in the opposite direction. A perfectly positive relationship of $+1$ indicates the opposite: as X rises/declines in value, Y always moves in the same direction.

There are a few different formulas for Pearson's r. The first is considered an "illustrational" formula, because it illustrates the process, but it can be cumbersome to use:

$$r = \frac{\sum\left[(X - \overline{X})(Y - \overline{Y})\right]}{\sqrt{\left[\sum(X - \overline{X})^2 * \sum(Y - \overline{Y})^2\right]}}$$

The problem with this equation is that it requires you to subtract the average from each X and Y value line by line, which would take forever and a day in large data sets. Fortunately, the equation can be modified so that that task is unnecessary:

$$r = \frac{N\sum XY - (\sum X)(\sum Y)}{\sqrt{\left[N\sum X^2 - (\sum X)^2\right]\left[N\sum Y^2 - (\sum Y)^2\right]}}$$

Most of the time, you'll want to use the second equation. Even though it looks more difficult, it is actually much easier to use.

Take note of the $(\Sigma X)^2$ and $(\Sigma Y)^2$ in the denominator. According to BEDMAS, the order of operations that we discussed in Chapter 2 (Brackets-Exponents-Division-Multiplication-Addition-Subtraction), the calculations within the parentheses must be performed first, then the ones outside them. This means that the X and Y values must be summed *first*, before raising them to the power of two. People often forget to do this the first time they calculate r, and calculate it incorrectly as a result.

With a little care, you won't be one of those people. To make sure of that, we'll demonstrate the calculation of r with an example: Suppose we are interested in the relationship between a person's age and the age of their spouse in colonial Canada (or New France as it was then known) in 1,665 to 1,666. These data are available because Jean Talon, Intendant of Justice, Police, and Finance from 1,665 to 1,668 and 1,670 to 1,672, decided that the best way to learn about the colony was to take a numerical inventory of its inhabitants. In North America's first census, Talon enumerated the 3,278 residents of New France, a critical step in establishing New France as a self-sufficient settlement.[1]

These records, an interesting and important part of Canada's history, can be used to demonstrate Pearson's r. As with most other measures of association, it is helpful to arrange your data in a table first so that you can calculate the values of interest easily. Table 14.1 shows these data for five randomly selected cases from the 513 suitable for analysis (unmarried people were dropped, as were those with missing data, etc.). In the table, X represents the age of the husband and Y the age of his wife. As we've done so many times already, it is useful to

TABLE 14.1	Age of Married Couples in 1666 New France				
Observation #	X	Y	X^2	Y^2	XY
1	41	40	1,681	1,600	1,640
2	36	47	1,296	2,209	1,692
3	40	30	1,600	900	1,200
4	27	18	729	324	486
...	...	...	...	...	...
513	42	28	1,764	784	1,176
Sum	19,021	14,808	764,779	497,544	593,371

Source: 1881 Census of Canada 100% sample file
Note: There is only one observation per household, and only couples for whom both ages are listed are included. Sums reflect *all* observations, not only those shown above.

hypothesize a relationship between the variables. Since Pearson's *r* is a directional measure, we should capitalize on the ability to indicate the direction of the relationship.

> H_1: **The older a husband is, the older his wife will be.**
> H_0: **There is no relationship between the age of a husband and the age of his wife.**

Once these data are organized and each of the columns is summed, it is easy to calculate *r* by inserting the appropriate values. Note that the sum at the bottom of each column pertains to *all* observations, not just those shown in the table.

A ROUGH INTERPRETATION OF *r*

The calculated value of +0.686 has little meaning, unless we read it with some guidelines in mind. Typically, a value between ±0.01 and ±0.30 is considered a weak correlation, ±0.31 to ±0.70 is a moderate correlation, and ±0.71 to ±1 suggests that the variables are strongly correlated. Here, the value of 0.686 suggests a conclusion that in New France a husband's age was a moderate and positive predictor of the age of his spouse. Typically, we'd have to make sure that *r* is statistically significant before we can assess our hypotheses (we'll look at that in a moment), but here we have the entire population in our dataset (rather than just a sample), so we can say that we have cause to reject the null hypothesis without assessing significance.

You should note that *r* is important because it tells you what happens to one variable, *X*, as the value of the other variable, *Y*, changes. In our example, the value is positive, so we can say that, on average, as a person's age increases so does the age of his or her spouse. If the value was negative, we would say the opposite: on average, as a person's age increases, the age of his or her spouse *decreases*.

BOX 14.1

Pearson's *r*: The Steps

1. Using a spreadsheet program, square each value of the independent variable *X*.
2. Square each value of the dependent variable *Y*.
3. Find *X* * *Y* for each observation.
4. Sum *X*, *Y*, the squared values of *X* and *Y*, and the *XY* product.
5. Pearson's *r* can be solved by using the following equation:

$$r = \frac{\sum\left[(X - \overline{X})(Y - \overline{Y})\right]}{\sqrt{\left[\sum(X - \overline{X})^2 * \sum(Y - \overline{Y})^2\right]}}$$

Values between ±0.001 and ±0.30 are considered weak correlations, from ±0.3001 to ±0.70 moderate correlations, and from ±0.7001 to ±1 strong correlations.

A VISUAL REPRESENTATION OF *r*

To further illustrate how *r* describes bivariate relationships between two interval/ratio variables, let's look at a couple of graphs, each with a different set of data. In Figure 14.1, the independent variable *x* is positively related to *y*, with a Pearson's *r* value of 0.25. The dots represent (simulated) values of *x* plotted against *y*. The straight line represents fitted, or expected, values. Although an approximate relationship between *y* and *x* is detectable, the fit line doesn't do a very good job of representing the relationship. Note that if Pearson's *r* was negative, for example −0.25, the line would slope downward.

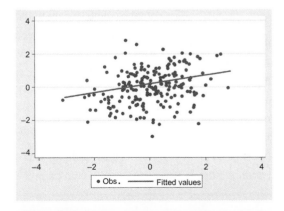

FIGURE 14.1 | An Illustration of a Pearson's *r* Value of 0.25 Using Simulated Data

BOX 14.2

It's Your Turn: Calculating Pearson's *r*

Marcus has been involved with a number of student groups during his undergraduate career, and has loved that part of his life. As he nears the end of his degree program, he has started to wonder if he will be able to keep this up while working, especially since he expects to have a job that will demand a lot of his time. It seems to him that there won't be enough hours in the day, but he has often read about people who manage to juggle organizational involvement and successful careers. Are these people exceptional, or are they the norm? As a research question, he wonders if an increase in work hours has a negative correlation with organizational involvement.

To study this, Marcus uses the Survey on Social Engagement (gss 17) Public Use Microdata File (target population of Canadians over 15, excluding those in Yukon, the Northwest Territories, and Nunavut, and full-time residents of institutions). Since he is concerned about his own prospects, Marcus has decided to limit the sample to men, and only those who have completed high school. Since this is a huge data set and Marcus doesn't have a computer, he decides to take a random sample of 15 people. He is careful to make sure that none of the 15 are missing information about either number of hours worked or number of civic groups belonged to, his two variables of interest. Only individuals who were involved in at least one civic group are included, since Marcus wants only people with some likelihood of involvement. He also limits the number of hours worked to 74 or less (individuals who worked over 75 hours were grouped together, which changed the

variable to an interval variable from being a ratio variable). The data are shown in the table below:

Respondent	Hours of work/ week	Number of civic groups
1	38	2
2	40	2
3	60	2
4	50	2
5	60	2
6	50	4
7	35	1
8	50	2
9	36	2
10	30	3
11	65	1
12	45	1
13	48	3
14	40	2
15	55	3

Source: Survey on Social Engagement (gss17)

1. Construct and complete a table like Table 14.1.
2. Calculate the value of *r*.
3. What can you say about the relationship between the variables based on your calculation?
4. Marcus was able to borrow a friend's computer. He re-ran the analysis with the full weighted sample (with the same exclusions described above). The Pearson's *r* value was 0.058. How does this compare to your value?

The solution for Box 14.2 can be found on page S-39.

With a stronger positive association (as r increases), we expect the average distance between a particular observation and the line to shrink, indicating a reduction in estimation error. This can be seen in Figure 14.2, where a Pearson's r value of 0.50 is illustrated.

A close examination of Figure 14.2 suggests that the observations are closer to the line than in Figure 14.1. The convergence becomes more obvious when Pearson's r increases to 0.75, which happens in Figure 14.3. In Figure 14.4, variable x finally has a perfect positive relationship to y. This demonstrates that by knowing a person's score on an independent variable (x), the score on the dependent variable (y) can be predicted. Thus, *all* of the observed values lie perfectly on the line of best fit.

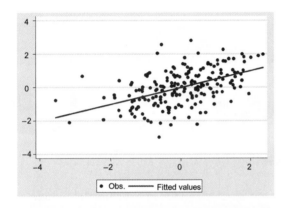

FIGURE 14.2 | An Illustration of a Pearson's r Value of 0.50 Using Simulated Data

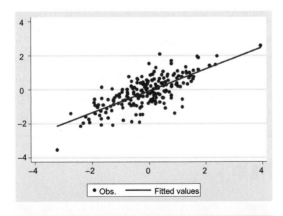

FIGURE 14.3 | An Illustration of a Pearson's r Value of 0.75 Using Simulated Data

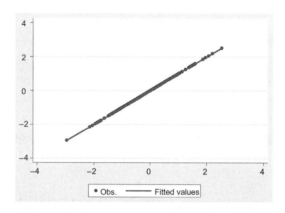

FIGURE 14.4 | An Illustration of a Pearson's *r*
Value of 1.0 Using Simulated Data

BOX 14.3

Pearson's Correlation Coefficient: The History of a Term

Pearson's *r* is an indicator of how closely two variables are related and designates the degree of a linear relationship. Pearson called his method for calculating this coefficient the product, which he derived in 1896 and called the "moment method" (Porter, 1989). He developed it while working on regression analysis and by taking up Galton's work, for it was Galton who first suggested the indicator, in the context of heredity. Although Pearson published his method in an 1895 paper, it was not received with much fanfare. Francis Galton himself was one of the paper's reviewers, and thought it should be published rather than read out loud in a lecture. In Galton's words, "It would be too dull to *read*" (Stigler, 1986: 344).

The attribution for this coefficient brings up important issues about who gets credited with developing statistical methods. Although Pearson can be credited with much of the work, he did not operate in a vacuum. As I mentioned before, *r* also stems from Galton's research. Further, Pearson and statistician Francis Edgeworth corresponded and reviewed each other's work. Though Pearson did credit Edgeworth did early on, referring to "Edgeworth's theorem," in his later work he did not do so.

EXPLAINED VARIANCE

Using Pearson's *r*, it is possible to determine how much of the variation in a variable can be explained with the use of other variables. The value of zero does not reflect a relationship between two variables, but a value of +1 indicates a perfect positive relationship, and a value of −1 indicates a perfect negative relationship. Values between −1 and +1 do not have a direct interpretation, unless you're comfortable with interpreting values in terms of standard deviations.

To determine the variation, we find the coefficient of determination by squaring r, yielding r^2. The coefficient of determination is the percentage of all variation in the dependent variable that can be explained by the values of the independent variable. The variable r^2 is the percentage by which errors are reduced when the information found in the independent variable is incorporated into the prediction.

This introduces **explained variation** and **unexplained variation** in the dependent variable. Explained variation is how much more accurate a prediction becomes when the independent variable, X, is taken into account. Unsurprisingly, unexplained variation is the remaining prediction error, which could be due to variables that weren't included as predictors, measurement error, or random error. The sum of the explained variation and unexplained variation of a variable is equal to its **total variation**.

A MORE PRECISE INTERPRETATION OF r

Looking at what the calculation of r achieves makes it possible to move beyond examining rough patterns between variable relationships. The calculation for r standardizes the values of each variable, allowing correlation coefficients to be compared without worrying about how many values each variable has, or what their standard deviation is. When each variable is standardized, r refers to the degree of correspondence between a person's z-score on one variable (X) and their z-score on another variable (Y), measuring the relationship between the average person's score in standard deviation units on one variable and their standard deviation score on a second variable. In an instance where $r = 1$, a person with a variable that has a change in the z-score from zero to two on one variable of interest will see a corresponding increase of a z-score of two on the other variable of interest. Conversely, an r value of -1 will translate to a z-score of $+1$ on one variable and a score of -1 on another. Remember, r is a measure of what happens to one variable as the value of another variable changes.

THE CORRELATION MATRIX

A **correlation matrix** is used to show correlations between variables and all of the possible relationships between variables in a grid.

Suppose that we wanted to study the relationship between incidents of domestic violence and unwanted sexual acts perpetrated by an ex-spouse/domestic partner, because we want to know if violence and unwanted sexual acts are interchangeable techniques for asserting dominance, or if they are qualitatively different. To determine this, we could use the eighteenth wave of the General Social Survey (GSS), Public-Use Microdata File (the Victimization Survey) to construct a correlation matrix between the occurrence and frequency of violent and unwanted sexual acts (see Table 14.2).

A typical correlation matrix presents a series of numbers in a triangular pattern. Each cell represents the correlation between the variables that are listed above and to the left of, the number. For example, the number 0.2391 refers to the correlation between the number

TABLE 14.2 | Correlation between Violent Acts and Unwanted Sexual Acts between Spouses/Partners

	# Violent acts	# Unwanted sexual acts
# Violent acts	1.0000	
# Unwanted sexual acts	0.2391	1.0000

Source: 2004 General Social Survey, Public Use Microdata File
Note: Includes persons aged 15 or older in Canada, excluding residents of the three territories and full-time residents of institutions (Statistics Canada, 2005).

of unwanted sexual acts and the number of violent acts. In a correlation matrix, the diagonal that runs from the top left cell to the bottom right cell, which refers to the correlation between a variable and itself, will always be one. Using Table 14.2, we can see that there is a weak relationship between violent acts and unwanted sexual acts committed by and against domestic partners. That weak relationship suggests that there are other factors involved with both those phenomena.

Although the primary focus of this chapter is bivariate relationships, a correlation matrix can be used for more than two variables. A correlation matrix can contain as many relevant variables as you can imagine.

USING A *t*-TEST TO ASSESS THE SIGNIFICANCE OF *r*

When using r, it is usually necessary to determine if we can assume that the relationships we observe in the sample also exist in the population (remember that our 1666 census example included the entire population of New France). If a sample we drew from the population had high sampling error, that would make it impossible to be confident about the inferential capacity of the r-value we calculate.

By mathematically manipulating r, we can use t-distributions to assess its representativity. Remember that t-distributions are closely related to the z-distribution, except that t-distributions make adjustments (largely to the tails) for sample size. The first step is to select the appropriate t-distribution by using the degrees of freedom. Because there are two known parameters (two variables we know the values for), the degrees of freedom are equal to $(N - 2)$, where N is equal to the sample size. If, for example, we had a sample of 22 people and we wanted to be 95 per cent confident of the generalizability of our results, we would need a t-value of at least 2.086. To get this value, we look at the row for $df = 20$ (remember to look at $n - 2$ degrees of freedom) in Appendix B, and look for a 0.05 level of significance in a two-tailed test (remember that levels of significance are usually stated as alpha values in a t-distribution, and can be calculated as one minus your desired confidence interval). This value is known as $t_{critical}$.

The other value we need to calculate is $t_{observed}$, which is done using this formula:

$$t_{observed} = r\sqrt{\frac{n-2}{1-r^2}}$$

Using the same example we used to calculate the correlation matrix (Table 14.2) and a hypothetical sample size of 22 observations:

$$t_{observed} = r\sqrt{\frac{n-2}{1-r^2}}$$

$$= 0.2391\sqrt{\frac{22-2}{1-0.2391^2}}$$

$$= 0.2391\sqrt{\frac{20}{1-0.572}}$$

$$= 0.2391 * 4.6058$$

$$= 1.101$$

Since the $t_{observed}$ value of 1.101 is below the critical value of 2.086, we cannot be 95 per cent confident that the sample r value of 0.2391 did not occur by chance. Based on our sample of 22 respondents, we cannot be certain that there is a correlation between violent and unwanted sexual acts between ex-spouses/domestic partners.

ASSUMPTIONS OF LINEARITY

Pearson's r provides a rough and ready measure of the relationship between two interval/ratio variables. The variable r assumes that the relationship between two variables is the same, regardless of what the values of either of these variables is. This is called linearity, and it can be problematic at times. Let's see why this is the case with an example.

Imagine that we wanted to identify the relationship between age and amount of time spent on entertainment. We expect that teenagers have more time than their parents do to go to movies, dance clubs, or malls. We also assume that retirees have a high proportion of spare time too. This suggests that the relationship between age and time spent on entertainment is not linear; the rate at which available time to spend for entertainment increases is not consistent across the range of ages. There could be a very strong and positive relationship across the teenage years, after which the relationship begins to decline as many Canadians buy houses, get married, have children, develop their careers, etc. Finally, as people get older, their children might leave home, they might begin to work less, etc., and they have more spare time again, affecting the relationship between entertainment and age. To consider how this relationship might look, look at Figure 14.5.

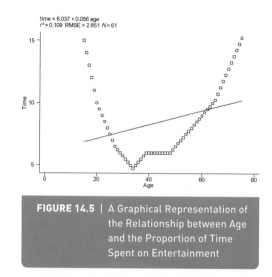

time = 6.037 + 0.056 age
r^2 = 0.109 RMSE = 2.851 N = 61

FIGURE 14.5 | A Graphical Representation of the Relationship between Age and the Proportion of Time Spent on Entertainment

The curvilinear pattern of circles represents the actual relationship between age and time, and the straight line represents the relationship described by r (actually, this is known as the least squares regression line, but we'll talk about that later). Without manipulating one or both of the variables (for example, by taking their logarithms), we must be content with summarizing the relationship with a straight line. Unfortunately, as the diagram shows, the line is not an accurate or sensitive representation of the relationship, and there isn't much we can do about it without complicating things. For our purposes, the generalization provided by that straight line will have to do.

Before embarking on a deeper discussion of the fit line, a brief discussion about using variables measured at different levels is necessary. Most measures of association assume that both variables are measured at the same level and that you are working with two nominal, ordinal, or interval/ratio variables. However, this is often not the case. When that happens, you'll find yourself in a position where you need to assess the association between variables by using different levels of measurement. Don't worry, there are a few short guidelines that we can apply to help us through this added layer of complexity.

MEASURING ASSOCIATION BETWEEN INTERVAL/RATIO AND NOMINAL OR ORDINAL VARIABLES: USING THE LOWEST COMMON MEASURE OF ASSOCIATION

Although previous chapters presented the measures of association as being specifically for one level of measurement, it is possible, under certain circumstances, to use the measures for other levels of measurement. The measure of association can always be used on variables measured *above* the level of complexity for which they were designed.

Recall that there are essentially three levels of measurement: nominal, ordinal, and interval/ratio. If we were working with two nominal variables, we could choose between phi,

Cramer's V, or lambda, depending on the nature of the variables and the information we seek. However, if we are looking at a nominal by ordinal relationship, we could use any of those three measures (remember that we only use phi for a 2 by 2 relationship). Since these measures are non-directional, they can be used even if one of the two variables can be ranked. By using the measure of association for the variable at a lower level of measurement, we "discard" the additional information in the ordinal variable.

However, the opposite is not possible—a nominal variable cannot be "infused" with information that would allow it to be ranked. If we wanted to look for a relationship between visible minority status and attitudes about the seriousness of climate change (coded as extremely serious, very serious, not very serious, and not at all serious), we would use a nominal level of measurement, because ranking information for the ordinal variable, climate change, could be discarded to make it a nominal variable. However, it is not possible to rank visible minority categories, so we would choose a measure of association for nominal variables.

Demoting the level of measurement for particular variables is a technique that can be used for several combinations of variables. For ordinal and interval/ratio variables, it is necessary to discard the information on differences between response categories in the interval/ratio variables, and treat that variable as ordinal. To measure the association between attitudes toward the seriousness of climate change and income in dollars, we would have to choose from gamma, *rho*, Somer's *d*, or Kendall's tau-*b*.

EVERYDAY STATISTICS

Causal Relationship?

Over the years, many health professionals have identified a link between smoking and the likelihood of getting cancer. According to the Canadian Cancer Society, 30 per cent of all cancer deaths are due to smoking and 85 per cent of all lung cancer cases can be attributed to smoking. Because of these findings, many programs have been initiated to increase awareness of the link between smoking and cancer.

. . . .

Q: Do you think that we can assume a causal relationship between smoking and cancer based on the research that suggests the two are strongly correlated?

GLOSSARY TERMS

Correlation matrix (p. 175)   Total variation (p. 175)

Explained variation (p. 175)   Unexplained variation (p. 175)

PRACTICE QUESTIONS

1. The following data from the 1971 Census of Canada describe two pieces of information about 10 families.

Family number	Total income ($)	# People in family
1	1,330	2
2	800	4
3	1,200	5
4	1,600	4
5	900	6
6	6,144	4
7	3,490	2
8	1,310	4
9	5,670	3
10	1,330	2

Source: 1971 Census of Canada

  a. Develop a set of research hypotheses about the relationship between family income and family size.
  b. Calculate r.
  c. Assess the statistical significance of r by using a t-test.
  d. Now, assume that you have the same column totals for X, Y, XY, X^2, Y^2, but that your sample size is increased to 100. Now determine the statistical significance. Is there a difference from what you calculated above?

2. Consider the following plot for the values of total income and family size. Do you think that a line summarizing the association will slope upwards or downwards?

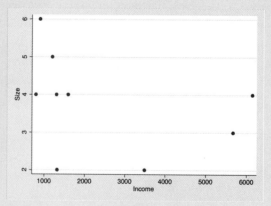

3. Chris and Josie like to eat out at restaurants, and they are worried that they are spending too much, in part because they tend to follow each other's lead in the price of the entrée they order. They are both aspiring statisticians and are therefore keen to apply what they just learned about Pearson's r, even though they will only be able to draw conclusions about whether they tend to spend as much as each other (we don't know if they actually follow each other, or if they independently choose similarly priced entrées). Help them determine if this concern is warranted by drafting a set of research hypotheses, keeping in mind the limitations of Pearson's r in this instance.

4. To help you test the hypotheses you composed in #3 above, Chris and Josie eat at a restaurant eight times and decide to keep track of their expenditures. Calculate the value of Pearson's r for their expenses.

Chris	Josie
4	5
12	20
13	8
14	6
8	11
3	10
5	6
6	9

5. Determine the statistical significance of your calculation. Does this lead you to reject or fail to reject your null hypothesis above?

6. Now you must report back to Chris and Josie. What would you tell them about their concerns based on your hypothesis test? Does each of them tend to spend as much as the other?

Answers to the practice questions for Chapter 14 can be found on page S-14.

CHAPTER 15

One-Way Analysis of Variance

LEARNING OBJECTIVES

Now that many of the techniques for measuring bivariate relationships have been covered, this chapter will discuss the final technique for identifying relationships between two variables in this text: one-way analysis of variance (ANOVA). Topics will include:

- what a one-way ANOVA is;
- when it should be used;
- how to calculate within-group sums of squares, between-groups sums of squares, and total sums of squares, the three main components of one-way ANOVAS;
- how to use the F-distribution with ANOVA.

INTRODUCTION

The last few chapters have been about strategies for identifying the existence and strength of a relationship between two variables. This chapter will build on what we've learned by discussing another method for identifying associations between variables measured at different levels. We'll focus on interval/ratio dependent variables, and nominal or ordinal independent variables that have more than two categories by discussing a procedure known as **ANOVA**, or the **ANalysis Of VAriance**.[1]

WHAT IS ANOVA?

ANOVA is a little like a t-test. The t-test can be used in any situation where a comparison between two groups on a continuous variable is desired. The t-test is useful, but what if we want to compare more than two groups?

For example, say we want to compare the level of control an individual feels he or she has over his or her own life, checking to see if it differs by religion by using Statistics Canada's 2003 Social Engagement Survey. Specifically, we want to compare the differences across Roman Catholics, Protestants, members of the United Church, and people with no religious affiliation.

Table 15.1 shows the average levels of mastery for each group.

Higher scores indicate superior mastery. A glance at the columns suggests that there are differences across religious groups, but we do not know if the differences are the result of chance, sampling error (most of the time, we can't distinguish between the two), or differences that exist across groups. How can we find this out?

One way is to conduct a series of *t*-tests, comparing two groups at a time. How many *t*-tests would we have to do?

For **No Religion**, there would be three: NR-RC, NR-UC, and NR-P.
For **Roman Catholics**, there would be two: RC-UC, and RC-P (there are only two comparisons because Roman Catholics have already been compared with no religion).
For the **United Church**, there would be one: UC-P (the only remaining comparison to be made).

That's six *t*-tests. What's wrong with that? First, it's a computational nightmare. Can you imagine wrestling with the results of six *t*-tests? With that many calculations, the chance of making an error increases dramatically—or it does for me, anyway.

Even if you were precise with your calculator, the bad news is that conducting multiple *t*-tests (or any other analysis conducted repeatedly) increases **type one error**—as we discussed earlier, this means rejecting the null hypothesis when it should be retained—increasing the risk of making a bad judgment about your hypothesis. The more statistical tests conducted, the higher the likelihood of sampling error.

TABLE 15.1 | Average Levels of Mastery by Religious Affiliation, 2003 Social Engagement Survey

Observation #	Levels of mastery			
	No religion	Roman Catholic	United Church	Protestant
1	21	17	22	21
2	25	21	14	23
3	26	19	16	22
4	24	20	13	24
5	22	20	14	21

Source: Statistics Canada 2003 Social Engagement Survey (GSS17)

Recall that a 0.05 level of significance is used to assess hypotheses, meaning that we accept that 5 per cent of the time we will mistakenly conclude that the differences we observe in our sample actually exist in the population. If each of the t-tests in the sample containing six t-tests has a 5 per cent chance of yielding significant results by mistake, our 95 per cent significance level decreases to about 73.5 per cent (to get this number, multiply the independent probabilities, 0.95 * 0.95 * 0.95 * 0.95 * 0.95 * 0.95).

Clearly, a single statistical test to assess differences between more than two groups is necessary. That test is ANOVA, which can be thought of as an elaborated t-test. It compares three things:

- differences between means
- differences in values within samples
- differences in values across samples

Like a t-test, there is an internal logic to ANOVA. Each observation is different from the grand mean by some amount. There are two sources of this difference:

1. the independent variable
2. random unexplained error

ANOVA compares the variation around the mean within groups to the variation across groups. Is a Roman Catholic more likely to be similar to another Roman Catholic than to a person in another category? What about a Protestant to another Protestant, etc.? If the answer to these questions is yes, then we could conclude that there are religious differences in levels of personal mastery.

Although that description is oversimplified, it nicely captures what is going on with ANOVA. We need to go over several equations before we can compare variation within groups to variation between groups.

The first equation is the **sum of squares**, which is defined as the total variation of all observations from a **grand mean**. To determine whether there is more variation within groups than across groups, we need to identify the total variation available to be distributed between and across groups. This is the **total sum of squares**, or SS_{total}, and equals the total variation of all observations from the grand mean. The equation for SS_{total} is

$$SS_{total} = \sum (X - \overline{X})^2$$

Stated in words, the equation is a sum of the differences between individual observations (X) and the grand mean ($\overline{X}$). The result is squared to remove the negative numbers that would result from subtracting the means from a value that is below the mean, which would equal zero. For example, if a person had a mastery score of 15, subtracting the grand mean of 18.85 would yield −3.85. On their own, negative numbers would not be a problem, but here they are because they are summed, and therefore cancelled out by positive values. Remember that we take the sum of all deviations; since the mean is the midpoint of all values, the negative numbers resulting from values below the mean would cancel out all values above the mean. If deviations aren't squared, then the sum of the deviations will always equal zero.

Once the total sum of squares has been calculated, equations are used to calculate the differences within groups and the differences across groups. These terms are known as the sum of squares within groups (SS_{within}) and the sum of squares between groups ($SS_{between}$).

The equation for the sum of squares within groups is

$$SS_{within} = \sum (X - \overline{X}_{group})^2$$

This equation is strikingly similar to the equation for the total sum of squares. The major difference between the within-groups sum of squares and the total sum of squares is that instead of trying to calculate the total variation of *all* observations, we are trying to calculate the variation that exists *within* each group (we calculate deviations of each group member from their group mean, rather than the grand mean). For the equation, the difference is that the grand mean $\overline{X}$ is replaced by the group mean $\overline{X}_{group}$.

The final equation is a little different. Since we're interested in the variation across groups, each group is treated as an observation:

$$SS_{between} = \sum N_{group}(\overline{X}_{group} - \overline{X})^2$$

To find the sum of squares between groups, subtract the grand mean from each group mean, square the difference, multiply it by the number of observations in each group, and add the results across all groups.

EVERYDAY STATISTICS

When to Use ANOVA

ANOVA is often used in cases where the researcher is attempting to examine the outcome of a particular treatment on a sub-group of the population. In these types of experiments, there are often several sub-groups that receive a varying degree of treatment. Usually, one group does not receive the treatment. Once the treatment is over, the groups are compared to see which ones have changed noticeably.

Q: Why do you think ANOVA would be a good method to employ in the above situation?

THE SUM OF SQUARES: AN EASIER WAY

While it's possible to use those equations, they are a lot of work. You have to subtract the mean from each observation, which involves going through your data set line by line and calculating deviations. In a sample of 100,000 observations, that would be incredibly tedious and time-consuming, even with a spreadsheet program.

Luckily, there's an easier way: summing variables *before* taking differences. Since the mean is the midpoint of all values of a particular variable, it can be multiplied by the number of observations and squared, speeding up the calculation of the sums of squares. Unfortunately, you'll still need to calculate the sum of all observations and square it, but the following equations are still easy to work with:

$$SS_{total} = \sum X^2_{total} - N_{total} \overline{X}^2_{total}$$

$$SS_{within} = \sum X^2_{total} - \sum N_{group} \overline{X}^2_{group}$$

$$SS_{between} = \sum N_{group} \overline{X}^2_{group} - N_{total} \overline{X}^2_{total}$$

A few words of caution: First, for the total sum of squares and within-groups sum of squares, it is important to square the value of the observations (in each case, this first term in the equation) *before* summing them. The mean value in both of the second terms needs to be squared before being multiplied by either N_{total} or N_{group}. Second, when finding the sum of squares between groups, the group average and the grand mean need to be squared *before* being multiplied by N_{group} or N_{total}. Skipping either of these steps will result in the wrong value.

So what exactly is the sum of squares and why is it useful? The sum of squares is defined as the squared and summed measures of variance that exist between observations. It is a standardized measure of deviance from a measure of central tendency, which is why it periodically pops up in statistics. When two samples of the same size are being compared, a higher sum of squares indicates greater variation between observations.

The sum of squares is useful in certain circumstances, but, like the *t*-statistic, larger summed deviations depend in part on sample size. A higher sum of squares is more likely in an analysis of 100,000 observations than with a sample size of 10, suggesting that the sum of squares (total, within, and between) increases with either greater variation between scores, or sample size. When measuring variation between scores, the sum of squares must be standardized so that values can be compared regardless of sample size. This creates a standardized measure called the **mean square**.

The equation for the mean square within groups is

$$MS_{within} = \frac{SS_{within}}{df_{within}}$$

The equation for the mean square between groups is

$$MS_{between} = \frac{SS_{between}}{df_{between}}$$

You should recognize the sum of squares within groups and between groups in the numerator of the equation. The denominator is new. The symbols refer to the degrees of freedom within groups (df_{within}) and between groups ($df_{between}$). Calculating these values is fairly simple:

$$df_{within} = N_{total} - k$$

and

$$df_{between} = k - 1$$

where k = the number of groups you are comparing.

Remember that for the t-distribution, the degrees of freedom are defined as the number of values that are free to vary. Although the equations for degrees of freedom differ slightly, the logic is the same.

First, since we're estimating group means within the population by using sample means, only the number of observations in each group minus one can assume any value. Consequently, in each group there is one pre-determined value. We define df_{within} as $N_{total} - k$, since one value of each group is perfectly determined by all other values within that group, when the group mean is known.

Second, since we're calculating the observed variation between groups, we don't need to know the means for every group. If the grand mean is known, then the values for $k - 1$ groups will determine the value of the last group. Therefore, only $k - 1$ values for $df_{between}$ can vary freely.

THE *F*-DISTRIBUTION

By now, you should know that when statistical equations seek standardized numbers, it means that they're going to be assessed against a pre-established benchmark. These equations are no different, but now, instead of using the t- or z-distribution, we're going to use the F-distribution.

To assess values against the F-distribution, a test statistic must be calculated first. This test statistic is known as the F-ratio and is calculated using the following equation:

$$F_{observed} = \frac{MS_{between}}{MS_{within}}$$

Since $MS_{between}$ and MS_{within} are the only variables needed, we won't bother with MS_{total}. (I'm sure you'll agree that we have already covered enough equations in this chapter!)

Finally, we have enough information to assess our observed test statistic against the F-distribution, our predetermined benchmark. Like the t-distribution, the shape of the F-distribution depends on sample size. Unlike the t-distribution, the F-distribution depends on

$df_{between}$	2	3	4	5	6	7	8
df_{within}							
1	199.50	215.71	224.58	230.16	233.99	236.77	238.88
2	19.00	19.16	19.25	19.30	19.33	19.35	19.37
3	9.55	9.28	9.12	9.01	8.94	8.89	8.85
4	6.94	6.59	6.39	6.26	6.16	6.09	6.04
5	5.79	5.41	5.19	5.05	4.95	4.88	4.82
6	5.14	4.76	4.53	4.39	4.28	4.21	4.15
7	4.74	4.35	4.12	3.97	3.87	3.79	3.73
8	4.46	4.07	3.84	3.69	3.58	3.50	3.44
9	4.26	3.86	3.63	3.48	3.37	3.29	3.23
10	4.10	3.71	3.48	3.33	3.22	3.14	3.07
11	3.98	3.59	3.36	3.20	3.10	3.01	2.95
12	3.89	3.49	3.26	3.11	3.00	2.91	2.85
13	3.81	3.41	3.18	3.03	2.92	2.83	2.77
14	3.74	3.34	3.11	2.96	2.85	2.76	2.70
15	3.68	3.29	3.06	2.90	2.79	2.71	2.64
16	3.63	3.24	3.01	2.85	2.74	2.66	2.59
17	3.59	3.20	2.97	2.81	2.70	2.61	2.55
18	3.56	3.16	2.93	2.77	2.66	2.58	2.51
19	3.52	3.13	2.90	2.74	2.63	2.54	2.48
20	3.49	3.10	2.87	2.71	2.60	2.51	2.45
30	3.32	2.92	2.69	2.53	2.42	2.33	2.27
40	3.23	2.84	2.61	2.45	2.34	2.25	2.18
50	3.18	2.79	2.56	2.40	2.29	2.20	2.13
60	3.15	2.76	2.53	2.37	2.25	2.17	2.10
70	3.13	2.74	2.50	2.35	2.23	2.14	2.07
80	3.11	2.72	2.49	2.33	2.21	2.13	2.06
90	3.10	2.71	2.47	2.32	2.20	2.11	2.04
100	3.09	2.70	2.46	2.31	2.19	2.10	2.03
120	3.07	2.68	2.45	2.29	2.18	2.09	2.02
∞	3.00	2.61	2.37	2.22	2.10	2.01	1.94

TABLE 15.2 | The *F*-Distribution for 95 Per Cent Level of Significance

the number of groups. You need to look at both the within-group and between-group degrees of freedom. Table 15.2 is an abbreviated version of a table that lists the critical values of the *F*-distribution (the same table can also be found in Appendix D).

If you encounter degrees of freedom values that do not perfectly coincide with the provided values, always use the higher value. This will give you a more conservative basis for assessing your calculated *F*-statistic. For example, if you have a $df_{between}$ of 1 and a df_{within} of 118 (reflecting an independent variable with two categories, the equivalent of an independent samples *t*-test), choose a $df_{between}$ of 2 and a df_{within} of 120.

To help this sink in, let's keep using the example from before. Remember that we were comparing levels of mastery by four religious groups. For ease of reference, the earlier table is replicated in Table 15.3.

To work through the necessary equations, the first thing we do is square the individual *X* values and find the sums; see Tables 15.4 and 15.5.

Here are the equations again:

$$SS_{total} = \sum X_{total}^2 - N_{total}\overline{X}_{total}^2$$
$$SS_{within} = \sum X_{total}^2 - \sum N_{group}\overline{X}_{group}^2$$
$$SS_{between} = \sum N_{group}\overline{X}_{group}^2 - N_{total}\overline{X}_{total}^2$$

The X^2 values in Table 15.4 are useful for calculating the within-groups sum of squares (the sum of these values represents the first part of each equation) and the total sum of squares (the sum of the within-group sum of squares). We also need the grand mean and the group means, so we'll have to calculate a few more numbers before using the equations.

Now that we have all of the information we need, let's calculate the sums of squares, starting first with the total sum of squares.

$$\begin{aligned}
SS_{total} &= \sum X_{total}^2 - N_{total}\overline{X}_{total}^2 \\
&= (2802 + 1891 + 1301 + 2471) - 20(20.52)^2 \\
&= 8465 - 20(410.06) \\
&= 8465 - 8201.2 \\
&= 263.8
\end{aligned}$$

TABLE 15.3 | Average Levels of Mastery by Religious Affiliation, 2003 Social Engagement Survey

	Levels of mastery			
Observation #	No religion	Roman Catholic	United Church	Protestant
1	21	17	22	21
2	25	21	14	23
3	26	19	16	22
4	24	20	13	24
5	22	20	14	21

Source: Statistics Canada 2003 Social Engagement Survey (GSS17)

TABLE 15.4 | Average Levels of Mastery by Religious Affiliation, 2003 Social Engagement Survey

Observation #	No religion		Roman Catholic		United Church		Protestant	
	Levels of mastery							
	X	X^2	X	X^2	X	X^2	X	X^2
1	21	441	17	289	22	484	21	441
2	25	625	21	441	14	196	23	529
3	26	676	19	361	16	256	22	484
4	24	576	20	400	13	169	24	576
5	22	484	20	400	14	196	21	441

Source: Statistics Canada 2003 Social Engagement Survey (GSS17)

TABLE 15.5 | Average Levels of Mastery by Religious Affiliation, 2003 Social Engagement Survey

Observation #	No religion		Roman Catholic		United Church		Protestant	
	Levels of mastery							
	X	X^2	X	X^2	X	X^2	X	X^2
1	21	441	17	289	22	484	21	441
2	25	625	21	441	14	196	23	529
3	26	676	19	361	16	256	22	484
4	24	576	20	400	13	169	24	576
5	22	484	20	400	14	196	21	441
Σ	118	2,802	97	1,891	79	1,301	111	2,471
$\overline{X}$	23.6		19.4		15.8		22.2	
N	20		Grand Mean		20.25			

Source: Statistics Canada 2003 Social Engagement Survey (GSS17)

This calculation is fairly straightforward. The only thing you need to watch for is the order of operations in the second part of the equation. Remember to square the grand mean before multiplying it by the number of observations. Failing to do so will result in a calculation error. The total sum of squares represents the total amount of variation within our sample that can be explained by the sample's characteristics.

The next calculation is the within-group sum of squares. (Since we already calculated the first term in this equation when calculating the total sums of squares, we can take a shortcut here; the first term is 8,465):

$$SS_{within} = \sum X_{total}^2 - N_{group}\overline{X}_{group}^2$$

$$= 8465 - 5[(23.6)^2 + (19.4)^2 + (15.8)^2 + (22.2)^2]$$
$$= 8465 - 5 * 1675.8$$
$$= 86$$

For the between-group sum of squares, we can either use the equation, or we can subtract the within-group sum of squares from the total sum of squares. Recall that the total sum of squares represents the total amount of variation within the sample, and the within-group sum of squares represents the total variation within each group. The between-group sum of squares should be the difference between the two, but let's make sure.

The first part of the equation for the between-group sum of squares is the same as the last part of the equation for the within-group sum of squares. The second part is the same as the second part of the equation for total sum of squares. We can insert those values.

$$SS_{between} = \sum N_{group}\overline{X}^2_{group} - N_{total}\overline{X}^2_{total}$$
$$= 8379 - 8201.2$$
$$= 177.8$$

The answer should be the same as what we would get by subtracting the within-group sum of squares from the total sum of squares:

$$SS_{between} = SS_{total} - SS_{within}$$
$$= 263.8 - 86$$
$$= 177.8$$

It is, so we can be fairly certain that our calculations are correct. (To be even more certain, we should choose not to borrow $\sum N_{group}\overline{X}^2_{group}$ and $N_{total}\overline{X}^2_{total}$ from our previous equations, since any errors we made before will be embedded in them.)

Now that we have our sums of squares, the next thing to do is calculate the mean squares. To do so, we need the two degrees of freedom values:

$$df_{within} = N_{total} - k$$
$$= 20 - 4$$
$$= 16$$

and

$$df_{between} = k - 1$$
$$= 4 - 1$$
$$= 3$$

We can put these values into our equations for the mean square. First, for within-groups

$$MS_{within} = \frac{SS_{within}}{df_{within}}$$
$$= \frac{86}{16}$$
$$= 5.38$$

And then for between-groups

$$MS_{between} = \frac{SS_{between}}{df_{betweeen}}$$
$$= \frac{177.8}{3}$$
$$= 59.27$$

Finally, we can calculate our *F*-statistic:

$$F = \frac{MS_{between}}{MS_{within}}$$
$$= \frac{59.27}{5.38}$$
$$= 11.02$$

Next, we need to compare that value with the $F_{critical}$ value on the *F*-table. For degrees of freedom, 3 and 16 return the critical value of 3.24, and since 11.02 greatly exceeds that number, we can be 95 per cent confident that there is at least one significant difference in levels of mastery across religions in the population. In other words, we now know with 95 per cent certainty that at least two of our groups differ significantly in terms of mastery.

IS THIS NEW?

Although a lot of material has been covered in this chapter—especially equations—there are striking similarities between the techniques we've been using and the techniques for *t*-tests. We have already compared variances between samples with variance within samples to determine where the greater differences lay. ANOVA is an elaboration of this technique, because it makes it possible to compare more than two groups. Think of ANOVA as a *t*-test for more than two groups, with a lower probability of type one error.

LIMITATIONS OF ANOVA

Of course, ANOVA has limitations. Two of them in particular are of concern to us.

First, the assumption of equal variances across groups within the population; the idea is that each of the groups within a population has approximately the same distribution of values around the mean. Slight differences between groups are acceptable, but ANOVA becomes increasingly unusable when there are large differences. Therefore, it is a good idea to compare the variances prior to conducting an ANOVA.

Second is the determination of what a significant *F*-value means. When $F_{observed}$ exceeds $F_{critical}$, the only information provided is that the mean of at least one group in the sample is significantly different from that of the population as a whole. If we were interested in determining *which* group was different, we'd have to conduct a series of complicated **post-hoc** tests. These can be calculated by using statistical software, but my preference is to create a series of dummy variables and use them as predictors in a regression, which we'll discuss in the next two chapters.

Furthermore, since it is not possible to determine which group is different, or whether that group is significantly higher or lower than the others on an outcome of interest, hypotheses are typically non-directional and, in my opinion, often of limited use. So it is always good practice to generate hypotheses whenever you embark on a statistical exercise.

Ordinary least squares regression, covered in the next chapter, is superior to post-hoc tests because you can assess the statistical significance of differences while holding other characteristics constant. For example, the differences in levels of mastery across religious groups that we saw could be due to differences in the average age or level of education of each group. Suppose that mastery and religion are heavily correlated with age and education. It's possible then that the differences observed in an ANOVA are the result of one or both of the third

BOX 15.1

ANOVA: The Steps

1. Find the grand mean and the mean for each group.
2. Find group sums, sum of squared scores.
3. Find SS_{total}, SS_{within}, $SS_{between}$.
4. Find $df_{between}$, and df_{within}.
5. Find $MS_{between}$ and MS_{within}.
6. Obtain the F-ratio.
7. Compare $F_{observed}$ to $F_{critical}$.

BOX 15.2

One-Way ANOVA: History of a Term

In the mid-nineteenth century, the agriculturist James F. W. Johnston recognized a problem with agricultural analysis. Because of the importance of practical agricultural knowledge to individual and national economic development, its importance was acknowledged, but unlike fields such as physics, where researchers can control conditions, agriculture is not easily translatable to the laboratory. For example, if there are two crops with differing methods of production, how can the cause of differences in yield be determined? Influences can't be isolated, so there is no way to discern whether the treatment of a crop had a significant contribution to its behaviour and yield.

Gigerenzer et al. (1991) relate the story of how statistician and geneticist Ronald Fisher (1890–1962)

attempted to solve the problem. He aimed "to ascertain whether a difference in means between treated population and controls indicates the causal efficacy of the treatment" (73). Specifically, he wanted to know how to evaluate the application of manure or bone meal when the yield from plots is not constant, but has a particular distribution. When there is variation among plots not treated with bone meal or manure, how can the distribution of yield of certain plots be accounted for when an independent variable is introduced (fertilizer)? Fisher developed the statistical and systematic means for comparing within-group variance and the variance between groups to solve this problem—the F in F-ratios and the F-test comes from him.

or fourth variables. In a regression framework, it is possible to determine if that is the case. In a one-way ANOVA, it is not.

Many social science disciplines use ANOVA frequently, testifying to its utility. There have been numerous elaborations on the simple technique described in this chapter that address the concerns, such as MANOVA (multivariate analysis of variance). However, these are beyond what is necessary for an introductory statistics course.

GLOSSARY TERMS

Analysis of variance (ANOVA) (p. 182)
Grand mean (p. 184)
Mean square (p. 186)
Post-hoc (p. 192)

Sum of squares (p. 184)
Total sum of squares (p. 184)
Type one error (p. 183)

PRACTICE QUESTIONS

1. Sarah plans to start exercising so that she can lose weight. She wonders whether she will burn the same number of calories no matter what type of activity she does. Sarah chooses five different exercises and asks five different people the number of calories they burn by doing each activity for a period of one hour. Develop a research and null hypothesis to determine if this is true.

2. Consider the following data from Sarah's data collection technique.

Number of Calories Burned per Hour				
Bicycling	**House cleaning**	**Health club exercise**	**Yoga**	**Tennis**
236	207	325	236	413
321	249	401	312	599
345	292	452	345	604
292	302	474	281	434
301	222	353	301	477

   a. Construct and complete a table containing X^2, N, the average time spent on each activity, the sum of all the times, and the grand mean for all activities.
   b. Calculate SS_{total}, SS_{within}, and $SS_{between}$.
   c. Calculate df_{within} and $df_{between}$.
   d. Calculate MS_{within} and $MS_{between}$.
   e. Obtain the F-ratio.
   f. Compare $F_{calculated}$ to $F_{critical}$. What are the implications for your hypotheses?

3. Ann's friend Jen always tells her that she should buy more expensive jeans because they last longer. Ann asked five people how many days they wore the four types of jeans shown in the table before they were no longer able to wear them, to see if there are significant differences between the types of jeans and their durability. What are the research and null hypotheses that would allow you to test this prospect?

4. Here are the data from Ann's excursion:

	Durability of Jeans			
Observation #	Levi's	People's Liberty	Silvers	Guess
1	182	209	1,040	260
2	130	225	780	624
3	91	156	520	416
4	200	260	340	222
5	154	101	416	85

a. Construct and complete a table that contains the necessary information for finding $F_{calculated}$.

b. Compare $F_{calculated}$ to $F_{critical}$.

c. Do you find evidence to reject or fail to reject the null hypothesis?

5. Edmonton's three major malls (other than the West Edmonton Mall) are Kingsway, City Centre, and Southgate Mall. Here is a fictitious list of the number of daily visitors to each of the malls for four Saturdays in a row, measured in thousands. Calculate a one-way ANOVA to see if at least one of the malls is significantly different from the others in the number of visitors.

Date	Kingsway	City Centre	Southgate
Saturday, August 6, 2011	45	32	51
Saturday, August 13, 2011	32	47	55
Saturday, August 20, 2011	44	55	31
Saturday, August 27, 2011	43	41	30

Answers to the practice questions for Chapter 15 can be found on page S-16.

NOTE

1. Throughout this chapter, we'll only discuss one-way ANOVA, even though there are multiple ANOVA techniques. For brevity, here ANOVA will be used as shorthand to refer to one-way ANOVA.

PART III | MULTIVARIATE TECHNIQUES

CHAPTER 16

Regression 1—Modelling Continuous Outcomes

LEARNING OBJECTIVES

In this chapter, we're moving beyond bivariate techniques and focusing on analysis with more than two variables. Specifically, we'll look at:

- why and when multivariate analysis might be necessary;
- ordinary least squares (OLS) regression;
- how to calculate and interpret OLS coefficients, and how to identify statistical significance;
- standardized partial slopes;
- dummy variables.

INTRODUCTION

You probably expect your income to increase as you age, but do you know how to determine whether that is a reasonable expectation? Can you calculate the rate at which it will increase? You could run a bivariate correlation between age and income, but what if you believe that other variables, such as education, will also have an effect? What about if you're male or female? Black or white? A resident of Winnipeg or Halifax? How can you look at the relationship between two variables and still acknowledge that other variables matter?

So far, a lot of this text has been about levels of measurement, variance, and correlations between variables. In a way, this has all been "build-up" to the next two chapters. In this chapter, many of these things will come together with ordinary least squares regression, the multivariate technique of choice for continuous dependent variables. Chapter 17 will then cover logistic regression, which is often used with binary outcomes.

ORDINARY LEAST-SQUARES REGRESSION: THE IDEA

When two sets of numbers are plotted on a graph (say, age and income), and you think that you can see a general trend or relationship between the two sets, you might be tempted to draw a "trend line" (like the one we used in Chapter 14 to illustrate Pearson's r) to describe the relationship that you think you see. Although this can be done by eye, some quick calculations will probably result in a more accurate line. If you drew several lines, how would you know which line is best? Your goal is to find the line that best represents the relationship between individual scores on an independent variable and a dependent variable. You want the sum of the distances between the data points and the line to be as small above the line as below the line. That distance is known as the estimation error.

If all of the points were on a straight line, we could trace that line. This is rarely the case, so we must decide where to draw the line. To do that, we use regression. The shorthand term "regression" refers to a set of techniques that allow relationships between two or more variables to be identified and generalized (or summarized). For now, we'll consider only cases where the relationship between the variables is linear, though linearity isn't necessary with more complicated techniques. In the next chapter, we'll look at one such technique for modelling a non-linear relationship, the logistic curve.

Social scientists use computers to help them with regression. However, the best practitioners are also familiar with the "behind-the-scenes" calculations. In this chapter, we'll focus on calculating regression coefficients by hand, so that when you use Excel, SAS, STATA, SPSS, or any other program, you'll understand what the numbers in the output mean and how they were calculated. Although research with more than 50 independent variables is common, because of the complexity of the calculations for regression, we'll use only examples with far fewer independent variables.

Before we proceed, let's quickly review independent and dependent variables. Independent variables are those that elicit an effect on an outcome, whereas dependent variables are the outcomes you wish to explain. So, if you're looking at age and income, age is the independent variable and income is the dependent variable. How do we know this? Largely because it makes more sense to hypothesize that age has an effect on a person's income than it does to think that income affects a person's age.

If you are ever stuck trying to figure out which is which, think about temporal ordering—which occurs first? If you can answer this question, you can be pretty sure that you have distinguished independent variables from the dependent variable. Every person has an age long before they have an income—your age for the rest of your life was determined at birth, whereas countless things in your life will determine your income. To estimate a regression, it is vital to be able to identify independent and dependent variables.

ONWARD FROM BIVARIATE CORRELATION

To understand ordinary least squares regression, it is useful to think of it as an extension of a bivariate correlation between two interval/ratio variables. Like a bivariate correlation, Pearson's correlation coefficient measures the strength of the association between two variables (let's call them X and Y). However, unlike a bivariate correlation, it is possible to examine the strength of an association between Y and several variables (such as X and Z).

To illustrate, suppose that you wanted to look at the relationship between age and hours of sleep. You feel that years of schooling affects hours of sleep, but you aren't actually interested in this second relationship. Perhaps the most important feature of regression is that each relationship can be assessed without worrying about the impact of potential explanatory variables. If you were interested in the relationship between age and hours of sleep, but acknowledge that years of schooling probably has an effect on that relationship, you can "control" for years of schooling by entering it into the regression. The relationship that we observe between age and hours of sleep will represent the relationship after the effect of years of schooling has been removed. Regression assesses the effect of an additional variable, while holding the value of all other variables (except the dependent variable) at a constant value.

Think of it as trying to summarize the relationship between independent variable(s) and a dependent variable with a line (called the "least squares regression line" or "line of best fit"). It is the characteristics of that line that you are deriving with a regression.

BOX 16.1

Why Is Regression Called Regression?

The term "regression" is a bit odd. The origin of the term is an interesting one that brings us back to Francis Galton and his pea seeds.

Francis Galton (1822–1911) had a problem. He wanted to know, "How is it possible for a whole population to remain alike in its features, as a whole, during many successive generations, if the *average* produce of each couple resembles their parents?" (Walker, 1929:103).

To answer the question, he took several hundred pea seeds, sent them to friends and asked them to grow the seeds, keeping their soil constant, and to class the offspring according to parental size.

Then Galton asked his friends to return those peas. He weighed the parents of each pea seed and the pea seeds themselves, then divided them into classes. "The measurements . . . led him to his first statement of the law of regression: the mean of every batch of progeny was displaced from the general mean in an amount proportional to the displacement of their parents. The mean displacement of the offspring, however, was always less than that of their parents; they had, on the average, reverted part way back to the mean for the entire race" (Porter, 1986:286–287). The idea that developed into what we know now as regression was described as a regression, or reversion, of attributes (such as height) toward the mean. Even if height is hereditary, heights of successive generations continue to observe a normal distribution, and appear to be "pulled back" toward a new mean value, away from radical deviation.

REGRESSION: THE FORMULA

A little bit of basic geometry (the relationship between points and lines) should give you a better understanding of regression. Regression takes the following form:

$$Y = a + b_1x_{1i} + b_2x_{2i} + \cdots + b_nx_{ni} + e_i$$

where

- Y = the dependent variable
- a = the Y intercept
- b_1 = the partial slope of X_1 on Y
- b_2 = the partial slope of X_2 on Y
- b_n = the partial slope of X_n on Y
- x_{1i} = the first independent variable for individual i
- x_{2i} = the second independent variable for individual i
- x_{ni} = the nth independent variable for individual i
- e_i = error for individual i

The equation represents a formalized hypothesis about the relationship between the independent variables X and one dependent variable Y, acknowledging that each prediction is likely to carry at least some error, making the combination of the variables "miss" the actual score of the dependent variable by some margin. This margin is represented by e_i, an error term that each individual will have a distinct value for. Error is defined as the gap between predicted and observed values, the amount by which an estimate "misses" its mark. The addition sign between each partial slope coefficient/independent variable couplet implies an additive relationship, which means that each independent or explanatory variable has equal potential to affect the dependent variable.

For now, we assume that the relationship between independent variables and the dependent variable is linear, so it can be plotted as a straight line. The independent variables are summed to determine the slope of the line. Since each variable can contribute to the slope, they are referred to as **partial slope coefficients**. The term coefficient refers to a number or quantity that expresses the nature of the relationship between an independent variable and the dependent variable.

Let's look at a simple example: the relationship between age and income, using individuals of all ages. Since this is probably your first time using regression, we'll only look at one independent variable, age, even though it would be easy to think of numerous characteristics that shape income (gender, occupation, number of hours worked, years of education, etc.). The basic equation looks like this:

$$\text{Income} = a + b_1age_i + e_t$$

A regression takes the score of the independent variable (age) for each individual, and determines how that value relates to the dependent variable income.

The equation identifies three values: the y-intercept, the partial slope coefficient, and the individual error. We've already discussed partial slopes and errors, and you may remember from high school geometry that the y-intercept represents the value where the regression line (you may have called it the fit line) crosses the y-axis (note: now you finally know why you had to learn geometry!). The y-intercept refers to the point on the y-axis where the regression line crosses. The interpretation here is more nuanced because it also represents our prediction of a person's income when their scores on the independent variable of age are held constant at their lowest value. Since we are looking at people of all ages, the y-intercept will represent a person's expected income at zero years of age. It is always important to think about the ranges for all variables when estimating regression models, because they are critical to describing and understanding trends in your data. For example, if we include people of all ages, the y-intercept will refer to a person's expected income at age 0; if, however, we only include people age 15 and up (as is the case in the example below), then the y-intercept represents a person's expected income at age 15. The partial slope coefficient, which is actually the *only* slope coefficient in this case, represents the effect of an additional year of age on our income prediction, starting at the lowest value for that variable.

Usually, the partial slopes and y-intercepts are the values of greatest interest. Occasionally, it is interesting to look at the error, or the disparity between predicted values (our "guess" of a person's income) and actual values (what their income actually is). Now that we know what each term in the regression equation means, let's estimate the relationship between age and income by using the 2006 Census of Canada (see Table 16.1). We'll restrict the sample so that a person must have valid values on both variables. For now, we'll use a computer to do the calculations. In the next section, we'll learn how to calculate intercepts and coefficients.

Each computer program presents results differently. This regression was calculated with STATA, so you probably won't be able to interpret Table 16.1 on your own. For now, focus on the two values in the column with the heading "Coef." These are the coefficients for age (called agep in the 2006 public use census file) and the y-intercept (called _cons in STATA), respectively. The value of 17,795.57 tells us that our regression predicts that a person with zero years of age will be earning $17,795.57 (actually, since nobody under age 15 has valid income values on

TABLE 16.1 | Regression Output for a Single Independent Variable Model

Source	SS	df	MS		
Model	9.8500e+12	1	9.8500e+12	Number of obs = 645961	
Residual	4.6279e+14,645,959		716,439,688	F(1645959) = 13748.61	
				Prob › F = 0.0000	
Total	4.7264e+14,645,960		731,687,274	R-squared = 0.0208	
				Adj R-squared = 0.0208	
				Root MSE = 26,766	

Totincp	Coef.	Std. Err.	T	p›ltl	[95% Conf.	Interval]
agep	218.9251	1.867095	117.25	0.000	215.2657	222.5846
_cons	17,795.57	88.38844	201.33	0.000	17,622.33	17,968.81

Source: 2001 Census of Canada

the census, this represents income at age 15), and the agep coefficient tells us that the value is expected to increase by $218.93 for every additional year of age. Inserting these values into our equation above, *a* now carries a value of 17,795.57 and *b* is 218.93. For now, ignore the other columns, even though some of them (Std. Err., t, 95% Conf. Interval) may look familiar.

Graphing the relationship with a scatterplot can make it easier to visualize the relationship.

Although it may be difficult to see, Figure 16.1 shows that our estimate of the *y*-intercept (17,795.57) corresponds with where the line crosses the *y*-axis. Equally difficult to see is how the pitch of the regression line corresponds with this partial slope coefficient value (218.93) in our equation. These numbers should be identical. The equation describes the characteristics of the regression line and that the distance between the line and any given observation is the error.

You can probably see some similarities between regression and correlation by now. In some ways, regression is a correlation with many variables.

Regression allows you to predict the value of the dependent variable by using the information provided in independent variables. For example, if somebody was 25 years old, we could estimate their income as follows:

$$\text{Income} = 17795.57 + 218.93 age_i$$
$$= 17795.57 + 218.93 * 10$$
$$= 17795.57 + 2189.30$$
$$= \$19,984.87$$

Based on our regression equation, we can predict that a person who is 25 years old will earn $19,984.87. Why did we only add 10 years of age for someone who is 25? Because we estimated our regression for those over age 15, so we need to take the difference between lowest age and our age of interest, which is 25 − 15 = 10.

How accurate is that estimate? According to the 2006 census file, the actual average income for a 25-year-old is $21,663.40. Although our guess is pretty good—we're only off by

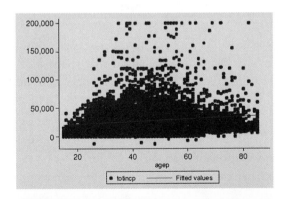

FIGURE 16.1 | Regression of Age and Income, 2006 Canada
Source: 2001 Census of Canada

$1,678.53—there are things we could do to get a more accurate estimate. One is to add more explanatory variables (education, gender, occupation, etc.), and another is to restrict the age range of our samples so that we are primarily looking at people in a more valid age range—say, age 25 to 55—since few 15-year-olds are likely to be working full-time. For now, let's just work with what we have and develop our understanding of the one independent variable model.

Now that we know how to estimate y by using slopes and intercepts, how are the y-intercept, the partial-slope coefficient, and the error terms obtained? We are kind of working backwards, but with some careful thought it is possible to imagine what some of the necessary information might be. Since the regression line is supposed to minimize errors (the average gap between observed values and predicted values should be as small as possible), we need an equation that will create a line of best fit where average distance between observations above the line are the same as, or as close as possible to, those below the line.

That makes sense: with the best fitting line, which is what the regression line is supposed to be, we want the average level of *under*estimation to be approximately equal to the average level of *over*estimation. If positive errors (those above the line) surpass negative errors, then our line will not cut midway through the data.

The line of best fit can also be stated as the sum of cross-product deviations from their mean of independent variable X and dependent variable Y, divided by the sum of squared deviations from its mean of independent variable X. This is the equation:

$$b = \frac{\sum (X - \bar{X})(Y - \bar{Y})}{\sum (X - \bar{X})^2}$$

where

- $\bar{X}$ = the mean value of variable X
- $\bar{Y}$ = the mean value of variable Y

The numerator is the sum of the deviations of the independent variable, multiplied by the deviations of the dependent variable. Remember that we're trying to identify how strongly the scores of Y depend on the scores of X. When observations have a high value of X alongside a high value of Y, a middle value of X alongside a middle value of Y, and lower X values alongside lower Y values, the numerator will be high, resulting in a larger partial coefficient.

What's going on with the denominator? Given that the size of the numerator partially depends on the range of values of X (if X has a large variance, then the numerator will be large, and vice versa), it is necessary to standardize these values. This is done by dividing the numerator by the squared deviations of X from the mean. These values are squared because if they are not, then the sum of deviations from the mean will be equal to zero. You might remember this from when we calculated variance and standard deviation.

Once the partial coefficient b is found, calculating the y-intercept and the error is easy. The y-intercept a is defined as

$$a = \bar{Y} - b\bar{X}$$

and error e is defined as

$$e = Y - \hat{Y}$$

where $\hat{Y}$ is the predicted value (the value of Y on the regression line at a particular value of X). The goal is to ensure that the estimation errors above the line (which would occur when our estimated value is lower than the actual value) are as close as possible to estimation errors below the line (when our estimated values are too high). We can do this by minimizing the sum of all errors. The problem with doing this is that when our line of best fit is optimally placed (the errors above the line equal those below it), the sum of all errors will be zero. For this reason, rather than look at the sum of errors, we typically compare the sum of squared errors, because squaring values will eliminate any negative values.

Let's illustrate this with an example. Using the 1971 Census of Canada Public Use File, we can use age at first marriage to predict family size, focusing on people who were 35-years-old in 1971. As with other statistical techniques, the calculations are cumbersome in large samples, so we'll restrict our analysis to 12 randomly selected observations. These observations appear in Table 16.2.

Let's revisit our equation for b:

$$b = \frac{\sum(X - \bar{X})(Y - \bar{Y})}{\sum(X - \bar{X})^2}$$

The first things we'll need to find are the means of family size (Y, the dependent variable) and age at first marriage (X, the independent variable).

TABLE 16.2 | Family Size and Age of First Marriage among 12 Randomly Selected Cases, 1971 Census of Canada

Age at first marriage (X)	Family size (Y)
21	4
32	2
21	3
25	5
24	1
17	3
22	5
21	4
22	2
22	5
28	2
26	3

For family size we get

$$(4 + 2 + 3 + 5 + 1 + 3 + 5 + 4 + 2 + 5 + 2 + 3)/12 = 3.25$$

For age at first marriage we get

$$(21 + 32 + 21 + 25 + 24 + 17 + 22 + 21 + 22 + 22 + 28 + 26)/12 = 23.42$$

We'll also need the sum of cross-product deviations of independent variable X and dependent variable Y from their means. This is a little harder to calculate, but a chart like the one in Table 16.3 will make things easier.

We are primarily interested in two pieces of information in Table 16.3, $\Sigma (X - \bar{X})(Y - \bar{Y})$, which is often referred to as the sum of products (SP), and $\Sigma (X - \bar{X})^2$, the sum of squares (SS).

Now that we have the sum of products, the sum of squares, and the means of the two variables, the equation for the partial slope is easy to solve:

$$b = \frac{\Sigma (X - \bar{X})(Y - \bar{Y})}{\Sigma (X - \bar{X})^2}$$
$$= \frac{-20.25}{168.92}$$
$$= -0.12$$

As is the intercept

$$a = \bar{Y} - b\bar{X}$$
$$= 3.25 - (-0.12) * 23.42$$
$$= 6.06$$

TABLE 16.3	Using Family Size and Age of First Marriage among 12 Randomly Selected Cases to Calculate Regression Coefficients, 1971 Census of Canada				
Age at first marriage (X)	Family size (Y)	$X - \bar{X}$	$y - \bar{y}$	$(X - \bar{X})(y - \bar{y})$	$(X - \bar{X})^2$
21	4	−2.42	0.75	−1.82	5.86
32	2	8.58	−1.25	−10.73	73.62
21	3	−2.42	−0.25	0.61	5.86
25	5	1.58	1.75	2.77	2.50
24	1	0.58	−2.25	−1.31	0.34
17	3	−6.42	−0.25	1.61	41.22
22	5	−1.42	1.75	−2.49	2.02
21	4	−2.42	0.75	−1.82	5.86
22	2	−1.42	−1.25	1.78	2.02
22	5	−1.42	1.75	−2.49	2.02
28	2	4.58	−1.25	−5.73	20.98
26	3	2.58	−0.25	−0.65	6.66
Mean = 23.42	Mean = 3.25			Sum = −20.25	Sum = 168.92

TABLE 16.4	Using Age of First Marriage among 12 Randomly Selected Cases to Calculate Predicted Family Size, 1971 Census of Canada		
Age at first marriage (X)	**Family size (Y)**	**Ŷ**	**e = Y − Ŷ**
21	4	3.54	0.46
32	2	2.22	−0.22
21	3	3.54	−0.54
25	5	3.06	1.94
24	1	3.18	−2.18
17	3	4.02	−1.02
22	5	3.42	1.58
21	4	3.54	0.46
22	2	3.42	−1.42
22	5	3.42	1.58
28	2	2.70	−0.70
26	3	2.94	0.06

To calculate the error, we need to generate **predicted values** for each observation: the predicted family size for each person, given the available information (their age at first marriage). We use our standard regression equation and the values we calculated above to find this:

$$Y = a + bX$$
$$= 6.06 - 0.12X$$

Next, we calculate predicted values for each observation, and by substituting values for X we calculate prediction errors with the following equation $e = Y - \hat{Y}$ (see Table 16.4).

MULTIPLE REGRESSION

In the previous example, we used models with only one independent variable and one dependent variable. Although this nicely illustrated the principle of ordinary least squares regression, such small models are rarely used in social science research. Typically, models will have more than one independent variable—in fact, analysts will usually include more than 50 independent variables in a single model. This makes for an extremely complex analysis that would be just about impossible without computers and statistical software packages.

The same equations are used for models with several independent variables, but there are more considerations. Any two independent variables will not only be correlated with the dependent variable but probably also with each other. Because of this, the independent effect of one variable cannot be isolated without looking at the impact of the other variables, and identifying the relationship between them. For example, the number of years that a Canadian immigrant has been in the country is related to his or her age. Of course, it is impossible to have

BOX 16.2

Regression with One Independent Variable: The Steps

1. Find the mean for each X and Y variable.
2. Subtract the mean from the value for each observation.
3. Square and sum these terms. Each value is known as the sum of squares.

$$SS_X = \sum(X - \bar{X})^2 \quad SS_Y = \sum(Y - \bar{Y})^2$$

4. Find the sum of products:

$$SP = \sum(X - \bar{X})(Y - \bar{Y})$$

5. Calculate b (the partial slope):

$$b = \frac{SP}{SS_X}$$

6. Calculate a (the y-intercept):

$$a = \bar{Y} - b\bar{X}$$

7. Calculate r:

$$r = \frac{SP}{\sqrt{SS_X SS_Y}}$$

been in Canada for longer than you've been alive, but older people have had the opportunity to be in Canada for much longer than young people, so we expect there to be a correlation between age and years in Canada. If we use both of these independent variables to predict a dependent variable, like the number of charities a person participates in, we would not be able to identify the independent impact of either age or years since migration without acknowledging that there is some relatedness, or **covariance**, between them.

Handling covariance can become complicated. Since we are dealing with correlations, we can return to bivariate correlations to help us understand regression with more than one independent variable. To remind you, here's the equation for a bivariate correlation between variables X and Y:

$$r_{xy} = \frac{N\sum XY - (\sum X)(\sum Y)}{\sqrt{[N\sum X^2 - (\sum X)^2][N\sum Y^2 - (\sum Y)^2]}}$$

We need to change the notation slightly to accommodate the new correlations we're measuring, resulting in the following three equations:

$$r_{X_1Y} = \frac{N\sum X_1Y - (\sum X_1)(\sum Y)}{\sqrt{[N\sum X_1^2 - (\sum X)^2][N\sum Y^2 - (\sum Y)^2]}}$$

$$r_{X_2Y} = \frac{N\sum X_2Y - (\sum X_2)(\sum Y)}{\sqrt{[N\sum X_2^2 - (\sum X_2)^2][N\sum Y^2 - (\sum Y)^2]}}$$

$$r_{X_1X_2} = \frac{N\sum X_1X_2 - (\sum X_1)(\sum X_2)}{\sqrt{[N\sum X_1^2 - (\sum X_1)^2][N\sum X_2^2 - (\sum X_2)^2]}}$$

These probably look daunting, but they're essentially the same equations that we used to calculate correlation in Chapter 13, except that the notation has changed to indicate that we're looking at different combinations of correlations.

Let's see how this works in practice. Recall from Chapter 14 that we used the 1666 census to illustrate correlation, so let's use that again to elaborate on regression with two independent variables. This time, both the age of the husband and the age of the wife will be independent variables, and we'll use that information to predict the number of children in the household. Let's suppose that we expect the age of the husband to be positively correlated with the age of the wife, and for the ages of both husband and wife to be positively associated with the number of children in the household. To get a better sense of what we're trying to do, let's take a look at the data in Table 16.5 (we'll focus on only 12 observations).

We need to calculate the correlations between all of the variables (since we already did that in Chapter 14, let's rely on computers here):

.corr spageage nchildhh (obs=12)

	wifage	husage	nchildhh
wifage	1.0000		
husage	0.7073	1.0000	
nchildhh	0.1485	0.6152	1.0000

TABLE 16.5 | Age of Husband and Wife and Number of Children among 12 Households, 1666 Census of Canada

obs #	wifage (X1)	husage (X2)	# child (Y)
1	40	41	0
2	47	36	0
3	30	40	5
4	18	27	0
5	37	50	7
6	50	62	4
7	32	30	3
8	40	54	6
9	41	36	1
10	20	27	1
11	36	36	2
12	32	37	5

Note: There is only one observation per household.

As you can see, our expectations are met. Each of the three correlations is positive, suggesting that age of husband is positively correlated with both age of wife and number of children in the household. Similarly, age of wife is positively correlated with age of husband and number of children in the household. Finally, we can infer from the previous two statements that number of children in the household is positively correlated with age of wife and age of husband.

Now that we have the **zero-order correlations** (correlations between variables without assuming any causal order), we need the equations for the partial correlation coefficient:

$$b_1 = \left(\frac{s_y}{s_{x1}}\right)\left(\frac{r_{x1y} - r_{x2y}r_{x1x2}}{1 - r_{x1x2}^2}\right)$$

$$b_2 = \left(\frac{s_y}{s_{x2}}\right)\left(\frac{r_{x2y} - r_{x1y}r_{x1x2}}{1 - r_{x1x2}^2}\right)$$

where s refers to the standard deviations of certain variables (which you learned how to calculate in Chapters 6 and 7), and r denotes the correlations between them.

Let's work through these equations to derive the partial slope coefficients:

$$b_1 = \left(\frac{s_y}{s_{x1}}\right)\left(\frac{r_{x1y} - r_{x2y}r_{x1x2}}{1 - r_{x1x2}^2}\right)$$

$$= \left(\frac{2.517}{9.612}\right)\left(\frac{0.1485 - 0.6152 * 0.7073}{1 - 0.7073^2}\right)$$

$$= (0.2618)\left(\frac{0.1485 - 0.4351}{1 - 0.5003}\right)$$

$$b_2 = \left(\frac{s_y}{s_{x2}}\right)\left(\frac{r_{x2y} - r_{x1y}r_{x1x2}}{1 - r_{x1x2}^2}\right)$$

$$= \left(\frac{2.517}{10.765}\right)\left(\frac{0.6512 - 0.1485 * 0.7073}{1 - 0.7073^2}\right)$$

$$= (0.2338)\left(\frac{0.6152 - 0.1050}{1 - 0.5003}\right)$$

When the coefficients are calculated, an interesting difference between these figures and the zero-order correlations emerges. Notice that b_2 remains positive, showing that the age of the husband remains positively correlated with the number of children in the household. At the same time, age of wife is now negatively related to the number of children in the household.

How can this be? The correlation between age of husband and age of wife was so strong that it obscured the negative relationship between the age of wife and the number of children in the household. This nicely illustrates the importance of regression analysis and explains why it is one of the most frequently used techniques in social science data analysis.

STANDARDIZED PARTIAL SLOPES (BETA WEIGHTS)

In the example, the partial slopes (b_1 and b_2) were in the original units of the independent variables. The coefficient refers to the expected increase in the dependent variable when there is a one-unit increase in the value of an independent variable. Since both independent variables were measured in years, it was easy to compare the relative impact of each variable. We know that the age of the husband had a more direct impact than the age of the wife because the coefficient was greater in magnitude.

To compare the relative effects of independent variables that are not measured in the same units, a beta weight (b^*) needs to be computed. Beta weights show how much change there is to *standardized* scores of Y when there is a one-unit change in the *standardized* scores of each independent variable, and controls for the effects of all other independent variables. With standardized betas, the independent variables do not have to be measured in the same units. Since calculating beta weights is really just a standardization technique that once again relies on standard deviations, the equation is simple:

$$b_{1*} = b_1 \left(\frac{s_1}{s_y} \right)$$

THE MULTIPLE CORRELATION COEFFICIENT

Recall Chapter 14, where r was used to identify the strength of the relationship between two variables. To get the per cent variation of one variable, we squared r. The same thing is possible using multiple regression, except that we are now able to assess the cumulative effect of several independent variables on one dependent variable, rather than just one on one correlations.

Although we already calculated the bivariate correlations, adding them together will overestimate the percentage of explained variation because of the correlation that exists between $X1$ and $X2$. Both might be explaining a similar portion of the dependent variable. Think of an apple as the dependent variable, with multiple slices representing the variable's variation. Regression aims to explain as much of the total variation (the whole apple) as possible; ideally, each independent variable will remove a slice of the apple. Since independent variables are frequently correlated with one another, there will be overlap in the slices that each independent variable will remove.

Consequently, the correlation of independent variables must be accounted for in the calculation of Pearson's r-squared R^2. The equation to do that is

$$R^2 = r^2_{y\,x1} + r^2_{y\,x1\,x2}(1 - r^2_{y\,x1})$$

or

$$R^2 = \frac{\sum (\hat{Y} - \bar{Y})^2}{\sum (Y - \bar{Y})^2}$$

We have most of the information we need to solve the equation. The only missing piece is r^2_{yx1x2}, which is calculated as

$$r^2_{y\,x1x2} = \frac{r_{yx2} - (r_{yx1})(r_{x1x2})}{\sqrt{1 - r^2_{yx1}}\sqrt{1 - r^2_{x1x2}}}$$

Applied to our 1666 example, we get

$$r^2_{yx1x2} = \frac{r_{x2y} - (r_{x1y})(r_{x1x2})}{\sqrt{1 - r^2_{x1\,y}}\sqrt{1 - r^2_{x1x2}}}$$

$$= \frac{0.6152 - 0.1485 * 0.7073}{\sqrt{1 - 0.1485^2}\sqrt{1 - 0.7073^2}}$$

$$= \frac{0.5102}{0.6991}$$

$$= 0.76$$

Now, we can solve for R^2:

$$R^2 = r^2_{x1y} + r^2_{yx1x2}(1 - r^2_{x1y})$$
$$= 0.1485^2 + 0.6530^2 * (1 - 0.1485^2)$$
$$= 0.0221 + 0.4264 * (0.9780)$$
$$= 0.4881$$

Now we know that age of husband and age of wife together explain about 48 per cent of the variation in the number of children in a household. Note that this result is substantially lower than when the two zero-order correlations are added together [$(0.1485 + 0.6152)^2 = 0.5832$]. This is due to correlation between variables.

REQUIREMENTS OF ORDINARY LEAST SQUARES REGRESSION

There are some fundamental assumptions behind ordinary least squares regression. You'll be familiar with most of them, because they've been covered elsewhere (particularly in our discussion of correlation).

1. All variables are interval/ratio, dichotomous, or dummy (discussed below).
2. All error terms are normally distributed.
3. There is linearity between variables. This means that the relationship between an independent variable and a dependent variable is the same across the range of both variables. For example, it is assumed that the relationship between years of schooling and number of hours worked per week is the same for a high school graduate as it is for somebody with a Ph.D.

4. Homoscedasticity. Random samples are necessary for significance tests, otherwise there will be non-random sampling error. This non-randomness can take many forms, but the most common is heteroscedasticity, where the variance of Y differs by X value. To illustrate heteroscedasticity, imagine the correlation of university grades with a person's previous high school grades. Somebody who earned a 65 per cent average in high school could (1) perform even worse in university because the material is more difficult, (2) continue to chug along, earning the same average, or (3) become interested in the curriculum offered in universities, thereby increasing their grades. Although the same three options exist for somebody with a 95 per cent average in high school, they are unable to increase their grades dramatically (it's pretty hard to get more than 100 per cent). Further, they are unlikely to fail miserably in university, suggesting that the range of grade for those with a 95 per cent average in high school will be smaller than it is for those with a 65 per cent average. The data in this example are heteroscedastic, and for regression we need them to be homoscedastic. Homoscedasticity occurs when the measure of variance in Y (likely the standard deviation) is consistent across values of X, whereas heteroscedasticity occurs when there is a difference in the measure of variance in Y across values of X.

DUMMY VARIABLES

The problem with ordinary least squares regression in the social sciences is that many variables of interest are measured at nominal and ordinal levels. For example, a common interest is the differences between men and women. This is problematic because it is not possible to rank respondents based on their sex, nor is it possible to measure the "distance" between men and women. Compare this to something like age, where we can determine the difference between two respondents based on their response (we know that a ten-year-old is five years older than a five-year-old). Does this mean that we can't use regression techniques for all variables?

Fortunately, the "distance" between response categories can be measured in a nominal or ordinal variable when there are only two response categories (typically, these variables are referred to as **dichotomous variables**, **binary variables**, or **dummy variables**). If we view the response categories of a dichotomous variable as being on two ends of a continuum (for example, males are on one end, and females are on the other), then we know that a person who identifies as male is 100 per cent more male than female. In this indirect way, we are able to quantify the distance between two categories in a dichotomous variable so that it can be used in a regression.

In the case of variables with more than two response categories (religion, region of residence, visible minority status), a "cheat," or simplifying process, is possible. If nominal and ordinal variables have more than two response categories they can be broken down into a series of dichotomous variables and then entered into a regression. This process is referred to as **dichotomization**.

Let's try an example. In the 1901 Census of Canada, every respondent was asked their race. There were four allowable responses: black, red, white, and yellow. In the census file, this information exists as a single nominal variable, "Race." Without modification, it is not possible to include this variable in a regression, because it is not possible to rank the four response categories, or to measure the distance between them, thereby violating OLS assumption one.

	D1	D2	D3	D4
TABLE 16.6	**Using 1901 Race Categories to Illustrate Dummy Variables**			
Red	1	0	0	0
Yellow	0	1	0	0
White	0	0	1	0
Black	0	0	0	1

Source: 1901 Census of Canada

To get around the problem, we need to create a series of new variables. Let's call them $D1$ through $D4$. As Table 16.6 illustrates, $D1$ assumes a value of one when a respondent identifies as red, and zero otherwise. $D2$ is set to one when a respondent identifies as yellow, and zero otherwise. In the same way, $D3$ and $D4$ identify white and black respondents, respectively.

We've created four new dichotomous variables out of one nominal variable. Since the new variables have only two values, zero and one, they can be used in an OLS regression. The new dummy variables use the same logic as the gender example. A person who has a value of one on variable $D1$ is 100 per cent redder than somebody with a value of zero.

Unfortunately, working with dummy variables is complicated by the necessity of having a **reference group**. The four dummy variables don't all need to be included in the regression. Only three are needed. Think about it: if a respondent has a score of zero on variable $D1$ (indicating that they are not red), $D2$ (they are not yellow), and $D3$ (they are not white), by default they must be black.

If we assume that everyone responded to the original race question, then we can infer a person's race using only three variables. Only $k - 1$ dummy variables need to be included, where k equals the number of response categories in the original variable or the total number of dummy variables.

There is no hard and fast rule for choosing the reference category. Researchers often choose the most common or populous group, although any group that's big enough is acceptable.

INTERPRETING DUMMY VARIABLE COEFFICIENTS

Interpreting dummy variable coefficients is more complicated than interpreting regular variables. Each coefficient refers to a one-unit increase in that particular variable, with all other variables set to zero. So the coefficient for somebody who is white represents the increased or decreased value of the dependent variable, *relative to the reference group*. This can be tricky, but an example should help to clarify it.

Returning to the 1666 data, imagine that we believe that families in which the parents are farmers will be larger than families in which the parents belong to other occupations. We believe that farmers will have more children because children provide cheap farm labour.

To assess this, we create a dummy variable "farmer" (1 = yes, 0 = no), and run the regression. This produces a coefficient with a value of 0.405, which can be interpreted this way: "Farmers in 1666 could be expected to have an average of 0.405 more children than non-farmers." Our suspicion is supported.

INFERENCE AND REGRESSION

As is the case for nearly all of the material we've covered in this text, regression analysis is typically conducted on samples even though it is the underlying population that is of interest. Given this, we must "infer" our sample results to the population. To do this, we use the material covered in several chapters in this text, most notably Chapter 14.

Up to this point in our discussion of regression, we have not thought about inference or statistical significance, even though it is a central part of what analysts consider when they look at regression results. To illustrate the importance of inference, let's continue with our earlier example of family size in 1971. Here is Table 16.3 again:

We want to assess the probability that b, the partial slope, is significantly different from 0 in the population. Said in words, we want to ensure that b does not have the same mean value for every value of X. Thinking about it in terms of plotting X and Y values, we do not want our least squares regression line to be perfectly horizontal.

TABLE 16.3	Using Family Size and Age of First Marriage among 12 Randomly Selected Cases to Calculate Regression Coefficients, 1971 Census of Canada				
Age at first marriage (X)	Family size (Y)	$X - \bar{X}$	$y - \bar{y}$	$(X - \bar{X})(y - \bar{y})$	$(X - \bar{X})^2$
21	4	−2.42	0.75	−1.82	5.86
32	2	8.58	−1.25	−10.73	73.62
21	3	−2.42	−0.25	0.61	5.86
25	5	1.58	1.75	2.77	2.50
24	1	0.58	−2.25	−1.31	0.34
17	3	−6.42	−0.25	1.61	41.22
22	5	−1.42	1.75	−2.49	2.02
21	4	−2.42	0.75	−1.82	5.86
22	2	−1.42	−1.25	1.78	2.02
22	5	−1.42	1.75	−2.49	2.02
28	2	4.58	−1.25	−5.73	20.98
26	3	2.58	−0.25	−0.65	6.66
Mean = 23.42	Mean = 3.25			Sum = −20.25	Sum = 168.92

Our calculation of *b* from the data above shows us that the *sample* value differs from 0, but we want to know about the *population*. We once again calculate *b* as

$$b = \frac{\sum (X - \bar{X})(Y - \bar{Y})}{\sum (X - \bar{X})^2}$$
$$= \frac{-20.25}{168.92}$$
$$= -0.12$$

Next, we need to calculate the standard error of our regression coefficient estimate. To do this, we need to once again recall the information from Table 16.4, with the addition of the sum of squared error estimates $(Y - \hat{Y})^2$:

TABLE 16.4	Using Age of First Marriage among 12 Randomly Selected Cases to Calculate Predicted Family Size, 1971 Census of Canada			
Age at first marriage (X)	Family size (Y)	$\hat{Y}$	$e = Y - \hat{Y}$	$(Y - \hat{Y})^2$
21	4	3.54	0.46	0.2116
32	2	2.22	−0.22	0.0484
21	3	3.54	−0.54	0.2916
25	5	3.06	1.94	3.7636
24	1	3.18	−2.18	4.7524
17	3	4.02	−1.02	1.0404
22	5	3.42	1.58	2.4964
21	4	3.54	0.46	0.2116
22	2	3.42	−1.42	2.0164
22	5	3.42	1.58	2.4964
28	2	2.70	−0.70	0.49
26	3	2.94	0.06	0.0036
				Sum = 17.8224

The sum of squared estimate errors is useful because it gives us a sense of how well our regression estimates approximates actual values. Once again, however, this number is sample-size dependent, which means that we must generate a standard error of the estimate by using the following equation:

$$s_{est} = \sqrt{\frac{(Y - \hat{Y})^2}{n - 2}}$$

This equation corrects for the effect of sample size, which is why we call it standardized. Inserting our values above, we get the following:

$$s_{est} = \sqrt{\frac{17.8224}{12 - 2}}$$
$$= 1.335$$

This is a standard error of the estimates, which gets us one step closer to the standard error of the coefficient b. To get this number, we use the following equation:

$$se_b = \frac{\sqrt{\frac{(Y - \hat{Y})^2}{n - 2}}}{\sqrt{(X - \hat{X})^2}}$$

We have nearly all of the values we need to calculate standard error of b. The numerator in the above equation is the standard error of the estimates, and the denominator is the square root of the sum of squares for X. We can get the value of 168.92 for the sum of squares for X from Table 16.3, giving us the following:

$$se_b = \frac{\sqrt{\frac{(Y - \hat{Y})^2}{n - 2}}}{\sqrt{(X - \hat{X})^2}}$$
$$= \frac{1.335}{\sqrt{168.92}}$$
$$= \frac{1.335}{12.997}$$
$$= 0.103$$

Finally, b is divided by the standard error of b and is then used to generate a t-statistic, which we usually assess at the 95 per cent confidence level. This can be assessed as a two-tailed test at $df = n - 2$:

$$t = \frac{b}{se_b}$$
$$= \frac{-0.12}{0.103}$$
$$= -1.165$$

Looking at Appendix B, we see a $t_{critical}$ value of 2.228, which is substantially higher than the absolute value of our $t_{observed}$ calculation of −1.168. Thus, we cannot be 95 per cent confident that our results would be seen in the population.

This is a lot of work, which is why we rely so heavily on statistical software to produce regression results. Every regression output will have a level of statistical significance and a confidence interval for each coefficient. Unless otherwise specified, the 95 per cent confidence interval will be reported by most programs.

BOX 16.3

Identifying the Statistical Significance of One Regression Slope Coefficient: The Steps

1. Calculate the regression slope coefficient by using the following equation:

$$b = \frac{\sum (X - \bar{X})(Y - \bar{Y})}{\sum (X - \bar{X})^2}$$

2. Determine the standard error of the estimate

error $s_{est} = \sqrt{\dfrac{(Y - \hat{Y})^2}{n - 2}}$

3. Calculate the standard error for b, using either of the following equations:

$$s_b = \frac{\sqrt{\dfrac{(Y - \hat{Y})^2}{n - 2}}}{\sqrt{(X - \hat{X})^2}} \text{ or } s_b = \frac{s_{est}}{\sqrt{(X - \hat{X})^2}}$$

4. Generate $t_{observed}$ as $t = \dfrac{b}{se_b}$

5. Compare $t_{observed}$ to $t_{critical}$, found in Appendix B at $df = n - 2$.

EVERYDAY STATISTICS

Regression and Retirement

In an interesting example of how regression helps sort out complicated processes, Myles, Hou, Picot, and Myers (2007) show that although earnings have risen among Canadian lone mothers since 1980, most of the increase has been due to the aging of the baby boomers. This is because the average age of a lone mother has been steadily rising since 1980, and since older people are likely to earn more, the change over time is largely due to a change in a key population characteristic of the lone mother population. For younger lone mothers, there was almost no change.

. . . .

Q: What do you think will happen to earnings among Canadian lone mothers once baby boomers start to retire?

A FINAL NOTE ON OLS REGRESSION

Although we have covered a lot, we have barely scratched the surface of regression. We have also not calculated regression coefficients with more than two independent variables, and we have calculated statistical significance with only one independent variable. Clearly, this chapter is only intended to give you a basic understanding of the most basic type of regression.

You'll encounter more complicated regressions in the more advanced statistics courses that (I hope) you'll take.

GLOSSARY TERMS

Binary variables (p. 213)

Covariance (p. 208)

Dichotomization (p. 213)

Dichotomous variables (p. 213)

Dummy variables (p. 213)

Partial slope coefficients (p. 201)

Predicted values (p. 207)

Reference group (p. 214)

Zero-order correlations (p. 210)

PRACTICE QUESTIONS

1. The following table contains data on the number of rooms and monthly rent for 12 houses. Yan wants to know if there is a relationship between the two variables. Help Yan out by answering the following questions:

Number of rooms (X)	Monthly rent (Y)
3	890
2	568
3	860
1	625
1	775
3	900
3	1,095
3	800
2	765
3	629
1	600
3	750

a. Find the mean for each X and Y variable.

b. Subtract the mean from the value for each observation.

c. Find the sum of squares for X and Y, and the sum of cross-products, using the following equations:

$$SS_X = \sum (X - \bar{X})^2$$
$$SS_Y = \sum (Y - \bar{Y})^2$$
$$SP = \sum (X - \bar{X})(Y - \bar{Y})$$

d. Calculate b (the partial slope):

$$b = \frac{SP}{SS_x}$$

e. Calculate a (the y-intercept):

$$a = \bar{Y} - b\bar{X}$$

f. Calculate r:

$$r = \frac{SP}{\sqrt{SS_X SS_Y}}$$

g. How much does the accuracy of your prediction of the value of the dependent variable increase if you know a person's score on the independent variable?

h. Generate predicted values for each observation.

i. What is the estimation error for each observation?

j. Is the slope coefficient statistically significant?

2. The city of Abbotsford is launching a study to identify the degree to which the number of people sharing a single dwelling affects the cost of utilities. Use the number of people living in a home to predict the amount charged per month.

Number of people (X)	Monthly charge
3	175
2	130
3	231
3	278
2	40
3	205.83
1	0
1	38.41
1	41.23
3	44.2
3	176
3	315

a. Calculate r to measure the association between the two variables above.

b. Calculate the standardized partial slope coefficient by using the following equation to calculate the standard deviations of X and Y (this is the equation for standard deviation in a sample):

$$s = \sqrt{\frac{\sum (X - \bar{X})^2}{n - 1}}$$

c. Calculate the slope coefficient from the data above.
d. What is the estimated monthly charge for a household that contains four people?
e. What is the standardized value of b?

3. One day Tess and Imogen became interested in identifying the factors behind curfews (largely because they think their parents are outliers in their expectations!). They hypothesize that age and grades are two strong explanatory factors, and that their parents should align their curfews with the more general trend. They asked all of their friends and family about their curfews. Tess and Imogen found that α was equal to 16.185. Below are the rest of the data they collected:

Person	Age	Grade (%)	Curfew in 24-hour clock, with minutes stated in decimal format (21.00 means 9 o'clock, 23.50 means 11:30, etc.).
1	12	85	21.00
2	18	78	23.50
3	13	64	20.00
4	12	78	20.25
5	14	56	22.00
6	17	98	22.50
7	21	70	23.75
8	20	59	23.00
9	19	90	22.50
10	15	87	19.50
11	17	63	22.75
12	17	74	23.00
13	16	91	22.25
14	14	77	20.00
15	16	65	22.00

a. Calculate b_1, the partial slope coefficient for age, and b_2, the partial coefficient for grades.
b. Which factor is more important? (Hint: standardize your coefficients.)
c. Tess has a 96 per cent average and is 17-years-old. Based on your regression results, what should her curfew be?

4. What will happen to r as the magnitude of a beta weight increases?

Answers to the practice questions for Chapter 16 can be found on page S-19.

CHAPTER 17

Regression 2—Modelling Discrete/Qualitative Outcomes with Logistic Regression

LEARNING OBJECTIVES

Ordinary least squares regression (OLS) is an excellent technique for multivariate analysis with continuous dependent variables. However, there are many situations where outcomes of interest are *not* continuous. In this chapter, we'll cover:

- why OLS might be inappropriate in these instances;
- logistic regression, a technique for modelling dichotomous dependent variables.

INTRODUCTION

Suppose you're trying to figure out what factors determine whether or not a person gets a mortgage, and you want to know how their earnings affect their chances. Since getting a mortgage is dichotomous—you're either approved or you're not—you know that there is an upper limit (getting a mortgage) and a lower limit (not getting a mortgage) to your outcome of interest.

If a person earns $1 an hour, they'll probably be rejected for a mortgage (assuming they have no savings to supplement their earnings). Similarly, if they earn $2 an hour, or even $3, their application is still likely to be rejected. The relationship between earnings and acceptance is relatively consistent at such low wages. Compare this to a scenario where a person earns $101 an hour. That person is *much* more likely to qualify for a mortgage. A person earning $100 an hour is also likely to qualify, suggesting that the relationship between earnings and mortgage is constant here as well. In both cases, we could say that the relationship between earnings and getting a mortgage is "flat."

Somewhere between these two extremes lies a more direct relationship. For example, earning $18 an hour may be below a critical threshold that $19 an hour is above. Earning that extra dollar that didn't matter much in the extremes could make a big difference here.

Using the ordinary least squares regression will oversimplify the relationship between earnings and getting a mortgage, leading to inaccuracies in certain ranges of the dependent variable. This is because ordinary least squares regression assumes that the same relationship exists between both variables at all ranges, even though this is obviously not the case.

In instances where an assumption of linearity cannot be made, there is a family of models that can be used to easily estimate binary outcomes. In this chapter, we'll look briefly at logistic regression, one of the simpler and more commonly used techniques. Logistic regression is a counterpart to OLS for binary outcomes.

LOGISTIC REGRESSION: THE IDEA

Although ordinary least squares regression can be used to estimate a binary outcome, and it is easy to do with all software packages, introducing a dichotomous outcome may violate the assumptions of ordinary least squares. The most significant assumptions (and useful for comparing OLS, as well as logistic regression) are about the assumed distribution of the dependent variable.[1] For OLS, the dependent variable must be continuous, and normally distributed. One of the problems with this assumption for dichotomous outcomes is that OLS coefficients will assume a normal distribution, with theoretical limits of $\pm\infty$ (plus or minus infinity), rather than a bounded or binomial distribution. With logistic regression, a dichotomous outcome variable is assumed from the outset, and coefficients are calculated with this in mind.

Another problem with using OLS regression for dichotomous variables is the assumption of a linear relationship between the outcome and other variables in the model. As the mortgage example demonstrates, this is often not the case. Results from an OLS regression could contain significant error, depending on the value of the independent variables.

Logistic regression solves these problems, and others, because

1. Independent variables do not have to be linearly related to the dependent variable.
2. Neither the dependent variables nor the error terms need to be normally distributed (the dependent variable *does* need to resemble one of the other distributions, but that is beyond this text).
3. Logistic regression does not assume homoscedasticity in variance across levels of the independent variable.[2]

LOGISTIC REGRESSION: THE FORMULA

Many principles of logistic regression are similar to those of OLS regression, but the language and symbols differ slightly. Logistic coefficients replace b (beta) coefficients, standardized logit coefficients (the log of the probability of an event) correspond with beta weights, and a pseudo-R^2 statistic is available to summarize the strength of the relationship (although the interpretation is not directly comparable to R^2 in OLS).

Practically speaking, logistic regression and least squares regression are almost identical. Both methods produce prediction equations, both have y-intercepts and coefficients (although raw logistic coefficients are much more difficult to interpret with some translation), and both sets of coefficients measure the predictive capability of independent variables on the outcome of interest.

To recap, OLS regression equations take the following form:

$$Y = a + b_1 x_{1i} + b_2 x_{2i} + \cdots + b_n x_{ni} + e_i$$

where

- Y = the dependent variable
- a = the Y intercept
- b_1 = the partial slope of X_1 on Y
- b_2 = the partial slope of X_2 on Y
- b_n = the partial slope of X_n on Y
- x_{1i} = the first independent variable for individual i
- x_{2i} = the second independent variable for individual i
- x_{ni} = the nth independent variable for individual i
- e_i = error for individual i

The key differences between logistic regression and OLS are the assumptions about the dependent variable, and the relationship between independent variables and the dependent variable. Instead of predicting the score of Y, an observed variable, logistic regression predicts the *probability* of an occurrence (well, actually, the log odds).

Imagine that beneath the surface of every dichotomous outcome variable is a latent, or underlying, propensity score. This score is unobserved, which means that it is not measured, and that we cannot see it. A score of one on this unobserved propensity variable means that the event will certainly occur (a person will get a mortgage), and zero means that it certainly will not (a person's mortgage application will be rejected). So far, the unobserved dependent variable corresponds with the observed dependent variable. Unlike the observed variable, which has only two values (zero and one), the unobserved variable has a range of values that are bounded by zero and one. Most individuals lie between zero and one—there's almost always a slight chance that a person will or will not get a mortgage—and the underlying propensity score is a useful way to understand differences between people.

Logistic regression does not directly predict the probability that our outcome Y is equal to one. Instead, it predicts the *log odds* that an observation will have an indicator equal to one, where the odds of an event are the ratio of the probability that an event occurs to the probability that it will not, often called an **odds ratio**. Stated as an equation

$$Odds\,(Y = 1) = \left[\frac{\Pr(Y = 1)}{\Pr(Y \neq 1)} \right]$$

This can be read as "the odds of Y being equal to one are equal to the probability of a positive occurrence over the probability of a negative occurrence." Remember that instead of modelling the odds, we model the natural logarithm of the odds. The following equation articulates that

$$LogOdds(Y = 1) = \ln\left[\frac{Pr(Y = 1)}{Pr(Y \neq 1)}\right]$$

You may also see the next equation as representing the log odds, but since exhausted probabilities are always equal to one, it is actually identical to the last one:

$$LogOdds(Y = 1) = \ln\left[\frac{Pr(Y = 1)}{1 - Pr(Y = 1)}\right]$$

The dependent variable is also referred to as the logit. Unlike OLS coefficients, which measure the effect of a one-increment change in the independent variable on the dependent variable, logistic coefficients reflect the effect of a one-increment change in the dependent variable on the *log odds* of the dependent variable.

Why use the odds instead of the probabilities? Sociologist Paul Allison (2000) describes odds as a more sensible scale for multiplicative comparisons (for example, how many *times* bigger is X_1 than X_2, whereas additive comparisons ask how *much* bigger is X_1 than X_2). Allison illustrates, using voting as an example; if person one has a probability of 0.30 of voting, and person two has a probability of 0.60, it's reasonable to claim that the probability of person two voting is twice as high as it is for person one. But a probability that is twice as high as 0.60 is impossible, because of the ceiling of one (the event definitely will occur) for the probability of an event.

Allison notes that this is not a problem on the odds scale, since a probability of 0.60 is equivalent to the odds of 1.5:

$$Odds = \frac{Pr(Y = 1)}{1 - Pr(Y = 1)}$$
$$= \frac{0.60}{1 - 0.60}$$
$$= 1.5$$

So we could say that one person is 1.5 times more likely to vote than the other person.

You are probably familiar with odds, especially if you've gambled or bought lottery tickets. In one well-known Canadian lottery, six numbers must be matched in order for a ticket to win the jackpot. The odds of this occurring depend on the 13,983,816 possible combinations that exist between the six numbers. The odds of winning are 1 in 13,983,816, or 0.0000000715 to 1 (most people will use the first expression since they prefer integers, but however you express it, winning is unlikely). To convert the number to a probability, use the following equation: the inverse of the equation for converting probabilities to odds is

$$probability = \frac{Odds\,(Y = 1)}{1 + Odds\,(Y = 1)}$$
$$= \frac{0.0000000715}{1 + 0.0000000715}$$
$$= 0.0000000715$$

I hope you can see that using the odds instead of probabilities makes it easier to grasp how unlikely your prospects of winning are.

Converting the probability to the odds removes the upper bound of the dependent variable (because it is no longer constrained by the value of one). Now only the lower value is constrained at zero, which can be addressed by using the log odds instead of the odds.

To illustrate, compare the three values in Table 17.1.

Several points on the table are noteworthy. First, notice how a probability of 0.5 (where an event is just as likely to occur as not to occur) corresponds with an odds ratio of one. Odds lie between zero and $+\infty$ (positive infinity), with one as a neutral value at which both outcomes are equally likely (which is why it corresponds with a probability of 0.5). Positive infinity means that odds can have any positive value with no limit to how large that number may be. Second, when the roles of the two outcomes are switched with odds, each value in the range zero to one is transformed by taking its inverse (one/value) to a value in the range one to $+\infty$. For example, if the odds of getting some form of cancer for males are one in nine, the odds of not getting cancer are nine to one.

On the other hand, log odds are completely symmetrical, and lie in the range of $-\infty$ to $+\infty$. The value where both outcomes are equally likely is zero (this might be considered the "neutral value"). When the roles of the two outcomes are switched, the log odds are multiplied by −1, but the number remains the same. So if the log odds of getting some form of cancer for males are 2.20, the odds of not getting it are −2.20.

TABLE 17.1 | Probabilities Compared to Odds and Log Odds

Probability	Odds	Log odds
0.01	0.01	−4.60
0.05	0.05	−2.94
0.10	0.11	−2.20
0.15	0.18	−1.73
0.20	0.25	−1.39
0.30	0.43	−0.85
0.40	0.67	−0.41
0.50	1.00	0.00
0.60	1.50	0.41
0.70	2.33	0.85
0.80	4.00	1.39
0.85	5.67	1.73
0.90	9.00	2.20
0.95	19.00	2.94
0.99	99.00	4.60

To illustrate how the log odds remove the upper and lower bounds, look at probability values of 0.01 and 0.99, the two extreme values. Although they are close to their theoretical limits of zero and one, it is possible to get much, much closer. We could have values of, say, 0.000000001 and 0.999999999, which would yield a log odds ratio of ±20.72. Although the increases would get smaller, it is possible to approach zero and one even more closely, so we give the log odds a range of $-\infty$ to $+\infty$.

As a further illustration, consider the bar charts of the distribution of a variable with propensity scores ranging between zero and one on 1,000 observations, found in Figures 17.1 to 17.3.

Figure 17.1 contains the probability scores. As you can see, variables are scattered almost evenly across the range, and the chart does not resemble a normal distribution. Instead, it is heavily bounded by zero and one, and, given that OLS models have an assumption of $\pm\infty$, you can see that there will be estimation error. Let's compare this with a plot of the odds in Figure 17.2.

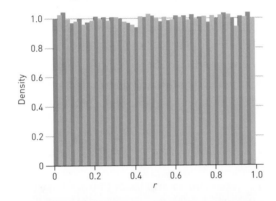

FIGURE 17.1 | Plot of Hypothetical Variable *r*, Stated as a Probability

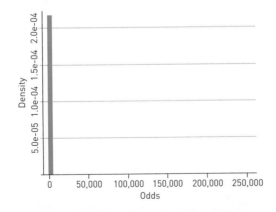

FIGURE 17.2 | Plot of Hypothetical Variable *r*, Stated as Odds Ratios

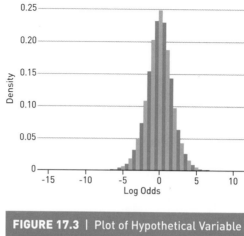

FIGURE 17.3 | Plot of Hypothetical Variable *r*, Stated as Log Odds Ratios

Figure 17.2 is better, in a way, because the constraint of an upper bound has been removed. The problem is that it still does not look like a normal distribution, so significant estimation error is still likely. Finally, compare this to the log odds in Figure 17.3.

Figure 17.3 is an almost perfectly normally distributed variable. By now, you should see that the log odds ratio of a dichotomous variable is the best option for a dependent variable.

MODELLING LOGISTIC REGRESSION

Thanks to log odds, the theoretical upper and lower bounds have been removed, and the similarities to OLS are now more obvious. Modelling the log odds of *Y*, instead of *Y*, produces a fairly familiar-looking equation:

$$LogOdds\,(Y = 1) = a + b_1 x_{1i} + b_2 x_{2i} + \cdots + b_n x_{ni} + e_i$$

where

- *LogOdds* $(Y = 1)$ is the natural logarithm of the odds of the dependent variable being one.
- a = the *Y* intercept
- b_1 = the partial slope of X_1 on *Y*
- b_2 = the partial slope of X_2 on *Y*
- b_n = the partial slope of X_n on *Y*
- x_{1i} = the first independent variable for individual *i*
- x_{2i} = the second independent variable for individual *i*
- x_{ni} = the nth independent variable for individual *i*
- e_i = error for individual *i*

To further illustrate logistic regression, let's look at an example. Suppose that we use the Ethnic Diversity Survey to fit a logistic regression equation that identifies the degree to which a person feels a strong sense of belonging in Canada, where *Y* = 1 if a person experiences a

TABLE 17.2 | Gender and Place of Birth as Predictors of Belonging, Stated as Raw Coefficients

- logit belong female Canada

Iteration 0:	log likelihood = −28161.371
Iteration 1:	log likelihood = −28128.081
Iteration 2:	log likelihood = −28128.079

Logistic regression

Number of obs	=	41695
LR chi2(2)	=	66.58
Prob > chi2	=	0.0000
Pseudo R2	=	0.0012

Log likelihood = −28128.079

belong	Coef.	Std. Err.	z	P > |z|	[95% Conf.	Interval]
female	.1600882	.0199796	8.01	0.000	.120929	.1992474
canada	.0337001	.0225676	1.49	0.135	−.0105316	.0779318
Cons	.2711552	.0219193	12.37	0.000	.2281941	.3141163

Source: Ethnic Diversity Survey Public Microdata File, 2002

strong sense of belonging and $Y = 0$ if they don't. We use sex of respondent ("female," where 1 = female, 0 = male) and place of birth ("Canada," where 1 = Canada, 0 = other country) as our two independent variables, producing the following predictive equation:

$$\text{Log Odds } (Y = 1) = \alpha + \text{female} + \text{Canada}$$

or

$$\log \left[\text{Pr(belong)}/\text{Pr(not belong)} \right] = \alpha + \text{female} + \text{Canada}$$

Estimating the equation in STATA gives us the results found in Table 17.2.

The interpretation of log coefficients is different from those of OLS regression. We can determine the direction of the relationship by looking at the sign of the coefficients. Since the coefficient for both female and Canada is positive, the log odds (and, therefore, the probability) of belonging is higher for females and those born in Canada (but notice that the second result is not statistically significant).

INTERPRETING THE COEFFICIENTS OF A LOGISTIC REGRESSION EQUATION

To get a better sense of the magnitude of difference, and to make interpreting the coefficients easier, we can exponentiate the results. Remember from Chapter 2 that exponentiation is the inverse function of the logarithm, so the log odds will be changed into the odds. This can be done using e, which is the inverse of the natural logarithm. The equation from the last example

$$\log[\Pr(\text{belong})/\Pr(\text{not belong})] = \alpha + \text{female} + \text{Canada}$$

becomes

$$[\Pr(\text{belong})/\Pr(\text{not belong})] = \exp(\alpha + \text{female} + \text{Canada})$$

Or, once the coefficients from the output are inserted

$$\log[\Pr(\text{belong})/\Pr(\text{not belong})] = \alpha + 0.160 * \text{female} + 0.034 * \text{Canada}$$

becomes

$$[\Pr(\text{belong})/\Pr(\text{not belong})] = \exp(\alpha + 0.160 * \text{female} + 0.034 * \text{Canada})$$

Alternatively, it could also be listed as

$$\Pr(\text{belong} = 1) = \frac{\exp(\alpha + 0.160 * \text{female} + 0.034 * \text{Canada})}{1 + \exp(\alpha + 0.160 * \text{female} + 0.034 * \text{Canada})}$$

This final example is just a more cumbersome form of the same equation.

Exponentiating the coefficients will give the odds ratio, which corresponds with a one-unit change in each independent variable. For example, we could convert the coefficient of 0.160 for female as

$$\text{OddsRatio}_{\text{female}} = e^{0.160}$$
$$= 1.174$$

For "Canada," we'd have

$$\text{OddsRatio}_{\text{Canada}} = e^{0.034}$$
$$= 1.035$$

Thus, the odds of a female feeling a sense of belonging is 1.174 times that of a male. Stated differently, a female is about 17 per cent more likely to feel a sense of belonging to Canada than a male.

For the variable "Canada," those born in the country are 1.035 times, or 3.5 per cent, more likely than those born elsewhere to feel a sense of belonging. Notice that we cannot be 95 per cent confident that this result exists in the Canadian population, given the low z-score of 1.49, and the corresponding significance (denoted in the output by the column P > $|z|$) of 0.135.

With odds ratios, we don't usually convert the intercept, because there isn't really a comparable reference group. For females, the odds ratio of 1.174 is the likelihood of females feeling a sense of belonging relative to males. For Canada, 1.035 compares people born in Canada to those born outside of Canada. The intercept simply denotes the point where the regression line crosses the y-axis, and there isn't any reason to state that as an odds ratio.

To convince you of the accuracy of our calculation of the odds ratios, let's compare them with the same odds calculated using STATA (see Table 17.3).

TABLE 17.3 | Gender and Place of Birth as Predictors of Belonging, Stated as Odds Ratios

logit belong female Canada, or

Iteration 0:   log likelihood = −28161.371

Iteration 1:   log likelihood = −28128.081

Iteration 2:   log likelihood = −28128.079

Logistic regression

		Number of obs	=	41695
		LR chi2(2)	=	66.58
		Prob > chi2	=	0.0000
Log likelihood = −28128.079		Pseudo R2	=	0.0012

belong	Odds Ratio	Std. Err.	z	P > |z|	[95% Conf.	Interval]
female	1.173614	.0234483	8.01	0.000	1.128545	1.220484
Canada	1.034274	.0233411	1.49	0.135	.9895236	1.081049

Source: Ethnic Diversity Survey Public Microdata File, 2002

Most software packages include an option to report the odds instead of the log odds (also referred to as the raw coefficients). Our calculations are identical to those produced in STATA. Also notice that the intercept is not reported.

As with OLS, logistic regression is far more intricate and complicated than the cursory overview provided here. The primary purpose of this chapter was to enhance your awareness and to provide some very basic information on a frequently used technique.

A NOTE ON ESTIMATING LOGISTIC REGRESSIONS

In OLS regression, a regression line is calculated with the explicit goal of minimizing the average distance between an observed value and a predicted value. This is done through a series of calculations, which we covered in Chapter 12. Unlike OLS, the coefficient estimates of a logistic regression are obtained through an iterative and complicated process called "maximum likelihood." For many social scientists, the intricacies of maximum likelihood are treated like a "black box," which means that we don't know or question how the results are obtained. Maximum likelihood is a very complicated procedure (and there are no truly gentle introductions to the topic that I'm aware of), so we will limit our discussion of it.

The goal of most statistical analysis is to produce a model that predicts our outcome of interest as often and/or accurately as possible. For our sense of belonging example above, we want intercept "female" and "Canada" coefficient values that predict whether a person feels belonging as accurately as possible (that is, where there are as few misses as possible).

Maximum likelihood works by fitting a trial equation to the data (often an OLS equation), and comparing the fitted equation to the observed values. Fitting an equation means deriving coefficient estimates. The first equation probably won't maximize the likelihood that we could replicate the results observed in our data set, since the OLS coefficients are likely inaccurate, so the coefficient estimates are tweaked over and over to improve the fit. Iterations stop when the improvement from one step to the next is suitably small, suggesting that the likelihood of replicating the results observed in our data set has been maximized.

Maximum likelihood is widely used in statistical analysis and is not limited to logistic regression alone. In fact, maximum likelihood is so flexible that it is possible to estimate an OLS regression by using maximum likelihood techniques. However, most of the software packages recommend against that since standard OLS techniques allow for greater flexibility.

EVERYDAY STATISTICS

Using Logistic Regression to Determine Mortgage Eligibility

Regression 2—Modelling discrete/qualitative outcomes with logistic regression

As mentioned at the beginning of this chapter, a logistic curve is a more appropriate way to model a dichotomous outcome than a linear regression model. This is because the relationship between an independent variable and a dependent variable is not the same at all values of the independent variable. To illustrate, consider the following figure:

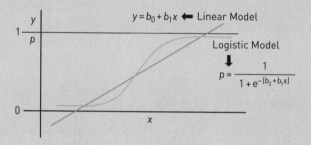

$$y = b_0 + b_1 x \;\; \longleftarrow \; \text{Linear Model}$$

Logistic Model

$$p = \frac{1}{1 + e^{-(b_2 + b_1 x)}}$$

Q: If 1 denotes mortgage acceptance and 0 denotes rejection, do you think people with income (shown on the x-axis) below the mean would be more or less likely to be accepted for a mortgage if ordinary least squares was used to determine eligibility?

GLOSSARY TERM

Odds ratio (p. 224)

PRACTICE QUESTIONS

1. Convert the following probabilities to odds ratios:
   a. 0.01
   b. 0.05
   c. 0.1
   d. 0.2
   e. 0.5
   f. 0.667
   g. 0.75
   h. 0.888
   i. 0.999

2. Convert the following logistic regression coefficients to odds ratios.
   a. −1.113
   b. 0.223
   c. 2.78
   d. 0
   e. −2.33
   f. −7.8

   Answers to the practice questions for Chapter 17 can be found on page S-25.

NOTES

1. At least in theory. Using OLS for dichotomous outcomes is becoming increasingly popular in certain circumstances, particularly when outcome probabilities range between 0.3 and 0.7.

2. A detailed explanation of what this means is also beyond this text, but, in short, independent variables do not need to have equal variances or standard deviation for each value of the dependent variable.

PART IV | ADVANCED TOPICS

CHAPTER 18

Regression Diagnostics

LEARNING OBJECTIVES

Although regression (both OLS and logistic) is a fairly straightforward technique (at least with the help of a computer), numerous hard-to-detect problems can arise in the data. This chapter will cover a few simple diagnostic techniques for regression, focusing in particular on the techniques for ordinary least squares (OLS) regression. We'll discuss:

- influential and outlying cases;
- leverage;
- non-normality in the error term;
- collinearity/multicollinearity.

INTRODUCTION

Suppose you ran an OLS regression to estimate the factors that determine a person's blood pressure, using the variables of body mass index, calories consumed per day, and whether a person drinks or smokes (both of these are dummy variables). You might get sensible coefficient estimates for the slope and the intercept, calculations for Pearson's r, standard errors, and just about everything else, but there could still be a problem with your model. How can that be?

The problem might be with how your summary measures—essentially, what the various components of a regression are—represent the data. The model you've estimated may be a bad summarization of the relationship between a series of independent variables and your dependent variable.

This chapter will cover how this happens and, more important, what can be done about it.

WHEN ORDINARY LEAST SQUARES REGRESSION GOES WRONG

In a 1973 article in *The American Statistician*, Francis Anscombe demonstrated how it was possible to have similar coefficients, correlations, and standard errors—just about everything between regressions—with very different data points.[1] To illustrate how that's possible, consider his original example in Table 18.1.

Anscombe demonstrated how it is possible to get identical univariate statistics (means, standard deviations) between x variables (x, $x4$) and y variables ($y1, y2, y3, y4$), as well as bivariate correlations (R^2), mean squared errors, sums of squares, etc. For our purposes, the most important revelation is that regression intercepts and coefficients can be identical, even though the data, when they are graphed on a scatterplot, look radically different.

To illustrate this better, we'll continue with Anscombe's original example, using four regressions and scatterplots for the data in Table 18.1 (these four plots are sometimes referred to as the "Anscombe Quartet"). In each figure, the regression output appears first, followed by the scatterplot (see Figures 18.1 to 18.4).

TABLE 18.1	Anscombe's Original 1973 Data for Illustrating Regression Diagnostics				
x	**y1**	**y2**	**y3**	**x4**	**y4**
10.00	8.04	9.14	7.46	8.00	6.58
8.00	6.95	8.14	6.77	8.00	5.76
13.00	7.58	8.74	12.74	8.00	7.71
9.00	8.81	8.77	7.11	8.00	8.84
11.00	8.33	9.26	7.81	8.00	8.47
14.00	9.96	8.10	8.84	8.00	7.04
6.00	7.24	6.13	6.08	8.00	5.25
4.00	4.26	3.10	5.39	19.00	12.50
12.00	10.84	9.13	8.15	8.00	5.56
7.00	4.82	7.26	6.42	8.00	7.91
5.00	5.68	4.74	5.73	8.00	6.89

Source: Anscombe, *The American Statistician*, 1973

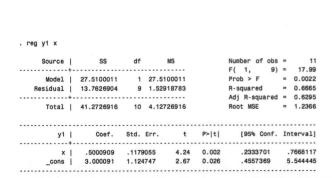

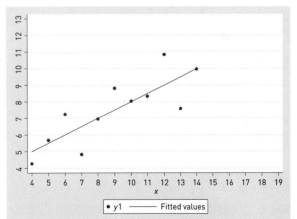

FIGURE 18.1 | Anscombe's Original Demonstration of the Need for Regression Diagnostics, Data Example #1
Source: Anscombe, *The American Statistician*, 1973

In each example, the regression results are identical. This means that the line of best fit is the same in each case, even though the observations have different values. In Figure 18.1, the relationship between the independent variables appears straightforward and relatively linear, with what appear to be randomly distributed errors. However, Figures 18.2 to 18.4 have very different relationships between the x and y variables.

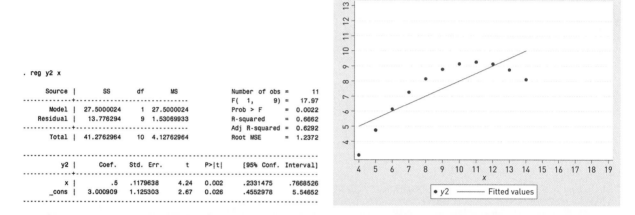

FIGURE 18.2 | Anscombe's Original Demonstration of the Need for Regression Diagnostics, Data Example #2
Source: Anscombe, *The American Statistician*, 1973

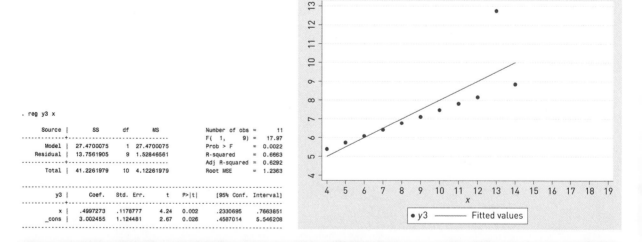

FIGURE 18.3 | Anscombe's Original Demonstration of the Need for Regression Diagnostics, Data Example #3
Source: Anscombe, *The American Statistician*, 1973

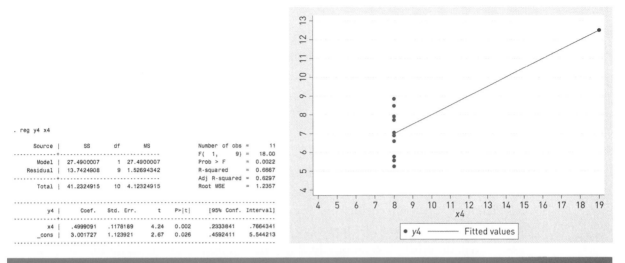

```
. reg y4 x4

      Source |       SS       df       MS              Number of obs =      11
-------------+------------------------------           F(  1,     9) =   18.00
       Model | 27.4900007      1  27.4900007           Prob > F      =  0.0022
    Residual | 13.7424908      9  1.52694342           R-squared     =  0.6667
-------------+------------------------------           Adj R-squared =  0.6297
       Total | 41.2324915     10  4.12324915           Root MSE      =  1.2357

-------------------------------------------------------------------------------
         y4 |      Coef.   Std. Err.      t    P>|t|     [95% Conf. Interval]
-------------+-----------------------------------------------------------------
         x4 |   .4999091   .1178189     4.24   0.002     .2333841    .7664341
      _cons |   3.001727   1.123921     2.67   0.026     .4592411    5.544213
-------------------------------------------------------------------------------
```

FIGURE 18.4 | Anscombe's Original Demonstration of the Need for Regression Diagnostics, Data Example #4
Source: Anscombe, *The American Statistician*, 1973

As a statistical issue, the similarity between regressions is problematic because it glosses over the obvious differences in the data. Without looking at the plots, we might conclude that each example does an equally good job of summarizing the nature of the relationship.

The scatterplots reveal something else. Ideally, we'd draw scatterplots whenever possible, but large samples make visualizing relationships increasingly difficult. Consider the plot of age of respondent and age of their spouse found in the 1666 census in Figure 18.5.

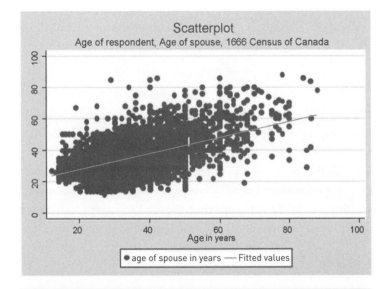

FIGURE 18.5 | Age of Respondent, Age of Spouse, 1666 Census of Canada

With large samples, identifying differences in relationships just by looking at visual data is difficult. We need to develop a set of tools to identify situations like the one in Figure 18.5. In the following sections, we'll cover some of the more common sources of error in regression specification. This usually involves examining the estimation error (also called a residual) to understand how well a regression approximates the observed relationship.

INFLUENTIAL CASES

By now, you probably know that there are several factors affecting how well a line of best fit describes the relationship between a dependent variable and its independent variables. One factor is the assumption that there are no observations eliciting an inordinate impact on the calculation of regression coefficients. For example, the observation with an x-value of 19 and a y-value of 13.5 in Figure 18.4 appears to have a greater effect on the calculation of the line of best fit than the other observations do. If that observation wasn't there, the line would probably have a different slope and intercept.

These observations are called influential cases. Although "influential case" has no firm definition, it is any case that exerts an extraordinary amount of influence on the slope and intercept. There are two types of influential cases: outliers and leveraged observations. An outlier refers to the distance an observation is from its estimated y-value (the distance between Y_i and $\hat{Y}_i$), and leverage measures the distance between an x-value and the mean for that variable (the gap between X_i and $\bar{X}$). Both can have a big impact on the representativeness of the regression coefficients.

To detect an influential case (either an outlier or a leveraged case), find the point where an observation begins to influence the regression results to an unusual degree. This can be guided by the nature of the study (for example, if we're studying housing and income, and we believe that the 15-year-old who earns $100,000 a year and owns a home is exceptional), or they can be identified statistically. There are many different ways to do this, but we're going to use Cook's Distance.

Cook's Distance

Introduced in the late 1970s by Dennis Cook, Cook's Distance, or Cook's D, determines the extent to which coefficient estimates (both slopes and intercepts) will change if a particular observation is removed from the analysis. To demonstrate, we'll work through one of Anscombe's original examples, relying on Lorenz's 1987 discussion of Cook's D (Lorenz, 1987).

First, obtain the predicted and residual values for each observation you're interested in determining the influence for. To help with that, Figure 18.3 is reproduced as Figure 18.6.

A good example of an influential observation would be the one with the highest y-value ($Y = 12.74$, $X = 13$). To get a sense of how much this observation influences the coefficients, calculate the predicted Y-value for observation i as

$$\hat{Y}_i = a + b_i x_i$$
$$= 0.5 + 3(13)$$
$$= 0.5 + 39$$
$$= 39.5$$

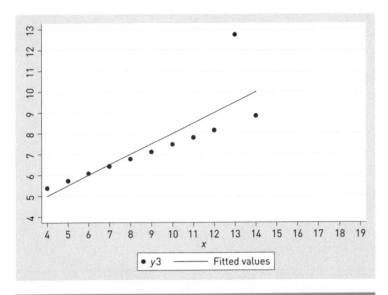

FIGURE 18.6 | Anscombe's Original Demonstration of the Need
for Regression Diagnostics, Data Example #3
Source: Anscombe, *The American Statistician*, 1973

The error is calculated as

$$e_i = Y_i - \hat{Y}_i$$
$$= 12.74 - 39.5$$
$$= -26.76$$

Next, determine the amount of influence an observation could have on the results by determining the distance of an average observation from the line of best fit. When X_i is far away from $\bar{X}$ (it is either a really high or a really low value), we say that it has a lot of leverage. To calculate leverage, use the formula

$$h_{ii} = \left[\frac{1}{n} + \frac{(X_i - X)^2}{\sum (X_i - X)^2} \right]$$
$$= \left[\frac{1}{11} + \frac{(13 - 9)^2}{110} \right]$$
$$= 0.236$$

In both the numerator and the denominator, the differences are squared so that the sum of values does not equal zero.

Finally, we calculate Cook's Distance as

$$D_i = \frac{e_i^2}{p(MSE)} \left[\frac{h_{ii}}{(1 - h_{ii})^2} \right]$$
$$= \frac{-26.76^2}{2(1.53)} \left[\frac{0.236}{(1 - 0.236)^2} \right]$$

BOX 18.1

Cook's Distance: The Steps

1. Obtain the predicted and residual y-values for each observation, using $\hat{Y}_i = a + b_i x_i$ to find $\hat{Y}_i$, and $e_i = Y_i - \hat{Y}_i$ to find the estimation error.

2. Calculate the leverage of each observation by using the following formula:

$$h_{ii} = \left[\frac{1}{n} + \frac{(X_i - \bar{X})^2}{\sum(X_i - \bar{X})^2} \right]$$

3. Calculate Cook's Distance as

$$D_i = \frac{e_i^2}{p(MSE)} \left[\frac{h_{ii}}{(1 - h_{ii})^2} \right]$$

4. Treat Cook's D values that exceed one with caution; seriously consider dropping values that greatly exceed one.

$$= \frac{716.0976}{3.06} \left[\frac{0.236}{0.584} \right]$$
$$= 234.019 * 0.404$$
$$= 94.544$$

where

- e_i = estimation error (calculated above)
- h_{ii} = The leverage of data point X_i. This refers to the ability of a particular data point to affect slope and intercept coefficients. High leverage denotes a strong capacity; low leverage denotes the opposite.
- MSE = Mean Squared Error
- P = the number of parameters (coefficients) being estimated. For us, it is two because there is a single slope coefficient and an intercept.

Cook's Distance values are meaningless by themselves, but any value below one is regarded as being tolerable for influence. Any observation that has a value exceeding one (such as the calculation for Figure 18.6) should be examined closely and possibly deleted. The farther from one a Cook's D value is, the stronger the case for deleting a particular observation.

HOMOSCEDASTICITY

As discussed in Chapter 16, homoscedasticity is the distribution of estimation errors across x-values. A regression is considered homoscedastic if the standard deviation of the estimation error for each value of x is roughly similar. If that condition is not met (we want it to be met), the model is heteroscedastic. Suppose you had an independent variable with

10 response categories; having a similar error variance across each response category would be important.

A real-life example is the relationship between total income and disposable income. If you wanted to determine whether people with large incomes have more or less disposable income, you could run an OLS regression, treating total income as the dependent variable, and disposable income as the independent variable. Most programs will estimate this model easily, even though the error variances are likely to be heteroscedastic. To demonstrate, think of how much more disposable income a person earning $100,000 could have compared to someone who earns $1,000. There is greater potential for us to "miss" with our estimate for the $100,000 earner than there is for the $1,000 earner, suggesting that the error variance will not be consistent across all values of x.

When the condition of homoscedasticity is not met for a particular variable, the accuracy of that coefficient can be questioned. Heteroscedasticity is complicated and often requires the use of different statistical models (such as weighted least-squares or heteroscedastic standard error) or for variables to be transformed by using a power transformation (particularly a logarithmic transformation). These can quickly become complicated so we'll only focus on identifying heteroscedasticity.

The easiest way to detect heteroscedasticity is probably to look at a residual versus a fitted value plot. To do that, use your statistical software to predict values for each observation, and plot the disparity across values of the independent variable. Figure 18.7 is an example conducted in STATA.

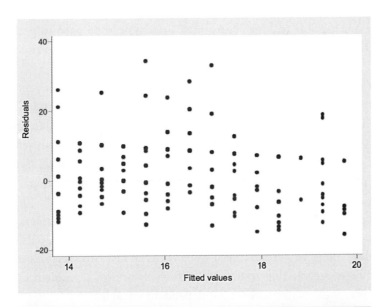

FIGURE 18.7 | Heteroscedastic Data in the Canadian Community Health Survey

Source: Canadian Community Health Survey Public Use Data, Wave 2.1

This plot shows the residuals from a model using the age of an individual to estimate the number of cigarettes that individual smokes per day. We can expect there to be wide variation at younger ages because, although there are likely to be some heavy smokers across all ranges, there are likely to be more casual smokers among young people, leading to the expectation of heteroscedasticity.

Although the full model includes all Canadians, to reduce the number of data points, only women living in Prince Edward Island are plotted in Figure 18.7. Notice how the dispersion of residual values (the y-axis) is not consistent across the fitted values (the x-axis). This suggests that there is greater variance at certain values of the independent variable than others. The variance gets smaller as age increases, which suggests that there is less variation in the number of cigarettes a person smokes as they age.

There are numerous statistical tests for heteroscedasticity (White's test, Bartlett's test, etc.); most are available in major statistical packages, but they go beyond what is appropriate for an introductory statistics course.

COLLINEARITY (A.K.A. MULTICOLLINEARITY)

Collinearity is found when independent variables, such as the two from our example, share a common line when graphed, in other words, have a linear relationship. To illustrate collinearity, let's continue with the example from the introduction: identifying the factors that affect a person's blood pressure. Suppose we suspect that there is a correlation between body mass index and calories consumed per day, two of our independent variables. If there was a perfect bivariate correlation between those two variables, how might that affect our regression coefficient estimates? First, including both variables as predictors is unnecessary because the information in one variable (calories consumed per day) can be used to perfectly predict a score on the other variable (BMI), and vice versa. The variables are essentially duplicates of one another.

Remember that for an ordinary least squares regression, coefficients represent the independent impact on the dependent variable of a one-unit increase in the independent variable of interest. Collinearity is important because the coefficients are calculated when all other independent variables are held to zero. When collinearity is strong, identifying the independent impact of BMI will be difficult, because whenever variable A is increased by one increment, so is the number of calories consumed. Finding the independent impact of either variable is virtually impossible because they are so intertwined.

Most of the time there isn't perfect collinearity between two variables. What happens instead is a more moderate correlation, for example a Pearson's r value of 0.9. This can still be problematic since collinearity doesn't need to be between just two variables to be a problem. Correlation between one variable and several others also poses a problem in the regression because collinearity is calculated across all independent variables.

EVERYDAY STATISTICS

How Do You Like Them Apples?: Collinearity

A classic example of a collinearity issue in demography is known as the "age-period-cohort" problem. An example of the problem would be as follows:

Suppose that you meet a grandfather, father, and son in a room, and each of them is eating an apple. The son tells you that he plans to consume three apples, the father tells you that he will eat two, and the grandfather will stop after one apple. If you were interested in explaining the differences across people, you'd face the following three possibilities:

1. The son is eating three apples because of his age. As he gets older, he will eat fewer apples. This would point to aging as the primary explanation for variation.
2. There is currently a convention in the society in which these three individuals live that allocates a disproportionate number of apples to the young. If the grandfather and father were permitted to eat as much as the son, they would. This suggests a period effect.
3. Since each person grew up in radically different eras, each may have different conventions about the suitable number of apples per consumer. Even when they were younger, the grandfather ate one apple, and the father ate two. This is the cohort effect.

Straightforward enough, but it is impossible to distinguish between these explanations in a regular regression because of collinearity, since the three variables are linear functions of each other (Age = Period – Cohort, Period = Age + Cohort, etc.). So the following equation will inevitably suffer from collinearity (and identification, but that's another issue). One solution, which has been subject to rigorous debate, is to assume that one of the three variables has no effect on the dependent variable.

. . . .

Q: Using the example of the apples above, can you think of why this might be a problem?

IDENTIFYING AND DEALING WITH MULTICOLLINEARITY

The easiest way to identify multicollinearity is probably to look at the variance inflation factor (VIF) for each variable. The VIF is a standardized version of Pearson's multiple correlation coefficient R^2. The equation for VIF is

$$VIF_{Xi} = \frac{1}{1 - R^2_{Xi}}$$

where R^2_{Xi} is equal to the multiple correlation coefficient from a regression of variable Xi on all other independent variables in a model. This suggests that each variable will have its own VIF value, because it will be the "dependent variable" in a model, with all other independent variables used as predictors. With a little thought, using a version of R^2 makes sense. Multicollinearity is expected, since it refers to how a particular variable is correlated with all other variables in a model—precisely what R^2 allows us to measure. The lowest value of VIF will be one (this would correspond to an R^2 value of zero), and the highest value is positive infinity ($+\infty$).

Although there is no clear consensus on what value of VIF points to multicollinearity, typically a conservative value of five or higher is deemed too high. However, often a lower value is more commonly used. Variables with values that exceed four are usually worthy of further investigation.

However you define multicollinearity, once you determine that your variables are too closely correlated, you have several options. The first one, dropping the problem variable, is the easiest and will immediately solve multicollinearity. The second option is more difficult: combining the two offending variables to form one composite measure. However, this method might not make sense in every situation, so you will want to consider transforming one or both of the variables. You could conduct a power transformation (such as exponentiating, or taking the logarithm of one of the variables), or you could means-centre your variable by resetting the variable so that the mean is set to zero and observations are measured by how they deviate from the new mean. Whichever transformation you choose, always use the transformed variable (rather than the old collinear one), and try to anticipate how the transformation might have changed the interpretation of your coefficients.

CONCLUSION

This chapter covered some of the diagnostic tools for identifying whether regression results are plausible and valid. As noted in the introduction, this is only a preliminary overview. There are entire courses dedicated to regression diagnostics. The aim of this chapter was to enhance your appreciation of the complexity of ordinary least squares regression.

PRACTICE QUESTIONS

Here are Anscombe's original fabricated data: (Anscombe, *The American Statistician*, 1973)

x	y1	y2	y3	x4	y4
10.00	8.04	9.14	7.46	8.00	6.58
8.00	6.95	8.14	6.77	8.00	5.76
13.00	7.58	8.74	12.74	8.00	7.71
9.00	8.81	8.77	7.11	8.00	8.84
11.00	8.33	9.26	7.81	8.00	8.47

x	y1	y2	y3	x4	y4
14.00	9.96	8.10	8.84	8.00	7.04
6.00	7.24	6.13	6.08	8.00	5.25
4.00	4.26	3.10	5.39	19.00	12.50
12.00	10.84	9.13	8.15	8.00	5.56
7.00	4.82	7.26	6.42	8.00	7.91
5.00	5.68	4.74	5.73	8.00	6.89

1. Calculate the means and standard deviation for all of the variables. When calculating the standard deviation, treat the observations as sample data (use $N - 1$ instead of N in your calculations).

2. The data point located at x-value = 1,000 and y-value = 500 could be considered an outlier. If this point didn't exist, what would happen to the slope (would it be higher or lower) and intercept (would it cross the y-axis at a higher or lower point)?

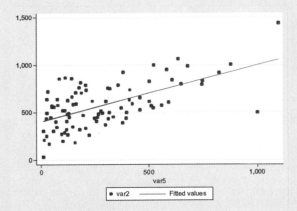

3. Here is a correlation matrix (Pearson's r value) for all the variables in the table above.

	x	y1	y2	y3	x4	x4
x	1.0000					
y1	0.8164	1.0000				
y2	0.8162	0.7500	1.0000			
y3	0.8163	0.4687	0.5879	1.0000		
x4	−0.5000	−0.5291	−0.7184	−0.3447	1.0000	
y4	−0.3140	−0.4891	−0.4781	−0.1555	0.8165	1.0000

Imagine that you estimated a regression of x and $x4$ on $y1$. Calculate VIF for x and $x4$. Remember that the table above reports r, not r^2.

4. Consider the following data, which were slightly modified from Anscombe's original:

x	y1
10.00	8.04
8.00	6.95
13.00	7.58
9.00	8.81
11.00	8.33
14.00	9.96
6.00	7.24
4.00	4.26
12.00	10.84
7.00	4.82
25.00	5.68

Here is some additional information:

- The means for x and $y1$ are 10.82 and 7.5, respectively.
- The mean squared error (MSE) is 4.464.
- The slope value is 0.0593 and the intercept value is 6.860.

Calculate Cook's Distance for the 11th observation. Is this observation a cause for concern? What about the 9th observation?

Answers to the practice questions for Chapter 18 can be found on page 318.

NOTE

1. In 1973, Anscombe was arguing for the importance of graphing raw data alongside regression analysis. As it happens, his example also beautifully illustrates the need for diagnostics.

CHAPTER 19

Strategies for Dealing with Missing Data

LEARNING OBJECTIVES

Researchers often have to deal with missing data, or observations that do not have information on all variables. Chapter 19 examines some of the strategies for dealing with incomplete data, including:

- non-response and its impact on validity;
- four kinds of missing data;
- single imputation of missing data;
- multiple imputation of missing data.

INTRODUCTION

Paul Allison begins his monograph on missing data by stating: "Sooner or later (usually sooner), anyone who does statistical analysis runs into problems with missing data" (2000, 1). Allison goes on to tell us that when practitioners are faced with these problems they must make several decisions that inevitably affect the conclusions that are made from the data.

There are three types of missing data in social surveys: household non-response, person non-response, and item non-response. Household non-response occurs when an entire household does not complete a questionnaire. This happens for various reasons, such as people not being at home, or being unwilling or unable to participate in the survey. Household non-response is difficult to deal with since there is no information available whatsoever.

Person non-response occurs when an interview is obtained from at least one household member, but not from one or more others in that household. Like household non-response, person non-response is the result of a person being unwilling, unable, or unavailable to answer survey questions. Person non-response is dealt with through editing and imputation of values with reasonable substitutes.

Item non-response occurs when a respondent completes only part of a questionnaire, leaving blanks for some information. Item non-response can occur for many reasons, including

1. A respondent refuses, or is unable, to provide requested information.
2. A respondent does not identify with any of the response categories and chooses to leave the question blank.
3. An interviewer fails to ask a question or an answer.
4. An interviewer makes an error when recording, or keying in, the response.

Since household and person non-response are usually handled by methodologists (which means that by the time you see a data set the data will have been cleaned up), in this chapter we'll look at item non-response, first by looking at the effects of non-response, then by looking at the four major types of missing data. Finally, we'll discuss common methods of dealing with these types of missing data.

WHAT EFFECT DOES NON-RESPONSE BIAS HAVE?

Non-response can have serious statistical consequences. In cases where an explanatory variable contains bias, consider the simple regression equation:

$$Y_i = \alpha + \beta_1 X_i + e_i \qquad (1)$$

where

- Y_i = some dependent variable
- α = constant term
- β_1 = coefficient for X_t
- e_i = error term
- X_i = explanatory variable with coefficient β

If instead of X_i; we observe $X^*_i + u_i$ (implying that $X^*_i = X_i + u_i$), where u_i = measurement error caused by non-random non-response, our new equation above would need to be modified accordingly:

$$Y_i = \alpha + \beta_1(X_i + u_i) + e_i \qquad (2)$$

Notice that there are now two error terms, e_i, and u_i, which can be simplified to form the compound error term z_i. One of the postulates of OLS regression—that error terms are not correlated with explanatory variables—has been violated with the introduction of non-response.

As a further illustration, consider a simple cross-sectional OLS equation with only one predictor variable, X, the average income of an individual, and one outcome, Y, the amount of money invested on the stock market per year (see Figure 19.1). Line one demonstrates the linear relationship between those two variables. However, there are problems with missing data: although the sample was randomly drawn, people with lower income levels were less likely to report their income. Therefore, lower-income earners are underrepresented, pulling line one

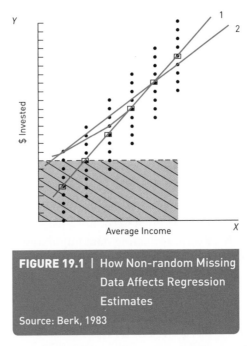

FIGURE 19.1 | How Non-random Missing Data Affects Regression Estimates

Source: Berk, 1983

upward at lower income amounts (see the curved line in the diagram). If we were to redraw the line of best fit, line two would replace line one as the best fitting line.

Clearly, validity—or the extent to which a variable is measuring what it is supposed to measure—has been compromised. The X variable, which allegedly measures respondent income, is no longer valid since it is doesn't measure what it purports to measure. This can be seen in the new line of best fit.

THE FOUR FORMS OF MISSING DATA[1]

To motivate the discussion, suppose that we have a very simple regression equation, denoted as

$$Y_i = \alpha + \beta_1 X1_i + \beta_2 X2_i + e_i \qquad (3)$$

Where Y = school average grade of a child in the last school year, $X1$ = mother tongue of the Person Most Knowledgeable (PMK) of the respondent, and $X2$ = income of PMK for the previous year. $X1$ and $X2$ are somewhat (though not completely) correlated with one another, and e is an error term. $X2$, the income of PMK for the previous year, is a problematic variable where some of the values are missing for reasons unknown. We could assume at least four possible reasons for the missing values (Little and Rubin, 1987):

1. $X2$ is Missing Completely at Random (MCAR), meaning that the non-response on this question is entirely independent of patterns in either Y or $X1$ (we say that the reason for "missingness" is contained in the error term e).
2. $X2$ is Missing at Random (MAR) but dependent on explanatory variable $X1$, so with certain values of $X1$ (such as mother tongue is neither French nor English), $X2$ is more likely to be missing.

3. *X*2 is Missing at Random but dependent on the focal outcome, and certain values of *Y* (e.g., if average grade is below 65 per cent) increase the probability that *X*2 will be missing.

4. Non-Ignorable Missing value (NIM): *X*2 is often missing when it is a certain value (e.g., income < $10,000).

Each of these four types of missing data is a non-response with different underlying causes, and all will have a different effect on coefficient estimates if left unaddressed. MCAR (#1) is unlikely to have any effect at all, MAR is likely to result in underestimated estimates of parameter *X*1 + *X*2 (for #2) or *X*1 + *Y* (for #3), and NIM (#4) is likely to result in a biased estimated relationship between income and average grades—low-income parents with high aspirations for their children would be underrepresented in the analysis.

The next section deals with various missing data imputation methods. Because of space considerations, weighting is omitted. Weights are usually invoked to correct for household or person non-response, but not item non-response.

WHAT TO DO ABOUT MISSING DATA?

Missing data can be dealt with in several ways. Some are very simple, and others require a solid grasp of statistical theory and practice.

1. Do Nothing: List-Wise and Pair-Wise Deletion

List-wise deletion: Delete all observations with missing data. In the previous example, anyone who didn't report their income was removed from the study.

Pair-wise deletion (or available case analysis): Use all available data to compute these means. For example, when creating a covariance matrix for two variables, only valid values are used. In a regression equation, observations with missing values will still contribute to coefficient estimates, so the observations with missing *X*1 or *X*2 values will still be included in some calculations. For example, observations with missing *X*1 values would be included when calculating the coefficient for *X*2. The impact of missing data is slightly lower with pair-wise deletion than with list-wise deletion. However, the two techniques tend to produce similar results in practice. List-wise deletion is probably the most popular method of dealing with missing data. In a survey of recent research articles in political science by King et al., list-wise deletion was found to be the method of choice in 94 per cent of all papers (2001: 49)[2].

List-wise deletion is problematic for several reasons. First, sample size is greatly reduced if problematic observations are deleted. Although sample size is not usually an issue with today's large data sets, it still places unnecessary constraints on the types of questions that can be asked.

The second, more serious, problem with list-wise and pair-wise deletion is that both hinge on the assumption that data are Missing Completely at Random (MCAR). Missingness often stems from the nature of the question, or survey, itself. To continue with the example, assuming that a random sample of people chose not to report their income, is very presumptuous. In a recent study using the NLSCY (National Longitudinal Survey of Children and Youth), Worswick (2001) found that parents whose native language was neither English nor French were less likely to participate in surveys. There are several possible reasons for this, one being that people have difficulty answering surveys that are not administered in their native tongue. Unless the missing data stem from research design—the missing data were planned or a question was not asked—there is almost always an underlying pattern to missing data, and the MCAR assumption is rarely justified.

2. Do Something: Single Imputation Strategies[3]

Best-guess imputation: The researcher views missing values in a quasi-subjective manner by, based on knowledge obtained from other variables. An example of a very successful Best Guess Imputation is what Steven Ruggles and Matthew Sobek did with the 1880 US census. Ruggles and Sobek were able to determine the relationship of all census respondents to the household head in the 1880 IPUMS data with remarkable accuracy (~99 per cent), through a series of best-guess imputations using age, sex, and order on the census schedule, among other things. Although Ruggles and Sobek were successful, other data sources do not lend themselves so easily to best-guessing techniques. When compared with subsequent censuses of Canada, the best-guess estimates of the visible minority indicator variable of the 1981 and 1986 censuses are not as accurate (1996 Census Codebook Online). One of the strengths of best guess is that it requires no assumptions about the nature of missingness or its distribution (King, 2002). Data can be MCAR, MAR, or NIM, and values can be imputed without affecting sample size.

Zero imputation: A score of zero (or some other arbitrary numeric indicator) replaces missing values and a dummy variable is added to control for the imputed value. This is not a true imputation method, because no plausible value is provided for the missing data, but researchers can use this method to retain problematic cases. Another use of zero imputation is as a predictor in a regression model, to determine whether or not the missing data are missing at random in relation to the dependent variable. If the effect of the dummy variable is not significant, a persuasive argument can be made for the appropriateness of list-wise deletion, since no significant effect is elicited on the dependent variable (this only addresses one type of MAR data; missingness could still depend on values of other independent variables).

Mean substitution: Replaces missing values with either the arithmetic average (for continuous data), or the most frequent value (for categorical data) of the variable, based on values from valid observations. This approach is simple; the mean value can be quickly calculated and analysis can proceed. The disadvantages include an underestimation of the standard error (through a reduction in the variance) and attenuation of correlations with other variables, producing overly optimistic fit statistics and significance levels (especially when values are not MAR or MCAR).

Hot deck: Use a value from another observation as a "donor" to replace the missing value. There are many methods for selecting suitable replacements: random selection of an observed value, or more complicated methods such as the Nearest Neighbour Imputation (NNI) methodology. For NNI (used for the 2000 Brazilian and US censuses, as well as the 2001 Canadian, Ukrainian, Swiss, and Italian censuses) the donor is not drawn at random, but selected according to data values on variables that the statistician hypothesizes to be the most salient predictors of the missing value. The assumption is that the data are missing at random and that there is a risk of using the same donor many times in small samples. This is a common method, but it's generally used before data are delivered to the end user.

Cold deck: Derive a missing value by using anything other than the same variable of that survey. It is the opposite of Hot Deck, in which non-respondent values are derived from respondent values for the same variable. Values from a covariate, or a previous survey, are often used to impute the missing value. Cold Deck relies entirely on the MAR assumption to arrive at estimates, since other correlates form the basis for selection of a missing value.

Y regression imputation: Run a preliminary regression on all observations, with the problematic variable as the focal outcome. A model for predicting the values of the missing data is derived from the regression. Missing values are filled by predicted regression values. The MAR assumption is heavily relied upon, and there is a significant underestimation of the standard error (predicted values are perfectly linear when Y is unobserved, but scattered when it is observed (King, 2001)).

$\hat{Y}$ regression imputation with random error term: Similar to regression imputation, except that error term is attached to the imputed value, allowing for an element of uncertainty in the estimate.

3. Do Multiple Things: Multiple Imputation

Multiple imputation: This is the most mathematically abstract and complex method of imputation, but also the most accurate and consistent. The basic idea is simple, although in practice it's less straightforward:

1. Determine the model of interest that incorporates random explanatory variables (missing and non-missing).
2. Make random draws for the missing values from the valid cases that have similar scores on the given focal variables, using one of the other imputation techniques.
3. Do this M times (usually between three and five), creating M complete data sets. Observed values remain the same in all data, but missing values are different in each data set.
4. Perform analysis on M data sets, as though data are not missing.
5. Combine estimates by taking the average of coefficients to produce a single estimate.

6. Calculate standard errors by averaging the squared standard error of M estimates. Calculate the variance of M parameter estimates across samples by taking the square root of the sampling variance mean, plus a coefficient variance multiplied by a "correction factor" of $1 + 1/M$ (to reward for increases in M).

EVERYDAY STATISTICS

Is There a Solution for This Missing Data?

In the Everyday Statistics box in Chapter 1, we discussed sampling error, the gap that exists between samples and populations, as it pertained to the 2011 Census of Canada. One of the concerns with imputing missing data is that sampling error is replicated through the imputation. If the sample is not a perfect microcosm of the population, problems in the sample will be reproduced by imputing values from other observations in the sample.

. . . .

Q: Do you think that the increase in sampling error because of switching from a mandatory census to a voluntary survey can be addressed by any of the strategies for dealing with missing data mentioned in this chapter?

MULTIPLE IMPUTATION: ADVANTAGES OVER SINGLE IMPUTATION

All other single imputation methods (except for the $\hat{Y}$ regression imputation with uncertainty element method) are essentially naive edits, those made with little or no knowledge about the person with missing values. The type-one errors are too high, confidence intervals are too narrow, and there is no compensation for the uncertainty about the right to impute. Once imputation has occurred, unknown values are indistinguishable from known values, and analysis proceeds as though the values were never missing.

Multiple imputation "builds in" a level of uncertainty (although there is no way of telling whether that level is the appropriate one), preserving, to some degree, the integrity and accuracy of the standard errors and model fit statistics. By running identical analyses on M data sets with slightly differing values for missing data, the non-observed values are less precise than observed values, and when coefficient estimates are combined, model uncertainty is retained.

MULTIPLE IMPUTATION: DISADVANTAGES

Multiple imputation has gained popularity with good reason; it is "the only general purpose statistical technique that can validly handle missing data problems" (Rubin, 1987). Unlike single imputation methods and deletion methods, estimates retain uncertainty elements to maintain the imprecision of the model resulting from working with data that are incomplete.

Unfortunately, multiple imputation is complicated to use and computer intensive. King, Honaker, Joseph, and Scheve (2001) found some time ago that on a data set with 1,000 observations and 100 variables, which is not uncommonly large, multiple imputation takes anywhere from 4 minutes (imputing values for 5 variables with about 5 per cent missing data) to 3.5 days (with 40 variables with 5 per cent missing data). Although computers today are no doubt faster, computation time can still be substantial. The other problem with multiple imputation is that each time it is used, different estimates are produced. Since quasi-random draws are taken from each variable, different values for each of the M data sets are selected each time, producing different results when combined.

Despite the advantages, multiple imputation might be too complex for the average user. Since version 11, SPSS has had a module entitled MVA, which allows users to perform many of the single imputation methods with easy-to-use and intuitive diagnostics to compare means and variance structures before and after imputation, and to assess change in model fit when imputed values are included.

WHAT DIFFERENCE DOES IT MAKE?

In the past, missing data in surveys were not thought to have a very big impact on generalizing results. This is largely because little work had been done to that point comparing respondents to non-respondents. However, since the early 1990s social scientists have begun to realize that missing data can have a significant effect on accuracym given the differences between respondents and non-respondents. As interest in correcting for missing data increases, software companies might begin to include more functions for multiple imputation. Whether multiple imputation will become the standard method for handling missing data in public-use data sets remains to be seen.

NOTES

1. Usually the four forms are reduced to three, since the two Missing at Random variants (#2 & #3) are usually handled similarly (Schafer, 1997).

2. Since political scientists, for example, often use countries as their unit of analysis, they are constantly dealing with small sample sizes, making list-wise deletion very "expensive" in terms of sample size. This suggests that list-wise deletion is even more common among sociologists.

3. Space permits discussion of only a very limited number of imputation techniques. A complete list would include Best Guess Imputation; Zero Imputation; Mean Substitution; Hot, Warm, and Cold Deck methods; and regression imputation methods, though many of the criticisms outlined here also pertain to these methods.

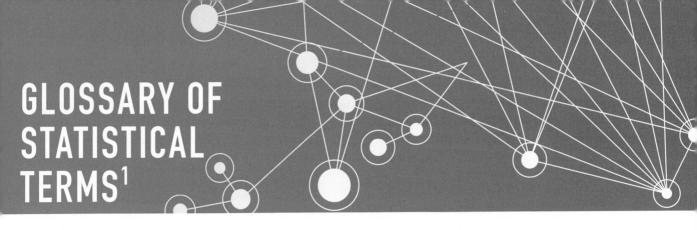

GLOSSARY OF STATISTICAL TERMS[1]

Absolute value The value of a number disregarding its positive or negative sign. It is denoted by a pair of '|' symbols: thus the absolute value, or modulus, of −2.5 is $|-2.5| = 2.5$.

Addition rule of probabilities To determine the probability of either of two mutually-exclusive (i.e., independent) events occurring, add the independent probabilities. For example, the probability of rolling a die to get a 1 or a 6 is determined by adding the two probabilities together $(1/6 + 1/6 = 1/3)$.

Alternative Hypothesis See **Research hypothesis**.

ANOVA A measure of the total variability in a set of data is given by the sum of squared differences of the observations from their overall mean. This is the total sum of squares (TSS). It is often possible to subdivide this quantity into components that are identified with different causes of variation (referred to as the within-in-group sum of squares and the between-group sum of squares). The mean square corresponding to RSS is often used as the yardstick for assessing the importance of the specified sources of variation. One method involves comparing ratios of mean squares with the critical values of an F-distribution.

Arithmetic average See **Mean**.

Associations Two variables are associated if they are not independent (i.e., if the value of one variable affects the value, or the distribution of the values, of the other). Thus, for a human population, height and weight are associated, and so are skin colour and ethnicity.

Asymptotic normality The distribution of a statistic is said to be asymptotically normal if the distribution of the statistic approaches a normal distribution as the sample size increases.

Axis scales The values that appear along the x-and y-axis of any plot.

Axis titles The titles used to describe the data on the x- and y-axis of any plot.

BEDMAS A mnemonic device for remembering the order of operations that stands for: Brackets Exponents Division Multiplication Addition Subtraction.

Bell curve A term used to describe the bell-like resemblance of a normal distribution.

Between-group sum of squares See ANOVA.

Bimodal Having two modes or modal classes.

Binary variables Any variable that has only two response categories.

Bivariate analysis Any analytical technique that requires two variables.

Bivariate relationships See **Associations**.

Bivariate statistics A suite of statistical procedures used to describe the relationship between two variables.

Categorical variables A variable whose values are not numerical. Examples include gender (male, female), paint colour (red, white, blue), and type of bird (duck, goose, owl).

Central limit theorem Proposed by Laplace, explaining the importance of the normal distribution for a large random sample of observations from a distribution with mean [mu] and variance. The distribution of the sample mean is approximately normal with mean [mu] and variance $\frac{1}{n}\sigma^2$, and the distribution of the sample total is approximately normal with mean n[mu] and variance no2. The phrase 'central limit theorem' appears in a 1919 article by von Mises.

Chi-square A statistical test to determine the similarity of the number of occurrences being investigated to the expected occurrences. The symbol for chi-square is X_2.

Concordant and discordant pairs Concordant pairs (in bivariate association) refer to a situation in which a positive (or negative) score on one variable corresponds with a positive (or negative) score on another variable. Discordant pairs describe the opposite situation, where a positive score on one variable corresponds with a negative score on another. Often used with ordinal data.

Confidence interval A confidence interval for an unknown population parameter is an interval calculated from sample values by a procedure such that if a large number of independent samples is taken, a certain percentage of the intervals obtained will contain the unknown population parameter. The term "confidence interval" was introduced in 1934 by Neyman.

Confidence limits The end points of a confidence interval.

Confidentiality The concern that an individual in a study can be identified by the information they provide.

Contingency tables A table displaying the frequencies for each combination of two or more variables. The variables are either categorical variables or numerical variables for which the possible outcomes have been arranged in groups. The term was first used by Karl Pearson in 1904. Each location in a table is called a cell, and the corresponding frequency is the cell frequency. Also called cross-classification, or cross-tabulation, tables.

Continuous variable A variable whose set of possible values is a continuous interval of real numbers x, such that $a < x < b$, in which a can be $-\infty$ and b can be $+\infty$.

Control A variable that has an effect that is of no direct interest. The analysis of the variable of interest is made more accurate by controlling for variation in the covariate.

Convenience sample A cheap method of obtaining a sample. An example would be interviewing supermarket customers. This would be a reasonable procedure provided that the purpose of the sampling was unrelated to the convenience of the sample (thus, it would be appropriate to ask the customers about car colour preferences, but not about food preferences).

Correlation matrix A square symmetric matrix in which the element in row j and column k is equal to the correlation coefficient between random variables X_j and X_k. The diagonal elements are always equal to one because the diagonal denotes a correlation between a variable and itself, and a variable is always perfectly correlated with itself.

Covariance The covariance of two random variables is the difference between the expected value of their product and the product of their separate expected values. For random variables X and Y,

$$Cov(X,Y) = E(XY) - E(X) \times E(Y)$$

Cramer's V In 1946, Cramer suggested that a measure of association could be based on the value of X^2. This is Cramer's V; it reduces to Phi in a 2 by 2 table.

Critical value of z or z(critical) or $z_{critical}$ An end point of a critical region. In a hypothesis test, comparison of the value of a test statistic with the appropriate critical value determines the result of the test. For example, 1.96 is the critical value for a two-tailed test in the case of a normal distribution and a 5 per cent significance level: thus, if the test statistic z is such that $|z| > 1.96$, then the alternative hypothesis is accepted in preference to the null hypothesis.

Degrees of freedom A parameter that appears in some probability distributions used in statistical inference, particularly the t-distribution, the chi-squared distribution, and the F-distribution. The phrase "degrees of freedom" was introduced by Sir Ronald Fisher in 1922.

Dependent variable The outcome of interest in a bivariate or multivariate analysis.

Dichotomization The process of transforming a categorical variable into a series of dummy variables.

Dichotomous or dummy variables A variable, taking only the values zero and one, derived from a polytomous categorical variable. If the categorical variable has k categories, then $(k - 1)$ dummy variables are required. For example, with four categories, the three dummy variables (xv, $x2$, $x3$) could be assigned the values (1, 0, 0) for category one, (0, 1, 0) for category two, (0, 0, 1) for category three, and (0, 0, 0) for category four. Dummy variables enable the inclusion of categorical information in regression models.

Direction Used to describe association; it can be either positive or negative.

Discrete (outcome) variables A dichotomous dependent variable.

Dispersion The amount of variety in a distribution of scores.

Distribution The set of values of a set of data, possibly grouped into classes, together with their frequencies or relative frequencies. In the case of random variables, the distribution is the set of possible values together with their probabilities in the discrete case and the probability density function in the case of a continuous variable.

Dummy variable See **Dichotomous variables**.

Empirical probability The estimated probability of an event calculated by using real data from a conducted experiment instead of theoretical sample space.

Experiment Any design that investigates the effects of a single explanatory variable in highly controlled conditions. Rarely used in social science research.

Explained variation The amount of variation in a dependent variable explained by one or more independent variables.

Face validity A test is said to have face validity if a reading of the items appears to reflect the areas that the test purports to measure.

F-distribution A theoretical relative frequency distribution of the ratio of two independent sample variances.

Frequency The number of times that a particular data value is obtained in a sample. For example, the frequency of 5 in the sample 4, 6, 5, 7, 4, 5, 2, 5 is 3. The sum of the frequencies is the sample size. The term is also used in connection with a set of values. For example, the number of people aged between 20 and 30, or the number of people with blue or green eyes.

Gaussian curve See **Normal curve**.

Grand mean When the data comes from different groups (e.g., "males" and "females"), the grand mean is the mean of all the values, regardless of their group.

Hypothesizing relationships A formal statement about the possibility of an association between two or more variables. Hypotheses must be mutually exclusive and exhaustive.

Independent variable Any variable that is believed to affect or explain the values of an outcome of interest in a bivariate or multivariate analysis.

Inferential statistical tests Involve generalizing from samples to populations, performing hypothesis testing, determining relationships among variables, and making predictions.

Interval—level of measurement A scale of measurement that can be used to measure the difference, or distance, between two general states or points, for example, the use of a ruler to measure length, the use of a stopwatch to measure a time interval, or the measurement of a musical interval (octave, fifth, etc.).

Inverse function If A is a function of B for variable f, then the inverse function for f is in the opposite direction, from B to A.

Kendall's tau-*b* A measure of association often used with but not limited to 2 by 2 tables. It is computed as the excess of concordant over discordant pairs. It is often used in 2 by 2 tables.

Kruskal and Goodman's gamma Kruskal and Goodman's gamma is a symmetric measure that varies from $+1$ to -1, based on the difference between concordant pairs (P) and discordant pairs (Q). Gamma is calculated as $(p - Q)/(p + Q)$.

Kruskal and Goodman's lambda For two categorical variables (A and B having, respectively, J and K categories) a measure with a probabilistic interpretation is Kruskal and Goodman's lambda, suggested by Goodman and Kruskal in 1954. Suppose that we are asked to guess the category of B for the next observation. An intelligent guess would be the category that was the most common so far.

Kurtosis A measure of whether data distribution is peaked or flat relative to a normal distribution.

Latent or unobserved concept An unobserved variable that may account for variation in the data and/or for apparent relations between observed variables.

Law of large numbers An empirical probability that will increasingly resemble its theoretical probability as the number of trials increases.

Least squares regression line Typically used with OLS regression. It is a line that best approximates the relationship between dependent variables and one or more independent variables.

Legend A box that describes the contents of a graph or chart.

Levels of measurement A term used to describe the relationship between response categories in any variable. See Nominal, Ordinal, Interval, and Ratio levels of measurement.

Line of best fit See **Least squares regression line**.

Logarithms An alternative notation for expressing an exponent; the inverse of exponentiation. It is often used with logistic regression.

Longitudinal surveys Any survey that observes the same respondent at more than one point in time.

Marginals If the cell frequencies of a (multidimensional) contingency table are totalled over one or more of the categorizing variables, the result is a set of marginal totals. For a two-dimensional table, the marginal totals are the row and column totals.

Maximum likelihood A commonly used method for obtaining an estimate of an unknown parameter of an assumed population distribution. The likelihood of a data set depends on the parameter(s) of the distribution or probability density function from which the observations have been taken.

Mean The mean of a set of N items of data $x_1, x_2, \cdots, x_n$ is $\bar{X} = \dfrac{\sum X_N}{N}$ which is the sum of all values of a variable, divided by the total number of observations used to calculate the sum. The mean is the most common measure of central tendency, and is usually denoted by placing a bar over the symbol for the variable being measured.

Mean square Used in ANOVA, it can be conceived as a standardized sum of squares that can be assessed against known distribution F.

Measure of central tendency Any measure of the tendency of quantitative data to cluster around some central value. The central value is commonly estimated by the mean, median, or mode, whereas the closeness with which the values surround the central value is commonly quantified using the standard deviation or variance. The phrase "central tendency" was first used in the late 1920s.

Median The middle value in any vector of numbers. When the number of numbers is even, the mean of the two middlemost numbers is used as the median.

Missing data Data that have not been collected by the respondent for a variety of reasons (refusal, uncertainty, etc.).

Mode The most common value in any vector of numbers.

Multimodal Any variable with more than one mode. Usually refers to variables with more than two modes.

Multiple correlation coefficient A measure of the linear dependence of more than one numerical random variable on another.

Multiplication rule of probabilities Observing two independent outcomes in succession is equal to the product of the probability of the two individual outcomes

Multivariate statistics Any technique that involves more than one variable. Usually refers to analysis with more than two variables.

Nominal—level of measurement Variable whose values are not numerical. Examples include gender (male, female), paint colour (red, white, blue), and type of bird (duck, goose, owl). A variable with just two categories is said to be dichotomous, whereas one with more than two categories is described as polytomous. The corresponding nouns are dichotomy and polytomy.

Non-integer Any number that is not whole.

Non-parametric test Any test that makes no distributional assumptions about the sample or population under investigation.

Non-probability/non-random sampling strategies Any sampling technique where individuals in a population do not have an equal probability of selection.

Normal, Gaussian, or Bell curve Any curve chat resembles the axial cross-section of a bell.

Normal score See **z-score**.

Normality The property of a random variable or population having a normal distribution.

Null hypothesis Any hypothesis that states that there is no difference between two samples on a variable of interest, for example positing that there is no difference in income between men and women.

Odds ratio The ratio of the odds on something occurring in one situation to the odds of the same event occurring in a second situation. An odds ratio of one implies that the odds of an event occurring (and hence the probability of its occurrence) are unaffected by the change in situation: they are independent of the situation.

One-tailed assessments See **One-tailed test**.

One-tailed test A statistical hypothesis test in which the values for which we can reject the null hypothesis are located entirely in one tail of the probability distribution.

Operationalize The practice of deciding how to measure a concept.

Order of operations A protocol for the order in which equations are solved. See BEDMAS.

Ordinal—level of measurement A categorical variable in which the categories have an obvious order (e.g., strongly disagree, disagree, neutral, agree, strongly agree), but the distances between categories cannot be accurately measured.

Ordinary least squares (OLS) regression The simplest and most frequently used of all statistical regression models. The model states that the random variable Y is related to the variable x by $Y = \alpha + \beta_x + \varepsilon$, where the parameters α and β correspond to the intercept and the slope of the line, respectively, and e denotes a random error.

Outliers An observation that is very different to other observations in a set of data.

Paired samples *t*-test or repeated measures *t*-test or *t*-test for dependent samples Any *t*-test with samples that are not completely independent from one another. An example of this would be people that are measured at different points in time.

Partial slope coefficients The slope coefficient between two variables (usually an independent variable and a dependent variable) after allowing for the effect of other variables.

Pearson's *r* A measure of the degree to which n pairs of values of random variables X and Y are related. When the correlation between two variables is positive, the values of one variable rise as the values of the other variable rise. The correlation is negative if the values of one variable rise as the values of the other fall.

Percentile A 1/100 slice of a sample or population that's been ranked and divided according to scores on one variable.

Phi See **Cramer's** *V*.

Pilot testing A preliminary test or study of a program or questionnaire used to try out procedures and make any needed changes or adjustments. A pilot test should always be conducted on people that are not part of the final sample.

Population The complete set of all people in a country, or a town, or any region (or just the number of such people). By extension the term is used for the complete set of objects of interest.

Post-hoc tests Any test that occurs after analysis has occurred.

Predicted values The values predicted by a model fitted to a set of data.

Probability The probability of an event is a number lying in the interval $0 <= p <= 1$, with zero corresponding to an event that never occurs and one to an event that is certain to occur.

Probability samples Any sampling technique where individuals in a population have an equal (or roughly equal) probability of selection.

Proportional reduction of error Any measure that indicates the degree to which an estimate is superior to a complete guess. It may also be interpreted as the per cent of explained variation in a dependent variable.

Qualitative outcome variables A dichotomous outcome variable.

Quota sample Any sample where the numbers of people in particular groups is used as criteria for selection.

Random process Any process in which results may not be certain.

Rates A rate is a special kind of ratio, of two measurements with different units, but usually with an intuitive denominator (such as kilometres per hour, cents per kilogram).

Ratio—level of measurement A scale of measurement where the difference, or distance, is measured between a state or point of interest and a standard state or point. For example, height above sea-level, distance from London, frequency of a musical note (in cycles per second), temperature in ° Kelvin (above absolute zero), clock-time (13:05 on 5 November 2001 AD). Confusingly, comparison of ratio scale measurements gives an interval scale, and in music an interval is measured by the ratio of the frequencies.

Ratios A stated relationship between two quantities. Rates are a special type of ratio.

Reference group, with dummy variables An omitted group for whom values can be derived from other variables in a model.

Regression equation An equation that represents a formal statement about a hypothesized relationship between a series of independent variables and one or more dependent variables.

Relationships See **Associations**.

Research hypothesis A specific, testable prediction about a relationship between two or more variables that is expected to emerge from an analysis.

Repeated measures *t*-test See **Paired samples *t*-test**.

Sample A portion of a population, often chosen for the purpose of statistical analysis.

Sample distribution of means A distribution that describes the variation in the values of the mean over a series of samples. Tends to asymptotically resemble the normal distribution.

Sample distribution of proportions A distribution that describes the relative frequency of an occurrence by comparing the mean to the sample size.

Sample space All theoretical possible outcomes of an event. Each probability is a fraction of the sample space, with the sum of all probabilities being 1.

Sampling error The degree to which a sample "misses" its population on quantities of interest.

Sampling frame A list of members of the population of interest.

Simple random sample The most basic form of probability sample, where members are chosen with reliance on randomly generated numbers.

Skewness If the distribution of a variable is not symmetrical about the median or the mean, it is said to be skewed. The distribution has positive skewness if, in some sense, the tail of high values is longer than the tail of low values, and negative skewness if the reverse is true.

Snowball sample A non-probability sampling method, where each person interviewed may be asked to suggest additional people for interviewing.

Somers' *d* A non-proportional reduction in error measure of association for ordinal data.

Sparsity The inverse of density, or the property of being scanty or scattered. In statistics, it typically refers to an area in a distribution where there are too few observations to confidently generalize from a sample to a population.

Spearman's *rho* A rank correlation coefficient that may be used as an alternative to Kendall's tau-*b*. Individuals are arranged in order according to two different criteria (or by two different people). The null hypothesis is that the two orderings are independent of one another. It is based on the differences in the ranks given in two orderings.

Standard deviation The square root of the variance. Karl Pearson introduced the term in 1893, using the symbol α in the following year.

Standard error of the mean The square root of the variance of a statistic, used to detect the accuracy with which a variable is measured in a particular analysis.

Standardized A variable that has the same unit of measurement as other variables, and is therefore appropriate for comparison. Converting all currencies to the US dollar, for example, allows you to compare currencies with a common metric. Standard deviations, rates, and ratios are also examples of standardization.

Standard score, normal score, or *z*-score The normal score corresponding to the kth largest of n observations is the expected value of the kth largest of n independent observations from a standard normal distribution.

Statistical significance The probability that an event or difference observed in a sample occurred by chance alone.

Stratified/hierarchical random sample The process of separating a sample into several groups, then randomly assigning subjects to those groups.

Student's *t*-distribution The form of the distribution was published in 1908 by Gosset, writing under the pen-name "Student," in the context of a random sample of size n from a population having a normal distribution. Often used with smaller samples because it is asymptotically equal to the normal distribution.

Sum of squares A measure of the variability in a set of data is given by the sum of squared differences of the observations from their overall mean. This variability can either be explained by a grouping variable (within-group sum of squares), or unexplained by a grouping variable (between-group sum of squares). The sum of these two is the total sum of squares.

Symmetrical Having similarity in size, shape, and relative position. Usually used to describe distributions on either side of a mean.

Systematic random sample A type of probability sample that starts at a random position on a list and selects every nth unit of a sampling frame until the desired sample size is reached.

Tau-c Like Kendall's Tau-b, except that adjustments are made for table size.

Theoretical probability Any probability generated from an infinite number of trials. Said differently, it is what the probability of an occurrence should be. For example, the theoretical probability of a coin landing heads is 0.5.

Total sum of squares See **Sum of squares**.

Total variation The amount of variation in a dependent variable that is available to be explained by an independent variable.

t-test A test to assess whether there is an equality of means between two variables having normal distributions and equal variances. Also called student's t-test.

t-test for dependent samples See **Paired samples t-test**.

Two-tailed assessment, two-tailed test A two-sided test is a statistical hypothesis test in which the values for which we can reject the null hypothesis are located in two tails of the probability distribution.

Type one error The chance of accepting the research hypothesis when the null hypothesis is actually true. Often called a false positive.

Type two error The chance of rejecting the research hypothesis when it is actually true.

Unexplained variation The amount of variation in a dependent variable that is not explained by one or more independent variables.

Unimodal Any variable with only one mode.

Univariate Pertaining to one variable.

Variable The characteristic measured or observed when an experiment is carried out or an observation is made. Variables may be non-numerical (see categorical variable) or numerical.

Variance A measure of the variability in the values of a random variable. It is defined as the expectation of the squared difference between the random variable and its expectation (often the mean).

Weights A derived value that denotes how many population observations are represented by a sample observation. For example, if an observation in a sample has a weight of five, then that person represents five people in the total population.

Within-group sum of squares See **Sum of squares**.

X-axis The scale that runs horizontally across a chart.

Y-axis The scale that runs vertically across a chart.

Zero-order correlations A correlation between two variables without any assumptions of temporal ordering or causality.

z-score See **Standard score**.

NOTE

1. Many of these definitions are used with permission from Graham Upton and Ian Cook. 2006. Oxford Dictionary of Statistics. Oxford: Oxford University Press.

APPENDICES

APPENDIX A

Area under the Normal Curve

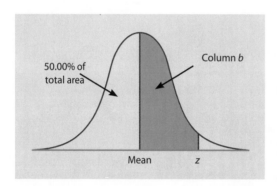

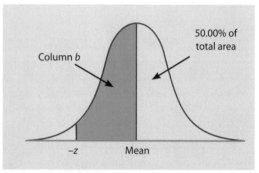

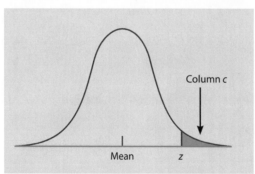

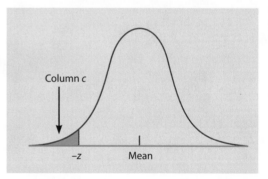

A	B	C	A	B	C
z	Area between mean and z	Area beyond z	z	Area between mean and z	Area beyond z
0.00	0.0000	0.5000			
0.01	0.0040	0.4960	0.41	0.1591	0.3409
0.02	0.0080	0.4920	0.42	0.1628	0.3372
0.03	0.0120	0.4880	0.43	0.1664	0.3336
0.04	0.0160	0.4840	0.44	0.1700	0.3300
0.05	0.0199	0.4801	0.45	0.1736	0.3264
0.06	0.0239	0.4761	0.46	0.1772	0.3228
0.07	0.0279	0.4721	0.47	0.1808	0.3192
0.08	0.0319	0.4681	0.48	0.1844	0.3156
0.09	0.0359	0.4641	0.49	0.1879	0.3121
0.10	0.0398	0.4602	0.50	0.1915	0.3085
0.11	0.0438	0.4562	0.51	0.1950	0.3050
0.12	0.0478	0.4522	0.52	0.1985	0.3015
0.13	0.0517	0.4483	0.53	0.2019	0.2981
0.14	0.0557	0.4443	0.54	0.2054	0.2946
0.15	0.0596	0.4404	0.55	0.2088	0.2912
0.16	0.0636	0.4364	0.56	0.2123	0.2877
0.17	0.0675	0.4325	0.57	0.2157	0.2843
0.18	0.0714	0.4286	0.58	0.2190	0.2810
0.19	0.0753	0.4247	0.59	0.2224	0.2776
0.20	0.0793	0.4207	0.60	0.2257	0.2743
0.21	0.0832	0.4168	0.61	0.2291	0.2709
0.22	0.0871	0.4129	0.62	0.2324	0.2676
0.23	0.0910	0.4090	0.63	0.2357	0.2643
0.24	0.0948	0.4052	0.64	0.2389	0.2611
0.25	0.0987	0.4013	0.65	0.2422	0.2578
0.26	0.1026	0.3974	0.66	0.2454	0.2546
0.27	0.1064	0.3936	0.67	0.2486	0.2514
0.28	0.1103	0.3897	0.68	0.2517	0.2483
0.29	0.1141	0.3859	0.69	0.2549	0.2451
0.30	0.1179	0.3821	0.70	0.2580	0.2420
0.31	0.1217	0.3783	0.71	0.2611	0.2389
0.32	0.1255	0.3745	0.72	0.2642	0.2358
0.33	0.1293	0.3707	0.73	0.2673	0.2327
0.34	0.1331	0.3669	0.74	0.2704	0.2297
0.35	0.1368	0.3632	0.75	0.2734	0.2266
0.36	0.1406	0.3594	0.76	0.2764	0.2236
0.37	0.1443	0.3557	0.77	0.2794	0.2207
0.38	0.1480	0.3520	0.78	0.2823	0.2177
0.39	0.1517	0.3483	0.79	0.2852	0.2148
0.40	0.1554	0.3446	0.80	0.2881	0.2119

(continued)

A	B	C	A	B	C
z	Area between mean and z	Area beyond z	z	Area between mean and z	Area beyond z
0.81	0.2910	0.2090	1.21	0.3869	0.1131
0.82	0.2939	0.2061	1.22	0.3888	0.1112
0.83	0.2967	0.2033	1.23	0.3907	0.1093
0.84	0.2995	0.2005	1.24	0.3925	0.1075
0.85	0.3023	0.1977	1.25	0.3944	0.1056
0.86	0.3051	0.1949	1.26	0.3962	0.1038
0.87	0.3078	0.1922	1.27	0.3980	0.1020
0.88	0.3106	0.1894	1.28	0.3997	0.1003
0.89	0.3133	0.1867	1.29	0.4015	0.0985
0.90	0.3159	0.1841	1.30	0.4032	0.0968
0.91	0.3186	0.1814	1.31	0.4049	0.0951
0.92	0.3212	0.1788	1.32	0.4066	0.0934
0.93	0.3238	0.1762	1.33	0.4082	0.0918
0.94	0.3264	0.1736	1.34	0.4099	0.0901
0.95	0.3289	0.1711	1.35	0.4115	0.0885
0.96	0.3315	0.1685	1.36	0.4131	0.0869
0.97	0.3340	0.1660	1.37	0.4147	0.0853
0.98	0.3365	0.1635	1.38	0.4162	0.0838
0.99	0.3389	0.1611	1.39	0.4177	0.0823
1.00	0.3413	0.1587	1.40	0.4192	0.0808
1.01	0.3438	0.1562	1.41	0.4207	0.0793
1.02	0.3461	0.1539	1.42	0.4222	0.0778
1.03	0.3485	0.1515	1.43	0.4236	0.0764
1.04	0.3508	0.1492	1.44	0.4251	0.0749
1.05	0.3531	0.1469	1.45	0.4265	0.0735
1.06	0.3554	0.1446	1.46	0.4279	0.0721
1.07	0.3577	0.1423	1.47	0.4292	0.0708
1.08	0.3599	0.1401	1.48	0.4306	0.0694
1.09	0.3621	0.1379	1.49	0.4319	0.0681
1.10	0.3643	0.1357	1.50	0.4332	0.0668
1.11	0.3665	0.1335	1.51	0.4345	0.0655
1.12	0.3686	0.1314	1.52	0.4357	0.0643
1.13	0.3708	0.1292	1.53	0.4370	0.0630
1.14	0.3729	0.1271	1.54	0.4382	0.0618
1.15	0.3749	0.1251	1.55	0.4394	0.0606
1.16	0.3770	0.1230	1.56	0.4406	0.0594
1.17	0.3790	0.1210	1.57	0.4418	0.0582
1.18	0.3810	0.1190	1.58	0.4429	0.0571
1.19	0.3830	0.1170	1.59	0.4441	0.0559
1.20	0.3849	0.1151	1.60	0.4452	0.0548

A	B	C	A	B	C
z	Area between mean and z	Area beyond z	z	Area between mean and z	Area beyond z
1.61	0.4463	0.0537	2.01	0.4778	0.0222
1.62	0.4474	0.0526	2.02	0.4783	0.0217
1.63	0.4484	0.0516	2.03	0.4788	0.0212
1.64	0.4495	0.0505	2.04	0.4793	0.0207
1.65	0.4505	0.0495	2.05	0.4798	0.0202
1.66	0.4515	0.0485	2.06	0.4803	0.0197
1.67	0.4525	0.0475	2.07	0.4808	0.0192
1.68	0.4535	0.0465	2.08	0.4812	0.0188
1.69	0.4545	0.0455	2.09	0.4817	0.0183
1.70	0.4554	0.0446	2.10	0.4821	0.0179
1.71	0.4564	0.0436	2.11	0.4826	0.0174
1.72	0.4573	0.0427	2.12	0.4830	0.0170
1.73	0.4582	0.0418	2.13	0.4834	0.0166
1.74	0.4591	0.0409	2.14	0.4838	0.0162
1.75	0.4599	0.0401	2.15	0.4842	0.0158
1.76	0.4608	0.0392	2.16	0.4846	0.0154
1.77	0.4616	0.0384	2.17	0.4850	0.0150
1.78	0.4625	0.0375	2.18	0.4854	0.0146
1.79	0.4633	0.0367	2.19	0.4857	0.0143
1.80	0.4641	0.0359	2.20	0.4861	0.0139
1.81	0.4649	0.0351	2.21	0.4864	0.0136
1.82	0.4656	0.0344	2.22	0.4868	0.0132
1.83	0.4664	0.0336	2.23	0.4871	0.0129
1.84	0.4671	0.0329	2.24	0.4875	0.0125
1.85	0.4678	0.0322	2.25	0.4878	0.0122
1.86	0.4686	0.0314	2.26	0.4881	0.0119
1.87	0.4693	0.0307	2.27	0.4884	0.0116
1.88	0.4699	0.0301	2.28	0.4887	0.0113
1.89	0.4706	0.0294	2.29	0.4890	0.0110
1.90	0.4713	0.0287	2.30	0.4893	0.0107
1.91	0.4719	0.0281	2.31	0.4896	0.0104
1.92	0.4726	0.0274	2.32	0.4898	0.0102
1.93	0.4732	0.0268	2.33	0.4901	0.0099
1.94	0.4738	0.0262	2.34	0.4904	0.0096
1.95	0.4744	0.0256	2.35	0.4906	0.0094
1.96	0.4750	0.0250	2.36	0.4909	0.0091
1.97	0.4756	0.0244	2.37	0.4911	0.0089
1.98	0.4761	0.0239	2.38	0.4913	0.0087
1.99	0.4767	0.0233	2.39	0.4916	0.0084
2.00	0.4772	0.0228	2.40	0.4918	0.0082

(continued)

A	B	C	A	B	C
z	Area between mean and z	Area beyond z	z	Area between mean and z	Area beyond z
2.41	0.4920	0.0080	2.81	0.4975	0.0025
2.42	0.4922	0.0078	2.82	0.4976	0.0024
2.43	0.4925	0.0075	2.83	0.4977	0.0023
2.44	0.4927	0.0073	2.84	0.4977	0.0023
2.45	0.4929	0.0071	2.85	0.4978	0.0022
2.46	0.4931	0.0069	2.86	0.4979	0.0021
2.47	0.4932	0.0068	2.87	0.4979	0.0021
2.48	0.4934	0.0066	2.88	0.4980	0.0020
2.49	0.4936	0.0064	2.89	0.4981	0.0019
2.50	0.4938	0.0062	2.90	0.4981	0.0019
2.51	0.4940	0.0060	2.91	0.4982	0.0018
2.52	0.4941	0.0059	2.92	0.4982	0.0018
2.53	0.4943	0.0057	2.93	0.4983	0.0017
2.54	0.4945	0.0055	2.94	0.4984	0.0016
2.55	0.4946	0.0054	2.95	0.4984	0.0016
2.56	0.4948	0.0052	2.96	0.4985	0.0015
2.57	0.4949	0.0051	2.97	0.4985	0.0015
2.58	0.4951	0.0049	2.98	0.4986	0.0014
2.59	0.4952	0.0048	2.99	0.4986	0.0014
2.60	0.4953	0.0047	3.00	0.4987	0.0013
2.61	0.4955	0.0045	3.01	0.4987	0.0013
2.62	0.4956	0.0044	3.02	0.4987	0.0013
2.63	0.4957	0.0043	3.03	0.4988	0.0012
2.64	0.4959	0.0041	3.04	0.4988	0.0012
2.65	0.4960	0.0040	3.05	0.4989	0.0011
2.66	0.4961	0.0039	3.06	0.4989	0.0011
2.67	0.4962	0.0038	3.07	0.4989	0.0011
2.68	0.4963	0.0037	3.08	0.4990	0.0010
2.69	0.4964	0.0036	3.09	0.4990	0.0010
2.70	0.4965	0.0035	3.10	0.4990	0.0010
2.71	0.4966	0.0034	3.11	0.4991	0.0009
2.72	0.4967	0.0033	3.12	0.4991	0.0009
2.73	0.4968	0.0032	3.13	0.4991	0.0009
2.74	0.4969	0.0031	3.14	0.4992	0.0008
2.75	0.4970	0.0030	3.15	0.4992	0.0008
2.76	0.4971	0.0029	3.16	0.4992	0.0008
2.77	0.4972	0.0028	3.17	0.4992	0.0008
2.78	0.4973	0.0027	3.18	0.4993	0.0007
2.79	0.4974	0.0026	3.19	0.4993	0.0007
2.80	0.4974	0.0026	3.20	0.4993	0.0007

A	B	C	A	B	C
z	Area between mean and z	Area beyond z	z	Area between mean and z	Area beyond z
3.21	0.4993	0.0007	3.61	0.4998	0.0002
3.22	0.4994	0.0006	3.62	0.4999	0.0001
3.23	0.4994	0.0006	3.63	0.4999	0.0001
3.24	0.4994	0.0006	3.64	0.4999	0.0001
3.25	0.4994	0.0006	3.65	0.4999	0.0001
3.26	0.4994	0.0006	3.66	0.4999	0.0001
3.27	0.4995	0.0005	3.67	0.4999	0.0001
3.28	0.4995	0.0005	3.68	0.4999	0.0001
3.29	0.4995	0.0005	3.69	0.4999	0.0001
3.30	0.4995	0.0005	3.70	0.4999	0.0001
3.31	0.4995	0.0005	3.71	0.4999	0.0001
3.32	0.4995	0.0005	3.72	0.4999	0.0001
3.33	0.4996	0.0004	3.73	0.4999	0.0001
3.34	0.4996	0.0004	3.74	0.4999	0.0001
3.35	0.4996	0.0004	3.75	0.4999	0.0001
3.36	0.4996	0.0004	3.76	0.4999	0.0001
3.37	0.4996	0.0004	3.77	0.4999	0.0001
3.38	0.4996	0.0004	3.78	0.4999	0.0001
3.39	0.4997	0.0003	3.79	0.4999	0.0001
3.40	0.4997	0.0003	3.80	0.4999	0.0001
3.41	0.4997	0.0003	3.81	0.4999	0.0001
3.42	0.4997	0.0003	3.82	0.4999	0.0001
3.43	0.4997	0.0003	3.83	0.4999	0.0001
3.44	0.4997	0.0003	3.84	0.4999	0.0001
3.45	0.4997	0.0003	3.85	0.4999	0.0001
3.46	0.4997	0.0003	3.86	0.4999	0.0001
3.47	0.4997	0.0003	3.87	0.4999	0.0001
3.48	0.4997	0.0003	3.88	0.4999	0.0001
3.49	0.4998	0.0002	3.89	0.4999	0.0001
3.50	0.4998	0.0002	3.90	0.5000	0.0000
3.51	0.4998	0.0002	3.91	0.5000	0.0000
3.52	0.4998	0.0002	3.92	0.5000	0.0000
3.53	0.4998	0.0002	3.93	0.5000	0.0000
3.54	0.4998	0.0002	3.94	0.5000	0.0000
3.55	0.4998	0.0002	3.95	0.5000	0.0000
3.56	0.4998	0.0002	3.96	0.5000	0.0000
3.57	0.4998	0.0002	3.97	0.5000	0.0000
3.58	0.4998	0.0002	3.98	0.5000	0.0000
3.59	0.4998	0.0002	3.99	0.5000	0.0000
3.60	0.4998	0.0002	4.00	0.5000	0.0000

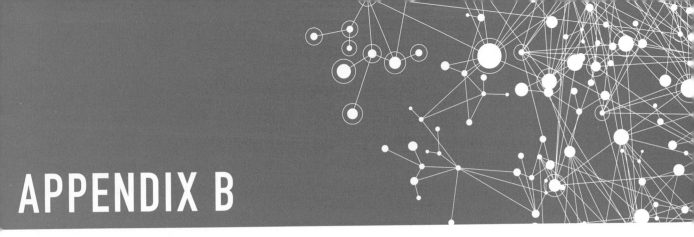

APPENDIX B

The Student's *t*–Table

For a One-Tailed Test:

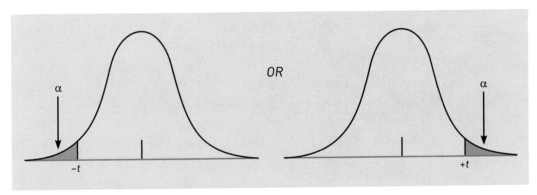

For a Two-Tailed Test:

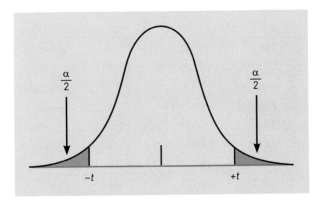

	Level of significance for one-tailed test					
	0.1	0.05	0.025	0.01	0.005	0.001
	Level of significance for two-tailed test					
df	0.2	0.1	0.05	0.02	0.01	0.002
1	3.078	6.314	12.706	31.821	63.657	318.313
2	1.886	2.920	4.303	6.965	9.925	22.327
3	1.638	2.353	3.182	4.541	5.841	10.215
4	1.533	2.132	2.776	3.747	4.604	7.173
5	1.476	2.015	2.571	3.365	4.032	5.893
6	1.440	1.943	2.447	3.143	3.707	5.208
7	1.415	1.895	2.365	2.998	3.499	4.782
8	1.397	1.860	2.306	2.896	3.355	4.499
9	1.383	1.833	2.262	2.821	3.250	4.296
10	1.372	1.812	2.228	2.764	3.169	4.143
11	1.363	1.796	2.201	2.718	3.106	4.024
12	1.356	1.782	2.179	2.681	3.055	3.929
13	1.350	1.771	2.160	2.650	3.012	3.852
14	1.345	1.761	2.145	2.624	2.977	3.787
15	1.341	1.753	2.131	2.602	2.947	3.733
16	1.337	1.746	2.120	2.583	2.921	3.686
17	1.333	1.740	2.110	2.567	2.898	3.646
18	1.330	1.734	2.101	2.552	2.878	3.610
19	1.328	1.729	2.093	2.539	2.861	3.579
20	1.325	1.725	2.086	2.528	2.845	3.552
21	1.323	1.721	2.080	2.518	2.831	3.527
22	1.321	1.717	2.074	2.508	2.819	3.505
23	1.319	1.714	2.069	2.500	2.807	3.485
24	1.318	1.711	2.064	2.492	2.797	3.467
25	1.316	1.708	2.060	2.485	2.787	3.450
26	1.315	1.706	2.056	2.479	2.779	3.435
27	1.314	1.703	2.052	2.473	2.771	3.421
28	1.313	1.701	2.048	2.467	2.763	3.408
29	1.311	1.699	2.045	2.462	2.756	3.396
30	1.310	1.697	2.042	2.457	2.750	3.385
31	1.309	1.696	2.040	2.453	2.744	3.375
32	1.309	1.694	2.037	2.449	2.738	3.365
33	1.308	1.692	2.035	2.445	2.733	3.356
34	1.307	1.691	2.032	2.441	2.728	3.348
35	1.306	1.690	2.030	2.438	2.724	3.340

df	Level of significance for one-tailed test					
	0.1	0.05	0.025	0.01	0.005	0.001
	Level of significance for two-tailed test					
	0.2	0.1	0.05	0.02	0.01	0.002
36	1.306	1.688	2.028	2.434	2.719	3.333
37	1.305	1.687	2.026	2.431	2.715	3.326
38	1.304	1.686	2.024	2.429	2.712	3.319
39	1.304	1.685	2.023	2.426	2.708	3.313
40	1.303	1.684	2.021	2.423	2.704	3.307
41	1.303	1.683	2.020	2.421	2.701	3.301
42	1.302	1.682	2.018	2.418	2.698	3.296
43	1.302	1.681	2.017	2.416	2.695	3.291
44	1.301	1.680	2.015	2.414	2.692	3.286
45	1.301	1.679	2.014	2.412	2.690	3.281
46	1.300	1.679	2.013	2.410	2.687	3.277
47	1.300	1.678	2.012	2.408	2.685	3.273
48	1.299	1.677	2.011	2.407	2.682	3.269
49	1.299	1.677	2.010	2.405	2.680	3.265
50	1.299	1.676	2.009	2.403	2.678	3.261
51	1.298	1.675	2.008	2.402	2.676	3.258
52	1.298	1.675	2.007	2.400	2.674	3.255
53	1.298	1.674	2.006	2.399	2.672	3.251
54	1.297	1.674	2.005	2.397	2.670	3.248
55	1.297	1.673	2.004	2.396	2.668	3.245
56	1.297	1.673	2.003	2.395	2.667	3.242
57	1.297	1.672	2.002	2.394	2.665	3.239
58	1.296	1.672	2.002	2.392	2.663	3.237
59	1.296	1.671	2.001	2.391	2.662	3.234
60	1.296	1.671	2.000	2.390	2.660	3.232
61	1.296	1.670	2.000	2.389	2.659	3.229
62	1.295	1.670	1.999	2.388	2.657	3.227
63	1.295	1.669	1.998	2.387	2.656	3.225
64	1.295	1.669	1.998	2.386	2.655	3.223
65	1.295	1.669	1.997	2.385	2.654	3.220
66	1.295	1.668	1.997	2.384	2.652	3.218
67	1.294	1.668	1.996	2.383	2.651	3.216
68	1.294	1.668	1.995	2.382	2.650	3.214
69	1.294	1.667	1.995	2.382	2.649	3.213
70	1.294	1.667	1.994	2.381	2.648	3.211

(*continued*)

	Level of significance for one-tailed test					
	0.1	0.05	0.025	0.01	0.005	0.001
	Level of significance for two-tailed test					
df	0.2	0.1	0.05	0.02	0.01	0.002
71	1.294	1.667	1.994	2.380	2.647	3.209
72	1.293	1.666	1.993	2.379	2.646	3.207
73	1.293	1.666	1.993	2.379	2.645	3.206
74	1.293	1.666	1.993	2.378	2.644	3.204
75	1.293	1.665	1.992	2.377	2.643	3.202
76	1.293	1.665	1.992	2.376	2.642	3.201
77	1.293	1.665	1.991	2.376	2.641	3.199
78	1.292	1.665	1.991	2.375	2.640	3.198
79	1.292	1.664	1.990	2.374	2.640	3.197
80	1.292	1.664	1.990	2.374	2.639	3.195
81	1.292	1.664	1.990	2.373	2.638	3.194
82	1.292	1.664	1.989	2.373	2.637	3.193
83	1.292	1.663	1.989	2.372	2.636	3.191
84	1.292	1.663	1.989	2.372	2.636	3.190
85	1.292	1.663	1.988	2.371	2.635	3.189
86	1.291	1.663	1.988	2.370	2.634	3.188
87	1.291	1.663	1.988	2.370	2.634	3.187
88	1.291	1.662	1.987	2.369	2.633	3.185
89	1.291	1.662	1.987	2.369	2.632	3.184
90	1.291	1.662	1.987	2.368	2.632	3.183
91	1.291	1.662	1.986	2.368	2.631	3.182
92	1.291	1.662	1.986	2.368	2.630	3.181
93	1.291	1.661	1.986	2.367	2.630	3.180
94	1.291	1.661	1.986	2.367	2.629	3.179
95	1.291	1.661	1.985	2.366	2.629	3.178
96	1.290	1.661	1.985	2.366	2.628	3.177
97	1.290	1.661	1.985	2.365	2.627	3.176
98	1.290	1.661	1.984	2.365	2.627	3.175
99	1.290	1.660	1.984	2.365	2.626	3.175
100	1.290	1.660	1.984	2.364	2.626	3.174
120	1.289	1.658	1.980	2.358	2.617	3.373
∞	1.282	1.645	1.960	2.326	2.576	3.090

Chi-Square

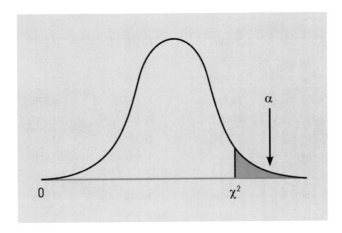

df	Critical values of chi-square Level of significance for two-tailed test				
	0.1	0.05	0.025	0.01	0.001
1	2.706	3.841	5.024	6.635	10.828
2	4.605	5.991	7.378	9.210	13.816
3	6.251	7.815	9.348	11.345	16.266
4	7.779	9.488	11.143	13.277	18.467
5	9.236	11.070	12.833	15.086	20.515
6	10.645	12.592	14.449	16.812	22.458
7	12.017	14.067	16.013	18.475	24.322
8	13.362	15.507	17.535	20.090	26.125
9	14.684	16.919	19.023	21.666	27.877
10	15.987	18.307	20.483	23.209	29.588
11	17.275	19.675	21.920	24.725	31.264
12	18.549	21.026	23.337	26.217	32.910
13	19.812	22.362	24.736	27.688	34.528
14	21.064	23.685	26.119	29.141	36.123
15	22.307	24.996	27.488	30.578	37.697
16	23.542	26.296	28.845	32.000	39.252
17	24.769	27.587	30.191	33.409	40.790
18	25.989	28.869	31.526	34.805	42.312
19	27.204	30.144	32.852	36.191	43.820
20	28.412	31.410	34.170	37.566	45.315
21	29.615	32.671	35.479	38.932	46.797
22	30.813	33.924	36.781	40.289	48.268
23	32.007	35.172	38.076	41.638	49.728
24	33.196	36.415	39.364	42.980	51.179
25	34.382	37.652	40.646	44.314	52.620
26	35.563	38.885	41.923	45.642	54.052
27	36.741	40.113	43.195	46.963	55.476
28	37.916	41.337	44.461	48.278	56.892
29	39.087	42.557	45.722	49.588	58.301
30	40.256	43.773	46.979	50.892	59.703
31	41.422	44.985	48.232	52.191	61.098
32	42.585	46.194	49.480	53.486	62.487
33	43.745	47.400	50.725	54.776	63.870
34	44.903	48.602	51.966	56.061	65.247
35	46.059	49.802	53.203	57.342	66.619
36	47.212	50.998	54.437	58.619	67.985
37	48.363	52.192	55.668	59.893	69.347
38	49.513	53.384	56.896	61.162	70.703
39	50.660	54.572	58.120	62.428	72.055
40	51.805	55.758	59.342	63.691	73.402

df	0.1	0.05	0.025	0.01	0.001
	Critical values of chi-square Level of significance for two-tailed test				
41	52.949	56.942	60.561	64.950	74.745
42	54.090	58.124	61.777	66.206	76.084
43	55.230	59.304	62.990	67.459	77.419
44	56.369	60.481	64.201	68.710	78.750
45	57.505	61.656	65.410	69.957	80.077
46	58.641	62.830	66.617	71.201	81.400
47	59.774	64.001	67.821	72.443	82.720
48	60.907	65.171	69.023	73.683	84.037
49	62.038	66.339	70.222	74.919	85.351
50	63.167	67.505	71.420	76.154	86.661
51	64.295	68.669	72.616	77.386	87.968
52	65.422	69.832	73.810	78.616	89.272
53	66.548	70.993	75.002	79.843	90.573
54	67.673	72.153	76.192	81.069	91.872
55	68.796	73.311	77.380	82.292	93.168
56	69.919	74.468	78.567	83.513	94.461
57	71.040	75.624	79.752	84.733	95.751
58	72.160	76.778	80.936	85.950	97.039
59	73.279	77.931	82.117	87.166	98.324
60	74.397	79.082	83.298	88.379	99.607
61	75.514	80.232	84.476	89.591	100.888
62	76.630	81.381	85.654	90.802	102.166
63	77.745	82.529	86.830	92.010	103.442
64	78.860	83.675	88.004	93.217	104.716
65	79.973	84.821	89.177	94.422	105.988
66	81.085	85.965	90.349	95.626	107.258
67	82.197	87.108	91.519	96.828	108.526
68	83.308	88.250	92.689	98.028	109.791
69	84.418	89.391	93.856	99.228	111.055
70	85.527	90.531	95.023	100.425	112.317
71	86.635	91.670	96.189	101.621	113.577
72	87.743	92.808	97.353	102.816	114.835
73	88.850	93.945	98.516	104.010	116.092
74	89.956	95.081	99.678	105.202	117.346
75	91.061	96.217	100.839	106.393	118.599
76	92.166	97.351	101.999	107.583	119.850
77	93.270	98.484	103.158	108.771	121.100
78	94.374	99.617	104.316	109.958	122.348

(continued)

df	Critical values of chi-square Level of significance for two-tailed test				
	0.1	0.05	0.025	0.01	0.001
79	95.476	100.749	105.473	111.144	123.594
80	96.578	101.879	106.629	112.329	124.839
81	97.680	103.010	107.783	113.512	126.083
82	98.780	104.139	108.937	114.695	127.324
83	99.880	105.267	110.090	115.876	128.565
84	100.980	106.395	111.242	117.057	129.804
85	102.079	107.522	112.393	118.236	131.041
86	103.177	108.648	113.544	119.414	132.277
87	104.275	109.773	114.693	120.591	133.512
88	105.372	110.898	115.841	121.767	134.746
89	106.469	112.022	116.989	122.942	135.978
90	107.565	113.145	118.136	124.116	137.208
91	108.661	114.268	119.282	125.289	138.438
92	109.756	115.390	120.427	126.462	139.666
93	110.850	116.511	121.571	127.633	140.893
94	111.944	117.632	122.715	128.803	142.119
95	113.038	118.752	123.858	129.973	143.344
96	114.131	119.871	125.000	131.141	144.567
97	115.223	120.990	126.141	132.309	145.789
98	116.315	122.108	127.282	133.476	147.010
99	117.407	123.225	128.422	134.642	148.230
100	118.498	124.342	129.561	135.807	149.449

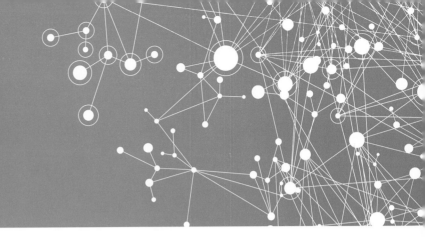

APPENDIX D

The *F*-distribution

$df_{between}$	2	3	4	5	6	7	8
df_{within}							
1	199.50	215.71	224.58	230.16	233.99	236.77	238.88
2	19.00	19.16	19.25	19.30	19.33	19.35	19.37
3	9.55	9.28	9.12	9.01	8.94	8.89	8.85
4	6.94	6.59	6.39	6.26	6.16	6.09	6.04
5	5.79	5.41	5.19	5.05	4.95	4.88	4.82
6	5.14	4.76	4.53	4.39	4.28	4.21	4.15
7	4.74	4.35	4.12	3.97	3.87	3.79	3.73
8	4.46	4.07	3.84	3.69	3.58	3.50	3.44
9	4.26	3.86	3.63	3.48	3.37	3.29	3.23
10	4.10	3.71	3.48	3.33	3.22	3.14	3.07
20	3.49	3.10	2.87	2.71	2.60	2.51	2.45
21	3.47	3.07	2.84	2.69	2.57	2.49	2.42
22	3.44	3.05	2.82	2.66	2.55	2.46	2.40
23	3.42	3.03	2.80	2.64	2.53	2.44	2.38
24	3.40	3.01	2.78	2.62	2.51	2.42	2.36
25	3.39	2.99	2.76	2.60	2.49	2.41	2.34
26	3.37	2.98	2.74	2.59	2.47	2.39	2.32
27	3.35	2.96	2.73	2.57	2.46	2.37	2.31
28	3.34	2.95	2.71	2.56	2.45	2.36	2.29
29	3.33	2.93	2.70	2.55	2.43	2.35	2.28
30	3.32	2.92	2.69	2.53	2.42	2.33	2.27
40	3.23	2.84	2.61	2.45	2.34	2.25	2.18
50	3.18	2.79	2.56	2.40	2.29	2.20	2.13
60	3.15	2.76	2.53	2.37	2.25	2.17	2.10
70	3.13	2.74	2.50	2.35	2.23	2.14	2.07
80	3.11	2.72	2.49	2.33	2.21	2.13	2.06

(continued)

$df_{between}$	2	3	4	5	6	7	8
90	3.10	2.71	2.47	2.32	2.20	2.11	2.04
100	3.09	2.70	2.46	2.31	2.19	2.10	2.03
120	3.07	2.68	2.45	2.29	2.18	2.09	2.02
∞	3.00	2.61	2.37	2.22	2.10	2.01	1.94

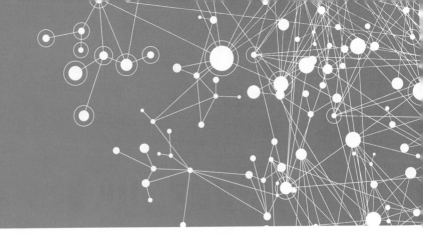

APPENDIX E

Area under the Normal Curve: A Condensed Version

A	B	C	A	B	C
z	Area between mean and z	Area beyond z	z	Area between mean and z	Area beyond z
0.0	0.0000	0.5000	2.0	0.4772	0.0228
0.1	0.0398	0.4602	2.1	0.4821	0.0179
0.2	0.0793	0.4207	2.2	0.4861	0.0139
0.3	0.1179	0.3821	2.3	0.4893	0.0107
0.4	0.1554	0.3446	2.4	0.4918	0.0082
0.5	0.1915	0.3085	2.5	0.4938	0.0062
0.6	0.2257	0.2743	2.6	0.4953	0.0047
0.7	0.2580	0.2420	2.7	0.4965	0.0035
0.8	0.2881	0.2119	2.8	0.4974	0.0026
0.9	0.3159	0.1841	2.9	0.4981	0.0019
1.0	0.3413	0.1587	3.0	0.4987	0.0013
1.1	0.3643	0.1357	3.1	0.4990	0.0010
1.2	0.3849	0.1151	3.2	0.4993	0.0007
1.3	0.4032	0.0968	3.3	0.4995	0.0005
1.4	0.4192	0.0808	3.4	0.4997	0.0003
1.5	0.4332	0.0668	3.5	0.4998	0.0002
1.6	0.4452	0.0548			
1.7	0.4554	0.0446			
1.8	0.4641	0.0359			
1.9	0.4713	0.0287			

APPENDIX F

Random Numbers between 1 and 1,000

388	250	87	729	502	962
185	60	160	117	714	496
524	19	360	95	784	800
494	6	951	606	40	530
603	504	919	973	620	320
203	167	195	920	447	756
690	647	821	594	111	918
10	899	275	191	22	988
930	816	335	717	413	470
65	993	620	201	66	949
332	273	128	656	220	326
717	477	37	580	905	421
832	51	422	106	204	42
16	194	916	364	507	405
390	34	243	464	912	453
868	609	556	252	554	487
164	347	163	588	898	889
958	537	166	119	826	880
996	365	168	214	106	644
876	774	271	625	74	821
738	929	550	471	762	994
31	793	556	1	752	300
198	595	960	200	288	362
302	997	409	337	253	310
694	994	8	41	24	456
511	204	686	941	546	70
500	622	64	467	752	448
153	339	447	609	339	938

698	662	134	248	285	532
4	511	701	892	178	943
197	635	960	22	672	440
492	959	399	654	111	174
937	986	741	947	730	734
979	538	226	541	809	445
541	911	105	613	974	961
359	728	913	159	281	951
938	20	224	702	166	998
581	341	124	55	592	881
709	660	216	59	29	162
15	411	172	825	192	174
191	959	230	161	873	915
788	928	56	915	785	881
586	951	839	161	155	239
485	415	627	971	840	824
595	329	648	985	251	18
856	523	860	788	172	525
359	681	246	157	928	997
419	94	519	199	200	593
699	256	903	339	303	140
93	418	735	486	801	21

APPENDIX G

Summary of Equations and Symbols

EQUATIONS

The arithmetic mean: $\overline{X} = \dfrac{\sum X_N}{N}$

The range: $\text{Range} = H - L$

Mean deviation: $\text{Mean Deviation} = \dfrac{\sum |X - \overline{X}|}{N}$

Variance: $\sigma^2 = \dfrac{\sum (X - \mu)^2}{N}$ or $s^2 = \dfrac{\sum (X - \overline{X})^2}{n - 1}$

Standard deviation: $\sigma = \sqrt{\dfrac{\sum (X - \mu)^2}{N}}$ or $s = \sqrt{\dfrac{\sum (X - \overline{X})^2}{n - 1}}$

Standard deviation of the difference between sample proportions:

$$s_{\overline{X}_1 \overline{X}_2} = \sqrt{P_u(1 - P_u)\dfrac{n_1 + n_2}{n_1 n_2}}$$

The standard score: $z = \dfrac{X - \mu}{\sigma}$ or $z = \dfrac{X - \overline{X}}{s}$

Standard error of the mean: $\sigma_{\overline{X}} = \dfrac{\sigma_X}{\sqrt{n}}$ or $s_{\overline{X}} = \dfrac{s_X}{\sqrt{n - 1}}$ or $s_p = \sqrt{\dfrac{p(1 - p)}{n}}$

Observed *t*-score: $t_{observed} = \dfrac{\overline{X} - \mu}{\sigma_X \sqrt{N}}$ or $t_{observed} = \dfrac{\overline{X} - \mu}{\sigma_{\overline{X}}}$ or $t_{observed} = \dfrac{\overline{X} - \mu}{s_{\overline{X}}}$ or

$t_{observed} = \dfrac{\overline{X} - \mu}{s_X / \sqrt{n - 1}}$

- **To assess r:** $t_{observed} = r\sqrt{\dfrac{n-2}{1-r^2}}$

Observed z-score:

- **In a sample:** $z = \dfrac{X - \overline{X}}{s}$

- **Between two sample means:** $z = \dfrac{(\overline{X}_1 - \overline{X}_2)}{s_{\overline{X}_1 - \overline{X}_2}}$

- **With proportions:** $z_{obtained} = \dfrac{P_{sample} - P_{population}}{\sqrt{P_{population}(1 - P_{population})/n}}$

Degrees of freedom:

- **for a t-test:** $df = n - 1$
- **for chi-square test of independence:** $df = (r-1)(c-1)$
- **When calculating the significance of difference between two means:** $df = (n_1 + n_2 - 2)$
- **When calculating the significance for Spearman's rho:** $df = n - 2$
- **Within groups in** ANOVA: $df_{within} = N_{total} = k$
- **Between groups in** ANOVA: $df_{between} = k - 1$

Confidence interval:

- **Confidence interval when z is known:** $\text{Confidence Interval} = \overline{X} \pm (z_{critical} * \sigma_{\overline{X}})$

$$\text{or}$$

$$\text{Confidence Interval} = \overline{X} \pm \left(z_{critical} * \frac{\sigma_X}{\sqrt{n}} \right)$$

- **Confidence interval when t is known:** $\text{Confidence Interval} = \overline{X} \pm (t_{critical} * s_{\overline{X}})$

$$\text{or}$$

$$\text{Confidence Interval} = \overline{X} \pm \left(t_{critical} * \frac{s_X}{\sqrt{n-1}} \right)$$

Chi-square: $\chi^2 = \sum \dfrac{(f_o - f_e)^2}{f_e}$

- **Expected cell frequencies:** $f_e = \dfrac{\sum column * \sum row}{n}$

Phi: $\phi = \sqrt{\dfrac{\chi^2}{n}}$

Cramer's V: $V = \sqrt{\dfrac{\chi^2}{(n)(\min{(r-1)}|(c-1))}}$

Lambda: $\lambda = \dfrac{E_1 - E_2}{E_1}$

Association between dummy and interval/ ratio variables, same group measured twice:

- **Differences between observations:** $\overline{X}_d = \dfrac{\sum d_i}{n}$

- **Standard deviation of differences:**
  $s_d = \sqrt{\dfrac{\sum(d - \overline{X}_d)^2}{n-1}} \;\; \text{or} \; s_d = \sqrt{\dfrac{\sum d^2}{n-1} - (\overline{X}_1 - \overline{X}_2)^2}$

- **Standard error of the difference between means (when the same group is measured twice):** $s_{\overline{d}} = \dfrac{s_d}{\sqrt{n-1}}$

- **t-observed for significance of differences:** $t = \dfrac{\overline{X}_1 - \overline{X}_2}{s_{\overline{d}}}$

Standard error of the difference between means:

- **When using z:** $s_{\overline{X}_1 - \overline{X}_2} = \sqrt{\left(\dfrac{s_1^2}{n_1 - 1} + \dfrac{s_2^2}{n_2 - 1}\right)}$

- **When using t:** $s_{\overline{X}_1 - \overline{X}_2} = \sqrt{\left(\dfrac{n_1 s_1^2 + n_2 s_2^2}{n_1 + n_2 - 2}\right)\left(\dfrac{n_1 + n_2}{n_1 n_2}\right)}$

Kruskal's gamma: $\gamma = \dfrac{N_{same} - N_{different}}{N_{same} + N_{different}}$

- **Testing significance:** $z_{obtained} = \gamma\sqrt{\dfrac{N_s + N_d}{N(1 - \gamma^2)}}$

Spearman's *rho*: $\rho_s = 1 - \dfrac{6 * \sum D^2}{N(N^2 - 1)}$

- **Testing significance:** $z_{obtained} = \rho_s \sqrt{\dfrac{N-2}{1-r_s^2}}$

Somer's d: $d = \dfrac{N_{same} - N_{different}}{N_{same} + N_{different} + Ties_y}$

- **Testing significance:** $z_{obtained} = d\sqrt{\dfrac{N_s + N_d}{N(1-d^2)}}$

Kendall's tau-b: $\text{tau-}b = \dfrac{N_{same} - N_{different}}{(N_{same} + N_{different} + Ties_y)(N_{same} + N_{different} + Ties_x)}$

- **Testing significance:** $z_{obtained} = \text{tau-}b\sqrt{\dfrac{N_s + N_d}{N(1-(tau\text{-}b^2))}}$

Pearson's r: $r = \dfrac{N\sum XY - (\sum X)(\sum Y)}{\sqrt{[N\sum X^2 - (\sum X)^2][N\sum Y^2 - (\sum Y)^2]}}$

Total sum of squares (ANOVA): $SS_{total} = \sum X_{total}^2 - N_{total}\overline{X}_{total}^2$

Within-group sum of squares (ANOVA): $SS_{within} = \sum X_{total}^2 - \sum N_{group}\overline{X}_{group}^2$

Between-group sum of squares (ANOVA): $SS_{between} = \sum N_{group}\overline{X}_{group}^2 - N_{total}\overline{X}_{total}^2$

Mean squares within groups: $MS_{within} = \dfrac{SS_{within}}{df_{within}}$

Mean squares between groups: $MS_{between} = \dfrac{SS_{between}}{df_{between}}$

F-ratio: $F_{observed} = \dfrac{MS_{between}}{MS_{within}}$

Ordinary least-squares regression (observed): $Y = a + b_1 x_{1i} + b_2 x_{2i} + \cdots + b_n x_{ni} + e_i$

Ordinary least-squares regression (expected): $\hat{Y} = a + b_1 x_{1i} + b_2 x_{2i} + \cdots + b_n x_{ni}$

- **Partial slope coefficient:** $b = \dfrac{\sum (X - \bar{X})(Y - \bar{Y})}{\sum (X - \bar{X})^2}$

- **y-intercept:** $a = \bar{Y} - b\bar{X}$

- **Error term:** $e = Y - \hat{Y}$

- **Correlations between X_1 and Y, X_2 and Y, as well as X_1 and X_2:**

$$r_{X_1Y} = \frac{N\sum X_1 Y - (\sum X_1)(\sum Y)}{\sqrt{\left[N\sum X_1^2 - (\sum X)^2\right]\left[N\sum Y^2 - (\sum Y)^2\right]}}$$

$$r_{X_2Y} = \frac{N\sum X_2 Y - (\sum X_2)(\sum Y)}{\sqrt{\left[N\sum X_2^2 - (\sum X_2)^2\right]\left[N\sum Y^2 - (\sum Y)^2\right]}}$$

$$r_{X_1X_2} = \frac{N\sum X_1 X_2 - (\sum X_1)(\sum X_2)}{\sqrt{\left[N\sum X_1^2 - (\sum X_1)^2\right]\left[N\sum X_2^2 - (\sum X_2)^2\right]}}$$

- **Per cent explained variance in Y:** $R^2 = r_{yx1}^2 + r_{yx1.x2}^2(1 - r_{yx1}^2)$ or

$$R^2 = \frac{\sum (\hat{Y} - \bar{Y})^2}{\sum (Y - \bar{Y})^2}$$

Where: $r_{yx1x2}^2 = \dfrac{r_{yx2} - (r_{yx1})(r_{x1x2})}{\sqrt{1 - r_{yx1}^2}\sqrt{1 - r_{x1x2}^2}}$

- **Standardized partial slopes:** $b_1^* = b_1\left(\dfrac{S_1}{S_y}\right)$

Logistic regression (observed): $LogOdds(Y = 1) = a + b_1 x_{1i} + b_2 x_{2i} + \cdots + b_n x_{ni} + e_i$

Logistic regression (expected): $LogOdds(\hat{Y} = 1) = a + b_1 x_{1i} + b_2 x_{2i} + \cdots + b_n x_{ni}$

- $Odds(Y = 1) = \left(\dfrac{\Pr(Y = 1)}{\Pr(Y \neq 1)}\right)$ or

   $LogOdds(Y = 1) = \left(\dfrac{\Pr(Y = 1)}{\Pr(Y \neq 1)}\right)$ or

   $LogOdds(Y = 1) = \ln\left(\dfrac{\Pr(Y = 1)}{1 - \Pr(Y = 1)}\right)$

- $Odds\ ratio_b = e^b$

Cook's Distance: $Di = \dfrac{e_i^2}{p(MSE)}\left[\dfrac{h_{ii}}{(1 - h_{ii})^2}\right]$

- **Leverage:** $h_{ii} = \left[\dfrac{1}{n} + \dfrac{(X_i - X)^2}{\sum (X_i - X)^2}\right]$

Variance Inflation Factor: $VIF_{Xi} = \dfrac{1}{1 - R_{XI}^2}$

SYMBOLS

a	The Y intercept (Chapter 16, p. 201)
α	Constant term (Chapter 19, p. 250)
ANOVA	The analysis of variance (Chapter 15, p. 182)
b_n	The partial slope of X_n on Y (Chapter 16, p. 201)
$b*$	Beta-weights (Chapter 16, p. 211)
c	The number of columns in a table (Chapter 12, p. 134)
D	Difference between rankings of variables (Chapter 13, p. 158)
D_i	Cook's Distance (or Cook's D) (Chapter 18, p. 240)
d	Somer's d (Chapter 13, p. 160)
d_i	Difference between scores (Chapter 10, p. 112)
df	Degrees of freedom (Chapter 9, p. 88)
$df_{between}$	Degrees of freedom between groups (Chapter 15, p. 187)
df_{within}	Degrees of freedom within groups (Chapter 15, p. 187)
ε_i	Error for individual i (Chapter 16, p. 201)
E_1	Classification error of dependent variable (Chapter 12, p. 141)
E_2	Classification error of independent variable (Chapter 12, p. 142)
f_e	Expected frequency (Chapter 12, p. 133s)
f_o	Observed frequency (Chapter 12, p. 133)
F	F-statistic (Chapter 15, p. 192)
$F_{observed}$	F-ratio (Chapter 15, p. 187)
GR	Growth rate (Chapter 3, p. 26)
h_{ii}	The leverage of data point X_i (Chapter 18, p. 242)
H	Highest value of a variable (Chapter 6, p. 51)
H_a/H_1	Alternative/research hypothesis (Chapter 10, p. 101)
H_0	Null hypothesis (Chapter 10, p. 101)
k	The number of groups being compared (Chapter 15, p. 187)
L	Lowest value of a variable (Chapter 6, p. 51)
MAR	Missing at random (Chapter 19, p. 251)
MCAR	Missing completely at random (Chapter 19, p. 251)
MS	Mean square (Chapter 15, p. 186)
$MS_{between}$	Mean square between groups (Chapter 15, p. 187)
MS_{within}	Mean square within groups (Chapter 15, p. 186)
MSE	Mean squared error (Chapter 18, p. 242)
n	Number of total observations in a sample (Chapter 8, p. 75)
N	Number of total observations (i.e., population size) (Chapter 6, p. 49)
NIM	Non-ignorable missing value (Chapter 19, p. 252)
NNI	Nearest neighbor imputation (Chapter 19, p. 254)
OLS	Ordinary least squares regression (Chapter 16, p. 212)
p	Probability (Chapter 4, p. 32)
P	Proportion (Chapter 10, p. 111)

P_u	The proportion of a population (Chapter 11, p. 124)
r	The number of rows in a table (Chapter 12, p. 134)
r	Pearson's r (Chapter 14, p. 169)
R^2	Pearson's multiple correlation coefficient r-squared (Chapter 16, p. 211)
s	The standard deviation of a sample (Chapter 6, p. 52)
s^2	The variance of a sample (Chapter 6, p. 62)
s_{est}	The standard error of the estimate (Chapter 16, p. 216)
s_P	The standard error of a proportion (Chapter 9, p. 90)
$s_{\bar{x}}$	The standard error of a sample (Chapter 8, p. 78)
$s_{\bar{x}_1} - s_{\bar{x}_2}$	The standard deviation of the difference between sample proportions (Chapter 11, p. 118)
se_b	The standard error of coefficient b (Chapter 16, p. 217)
$SS_{between}$	The total sum of squares between groups (Chapter 15, p. 185)
SS_{total}	The total sum of squares (Chapter 15, p. 184)
SS_{within}	The total sum of squares within groups (Chapter 15, p. 185)
t	t-distribution/Student's t-score (Chapter 9, p. 86)
tau-b	Kendall's tau-b (Chapter 13, p. 162)
u_i	Measurement error due to non-random non-response (Chapter 19, p. 250)
V	Cramer's V (Chapter 12, p. 139)
VIF	Variance inflation factor (Chapter 18, p. 245)
X	An independent variable (Chapter 16, p. 204)
x_{ni}	The nth independent variable for individual i (Chapter 16, p. 201)
$\bar{X}$	The mean of a variable (Chapter 6, p. 48)
$\bar{X}$	The mean of a sample (Chapter 9, p. 83)
X_i	An explanatory variable with coefficient β (Chapter 19, p. 250)
$\bar{X}_{group}$	The mean of a group (Chapter 15, p. 185)
Y	A dependent variable (Chapter 2, p. 9)
$\bar{Y}$	The mean of variable Y (Chapter 16, p. 204)
$\hat{Y}$	A predicted value of Y (Chapter 16, p. 204)
z	The z-score or standard score (Chapter 7, p. 58)
z_i	Compound error ($e_i + u_i$) (Chapter 19, p. 250)
β_1	The coefficient for X_i (Chapter 19, p. 250)
γ	Kruskal's gamma (Chapter 13, p. 155s)
λ	Lambda (Chapter 12, p. 143)
μ	The mean of a population (Chapter 7, p. 61)
ρ_s	Spearman's rho (Chapter 13, p. 157)
σ	The standard deviation of a population (Chapter 7, p. 61)
σ^2	The variance of a population (Chapter 9, p. 83)
$\sigma_{\bar{x}}$	The standard error of a population (Chapter 9, p. 84)
Σ	"The sum of" (Chapter 6, p. 49)
φ	Phi (Chapter 12, p. 136)
χ^2	Chi-square (Chapter 12, p. 133)

Solution Key for Practice Questions

CHAPTER 2

1. $10 + 15 = \mathbf{25}$

2. $10 + 15 - 5 = \mathbf{20}$

3. $10 - (-2) = \mathbf{12}$

4. $(10 + 15) - 5 = \mathbf{20}$

5. $(10 - 15) - 2 = \mathbf{-7}$

6. $10 * 15 = \mathbf{150}$

7. $10 * 15 - 5 = \mathbf{145}$

8. $10 * (15 - 5) = \mathbf{100}$

9. $10 * 15 - 15/5 = \mathbf{147}$

10. $10/5 * 15 - 5 = \mathbf{25}$

11. $(X * Y)^a + b = \mathbf{X^a * Y^a + b}$

12. $(X^a)\,(X^b) = \mathbf{X^{a+b}}$

13. $\sqrt{x} = \mathbf{X^{1/2}}$

14. if $e = 2.718$, $y = 5$, and $\ln 5 = 1.61$, then $e^{1.61} = \mathbf{5}$

Identify the levels of measurement (nominal, ordinal, interval, or ratio) for the following:

15. Percentage scores on a math exam: **Ratio**

16. Letter grades on a math exam: **Ordinal**

17. Flavours of ice cream: **Nominal**

18. Fitness training levels on an exercise machine classified as: Easy, Difficult, or Impossible: **Ordinal**

19. Ethnic origins: **Nominal**

20. Political parties: **Nominal**

21. Commuting times to school in kilometers: **Ratio**

22. Years between important historical events: **Ratio**

23. Age (in years): **Ratio**

24. Amount of money in your savings accounts: **Ratio**

25. Temperature on the moon, measured in degrees Celsius: **Interval**

CHAPTER 3

A. 1) Jorge was correct 37 times and incorrect 3 times. This translates into a ratio of 37:3.
   2) His score is calculated as 37/40, or 92.5 per cent.
   3) His percentile rank is calculated as 113/1,432, which equals 0.0789. Given this, we could say that he placed in the top 8th percentile.

B. 1) Ethel's contact rate would be calculated by first determining the percentage of people that she contacts, which is 432/541, or 79.9 per cent. When stated as a rate (percentages are essentially a rate per 100), we'd need to multiply the numerator and the denominator by 10, which would yield 799 per 1,000 people.
   2) Ethel's contact/non-contract rate is 432:109, which is roughly equivalent to 4:1.
   3) The participation rate as a percentage is 112:432, or 25.9 per cent.

C. The approval rate for Charles is calculated as 13/30, or 43.3 per cent; as a ratio, it is 13:17.

D. 1) In order to calculate what the population will be in exactly one year, the appropriate values need to be inserted into the population growth equation:

$$\text{Population}_{tn} = \text{Population}_{t0} * (1 + GR)^n$$
$$\text{Population}_{tn} = 34194937 * (1 + 0.01283)^1$$
$$\text{Population}_{tn} = 34194937 * 1.01283 = 34633658$$

The Canadian population will be approximately 34,633,658 in one year given the country's growth rate.

2) In order to calculate the population will be in 10 years, the population growth equation is used:

$$\text{Population}_{tn} = \text{Population}_{t0} * (1 + GR)^n$$
$$\text{Population}_{tn} = 34194937 * (1 + 0.01283)^{10}$$
$$\text{Population}_{tn} = 34194937 * 1.135966611 = 38844306$$

The Canadian population will be approximately 38,844,306 in 10 years, assuming that there is no change in the growth rate.

3) In order to calculate what the population was exactly 10 years ago, the population growth equation is used:

$$\text{Population}_{tn} = \text{Population}_{t0} * (1 + GR)^{n}$$
$$\text{Population}_{tn} = 34194937 * (1 + 0.01283)^{-10}$$
$$\text{Population}_{tn} = 34194937 * 0.880307563 = 30102061.69$$

The Canadian population was approximately 30,102,062 ten years ago, assuming that the growth rates are the same over time.

4) A new person is added to the population every 0.835 minutes, to find this take the difference between the 2010 population and the estimated population a year later gathered from question D1 (34,633,658 − 34,194,937 = 438,721), these are how many people are added during the course of a year, divide by 365 to get the number of people added per day, by 24 to get the number of people per hour, and then by 60 to get the number of people per minute.

CHAPTER 4

1. c

2. 2/5 or 0.4 or a 40 per cent chance

3. 1/36

4. 18/30 = 3/5

5. (0.52 * 0.52) 27 per cent

6. ((4/52) * (4/51) * (4/50)) = 64/132600 = 8/16575

7. There are 52 two cards in a deck and 13/52 chances of getting any one card of a particular suit. As each card is drawn the total number of cards that can be chosen of that particular suit (the numerator) decreases by one, as does the total number of cards in the deck (the denominator).

$$((13/52) * (12/51) * (11/50) * (10/49) * (9/48))$$

This results in a probability of 0.000495.

8. The probability that the essay questions Ryan hasn't studied for are on the exam is 2/8 = 0.25.
Because one essay question has already been chosen for the exam, the probability that the second essay Ryan has not studied for will appear on the exam is 1/7 = 0.143.
The probability that both questions Ryan has not studied for will appear on the exam is 0.25 * 0.143 = 0.04.

9. Since Julie was not a pirate 2 out of the 10 years, the probability that Julie will dress up as something other than a pirate is 2/10 or 1/5.

10. a) Your odds have been the same since you started.
    b) Your odds are the same as those around you.
    c) You have a 1/36 chance of rolling two fives.

CHAPTER 5

1. Dr. Knifewell might like to know that the data will probably be skewed to the right (positively skewed) and that it will likely be unimodal.

2. The data are unimodal and positively skewed.

3. The outlier is at the value 10,000. It appears to be flattening the normal curve, having a negative effect on the kurtosis value.

4. The distribution will become negatively skewed, or skewed to the left. The unimodal hump will also shift.

5. The impact of weather in Canada becoming more **volatile** will make the tails thicker because there will be more instances of high and low temperatures.

6. You would tell the cell phone provider that there are only a few customers (6/20) that exceed 500 airtime minutes a month. The distribution is positively skewed or skewed to the right.

7. You would expect outliers in the lower grade range because when a distribution is skewed to the left or negatively skewed the tail on the left is longer and the majority of the scores would actually fall to the right, which when plotted along a normal curve leaves outliers in the lower grade range.

8. Answer will vary.

CHAPTER 6

1. a) 7
   b) 248,000

2. Mean = 29.4, mean deviation = 30.9

3. Mean = 4.67, standard deviation = 1.84, variance = 3.39

4. The mean would be larger than the median and the histogram would be skewed with long right tail.

5. The median remains the same, but the mean is increased.

6. Income is almost always positively skewed, which will pull the mean past the median. Very few Canadians earn negative income (expect for some self-employed), suggesting that the distribution of income values hits a wall at $0. On the high side of the distribution there are many high earners, and these factors collectively produce a mean that exceeds the median.

7. All of the values will increase. The mean, median, and range will rise because of a broader set of age values, whereas the standard deviation will increase because of an increase in the average distance from the mean.

8. We would expect that the tails would be longer for a distribution with a larger standard deviation.

9. Remember that the mean deviation, standard deviation, and variance are measures of dispersion. Since Jessica is using the same number of minutes each month, the values for all three measures of dispersion is therefore zero.

10. There will be a larger number of lower values on the curve (the curve is negatively skewed) therefore the median value will be lower than the mean. The distribution is likely to be positively skewed, since Helen invests a lot of time right away and loses interest quickly. This suggests that there will be few small and many large time investments. Since the data will therefore be positively skewed, the median will be lower than the mean.

CHAPTER 7

1. Answers can be found by looking at column B of Appendix A.
    a) 0.3810
    b) 0.2995
    c) 0.4803
    d) 0.4131

2. Answers can be found in column C of Appendix A and, when z values are positive, subtracting the value from 1.
    a) Percentile rank $= 0.9878$ $(1 - 0.012)$
    b) Percentile rank $= 0.0475$
    c) Percentile rank $= 0.9236$ $(1 - 0.0764)$
    d) Percentile rank $= 0.3300$

3. Answers can be found in column C of Appendix A and, when z values are negative, subtracting the value from 1.
    a) 40.13 per cent of all cases are above a z-value of 0.25
    b) 88.69 per cent of all cases are above a z-value of -1.21 $(1 - 0.1131)$
    c) 11.31 per cent of all cases are above a z-value of 1.21
    d) 97.78 per cent of all cases are above a z-value of -2.01 $(1 - 0.0222)$

4. Answers can be found in column B of Appendix A.
    a) 59.64 per cent
    b) 12.88 per cent
    c) 83.53 per cent
    d) 7.69 per cent

5. Sigmund's percentile rank is 8.08. We get that number by calculating Z as:

$$z = \frac{X - \mu}{\sigma}$$
$$= \frac{45 - 52}{5}$$
$$= -1.40$$

The value comes from column C of Appendix A. Clearly, Sigmund didn't do very well.

6. Lesley did a bit better. From column C of Appendix A, $z = 0.4$ corresponds to 0.3446. Her percentile rank is 0.6554, which comes from subtracting 0.3446 (the area beyond z, or everyone that beat her) from 1. Here's the calculation for z:

$$z = \frac{X - \mu}{\sigma}$$
$$= \frac{54 - 52}{5}$$
$$= 0.40$$

7. Your child is quite bright, beating 93.7 per cent of all people that wrote the exam (this value comes from column C of Appendix A). This which corresponds to 0.0630. $1 - 0.0630 = .937$ percentile rank.

$$z = \frac{X - \mu}{\sigma}$$
$$= \frac{148 - 125}{15}$$
$$= 1.53$$

8. For Feng

$$z = \frac{X - \mu}{\sigma}$$
$$= \frac{76 - 80}{8}$$
$$= -0.50$$

This corresponds to 19.15 per cent (use column B).
For Lucy

$$z = \frac{X - \mu}{\sigma}$$
$$= \frac{94 - 80}{8}$$
$$= 1.75$$

This corresponds to 45.99 per cent (use column B).
65.14 per cent of all people are between these two scores.

9. Sixteen. Remember that only 5 per cent of all cases resides above or below 2 standard deviations, so knowing that the value for two standard deviations is 32 (120 − 88 = 32, 152 − 120 = 32) makes it easy to determine the value for one standard deviation.

10. a) Mean = 44.7, standard deviation = 13.01

    b) There are 6 hours that fall above or below ±1 standard deviation. There are no hours that fall above or below 2 or 3 standard deviations.

    c) Kody should go for early afternoon (between 1:00 and 2:00) because 28 per cent of chirps occur during this time.

CHAPTER 8

1. Since representativeness is the goal, a simple random sample would be preferred.

2. Given the focus on representativeness across facilities, a stratified random sample would be preferred.

3. Snowball samples are often used for vulnerable populations. A convenience sample might also be appropriate.

4. Since each instrument is needed in the sample, a stratified random sample would be preferred.

5. Given that the sample is random, selected cases will likely differ. Depending on how you chose to stratify, values here will also vary. There should only be six individuals in the sample.

6. a) Assuming that the Canadian population is 34,500,000, approximately 6,900,000 Canadians would have been administered the long-form census. Since the response is higher (94 per cent), approximately 6,486,000 would have completed the survey. This represents about 18.8 per cent of the entire Canadian population. Therefore, a long-form census questionnaire yields a higher response rate than the National Household Survey.

    b) Assuming that the Canadian population is 34,500,000, approximately 11,385,000 will be administered the National Household Survey. Since the expected response rate is 50 per cent, approximately 5,692,500 will complete the survey. This represents 16.5 per cent of the entire Canadian population.

CHAPTER 9

1. a)

	Men	Women
Mean	44.50	28.10
Standard deviation	8.68	8.54
Variance	75.39	72.99

   b) Standard error   2.75   2.70

c) For men (27.48, 61.52)
    For women (11.36, 44.84)

2. First calculate the mean, standard deviation, and the standard error:
    Mean = 10.92
    Standard deviation = 5.60
    Standard error = 1.14
    Then, find the appropriate t-value at $n - 1$ degrees of freedom:
    $t = 2.069$ for a 95 per cent confidence interval at $df = 23$.
    Confidence interval at 95 per cent: 8.33 < population mean < 13.05.
    We can be 95 per cent confident that the actual population mean for the number of hours students worked on their assignment was between 8.33 hours and 13.05 hours.

3. First, calculate the proportion standard of error:
    Standard error = 0.0670
    Confidence interval = 0.160, 0.520
    99 per cent confident that the real proportion lies between 0.160 percent and 0.520 percent

4. The standard error of a sample decreases as the number of observations increases. The confidence intervals increase as the number of observations increase, so we can be more confident in our results.

5. 71

6. Yes. Once you find the weight of the ninth cat, you have zero remaining degrees of freedom, because it is possible to find 10 values by knowing the sum or mean and $n - 1$ individual values.

7. 0.31376, 0.48624

8. a) One-tailed
    b) Two-tailed
    c) One-tailed
    d) Two-tailed
    e) One-tailed

9. Yes. The confidence interval for Roxio is 38,000 and 42,000, so your observational day is at the low end of a regular day.

10. 42.82, 73.58

CHAPTER 10

1. a) H_a = the amount of money raised will be different from the previous year
        H_0 = the amount of money raised will not be significantly different from the previous year

b) H_a = the amount of money raised will be greater than the previous year

H_0 = the amount of money raised will be equal or less than the previous year

2. a) $z = \dfrac{\overline{X} - \mu}{\sigma/\sqrt{N}}$

$= \dfrac{73 - 75}{8/\sqrt{5}}$

$= \dfrac{-2}{3.5776}$

$= -0.559$

b) The absolute value of 0.559 does not exceed the critical z-value of 1.96, suggesting that we cannot be 95 per cent confident in the superiority of Amber's new route.

3. $z = \dfrac{\overline{X} - \mu}{\sigma/\sqrt{N}}$

$= 31000 - 29000$

$= 27000/\sqrt{16}$

$= \dfrac{2000}{6750}$

$= 0.296$

Japer's income was significantly higher than the Canadian average, because the $z_{obtained}$ value does not exceed the critical value of 1.96.

4. We can be 95 per cent confident that the population proportion lies between 50.3 per cent (52 − 1.7) and 53.7 per cent (52 + 1.7).

5. There is an average of 4 leaves separating Ted's plants from his neighbour's, and both have a standard deviation of greater than 4, so we can't even be 68 per cent confident of the significance of the difference in means. Unfortunately, Ted cannot make a compelling case for basil superiority.

6. a) H_a = the girls will do significantly better than their competition

H_0 = the girls will do as equally well as the competition

b) H_a = the girls will do better or worse than their competition

H_0 = the girls will do as equally well as the competition

7. First calculate z for samples with proportions:

$$z_{obtained} = \dfrac{P_{sample} - P_{population}}{\sqrt{P_{population}(1 - P_{population})/n}}$$

$$= \dfrac{0.32 - 0.27}{\sqrt{0.27(1 - 0.27)/172}}$$

$$= \dfrac{0.05}{\sqrt{1.1459}}$$

$$= 1.477$$

$z_{obtained} = 1.477$. Because 1.477 does not exceed 1.96 (the critical value of z at 95 per cent confidence interval), we cannot say that there is a difference between Edmontonians and Albertans regarding their love for their home team at the 0.05 level.

8. Type two error

9. Increases

10. If you reject the null hypothesis, you are saying that the sample differs from the population on your outcome of interest.

CHAPTER 11

1. H_0 = There is no difference between the daily word counts of Leslie and Dayle.
   H_1 = Dayle's word count is significantly higher than Leslie's.
   This is a one-tailed test.

2. First, we need to calculate the mean and the sample standard deviation:
   For Leslie
   Mean = 519
   Sample standard deviation = 110.599
   For Dayle
   Mean = 495
   Sample standard deviation = 305.652
   With this information, we can calculate the standard error of the difference between means:

$$s_{X_1 - X_2} = \sqrt{\left(\frac{n_1 s_1^2 + n_2 s_2^2}{n_1 + n_2 - 2}\right)\left(\frac{n_1 + n_2}{n_1 n_2}\right)}$$

$$= \sqrt{\left(\frac{10 * 110.6^2 + 10 * 305.7^2}{10 + 10 - 2}\right)\left(\frac{10 + 10}{10 * 10}\right)}$$

$$= \sqrt{\left(\frac{1056848.5}{18}\right)\left(\frac{20}{100}\right)}$$

$$= \sqrt{58713.8 * 0.2}$$

$$= 108.36$$

Leslie's mean = 519 and Dayle's mean = 495, so Leslie has a higher average daily word count.

3. A t-test should be used because the sample size is small.

   Therefore, we calculate t as

$$z = \frac{\overline{X}_1 - \overline{X}_2}{s_{X_1 - X_2}}$$

$$= \frac{519 - 492}{108.36}$$
$$= 0.249$$

To find $t_{critical}$ calculate degrees of freedom as $df = (n_1 + n_2 - 2)$, which equals 18. At this level, $t_{critical} = 2.101$, which is much larger than $t_{observed}$, leading us to conclude that Leslie will beat Dayle.

4. H_0 = there is no difference between men and women on perceived life satisfaction

    H_1 = there is a difference between men and women on perceived life satisfaction

5. Since we have fairly large samples (>120), we can use the z-distribution and, consequently, the simpler calculation for the standard error of the difference between means:

$$s_{X_1 - X_2} = \sqrt{\left(\frac{s_1^2}{n_1 - 1} + \frac{s_2^2}{n_2 - 1} \right)}$$
$$= \sqrt{\left(\frac{7^2}{200 - 1} + \frac{5^2}{200 - 1} \right)}$$
$$= \sqrt{\left(\frac{49}{199} + \frac{25}{199} \right)}$$
$$= 0.610$$

This we use to calculate $z_{observed}$

$$z = \frac{\overline{X}_1 - \overline{X}_2}{s_{X_1 - X_2}}$$
$$= \frac{48 - 45}{0.610}$$
$$= 4.918$$

Comparing $z_{observed}$ to $z_{critical}$ value of 1.96, we can conclude that there are significant differences in the life satisfaction levels of men and women. Therefore, we would reject the null hypothesis.

6. H_0 = there is no difference between non-homeowners and homeowners concerning the importance of the distance to work

    H_1 = there is a difference between non-homeowners and homeowners concerning the importance of the distance to work

7. First, we need to calculate P_u:

$$p_u = \frac{n_1 P_{s_1} + n_2 P_{s_2}}{n_1 + n_2}$$
$$= \frac{201 * 0.76 + 218 * 0.68}{201 + 218}$$

$$= \frac{301}{419}$$

$$= 0.718$$

Next, we used P_u to calculate the standard error of the difference between means:

$$s_{X_1 X_2} = \sqrt{P_u(1 - P_u)\frac{n_1 + n_2}{n_1 n_2}}$$

$$= \sqrt{0.718(1 - 0.718)\frac{201 + 218}{201 * 218}}$$

$$= \sqrt{0.718(0.282)\frac{419}{43818}}$$

$$= \sqrt{0.202476 * 0.0095622803414122}$$

$$= \sqrt{0.0019361322744078}$$

$$= 0.0440015030925965$$

Finally, we calculate $z_{obtained}$:

$$z_{obtained} = \frac{\left(P_{s_1} - P_{s_2}\right)}{s_{\bar{X}_1 \bar{X}_2}}$$

$$= \frac{0.76 - 0.68}{0.044}$$

$$= 1.82$$

Comparing $z_{obtained}$ to $z_{critical}$ of 1.96, we can conclude that the differences are not statistically significant.

8. a) A t-test is more appropriate because the sample size is small.
   b) A one-tailed test is more appropriate because we are looking at a difference in one direction ("dogs have greater intelligence than cats").

9. First, we need to calculate the standard error of the difference between means:

$$s_{X_1 - X_2} = \sqrt{\left(\frac{n_1 s_1^2 + n_2 s_2^2}{n_1 + n_2 - 2}\right)\left(\frac{n_1 + n_2}{n_1 n_2}\right)}$$

$$= \sqrt{\left(\frac{93 * 12^2 + 28 * 12^2}{93 + 28 - 2}\right)\left(\frac{93 + 28}{93 * 28}\right)}$$

$$= \sqrt{\left(\frac{13392 + 4032}{119}\right)\left(\frac{121}{2604}\right)}$$

$$= \sqrt{146.42 * 0.05}$$

$$= \sqrt{6.804}$$

$$= 2.61$$

We can use this to calculate our t:

$$t = \frac{\overline{X}_1 - \overline{X}_2}{s_{\overline{X}_1 - \overline{X}_2}}$$

$$= \frac{75 - 79}{2.61}$$

$$= -1.53$$

To obtain the $t_{critical}$ value for 95 per cent confidence, we need to calculate our degrees of freedom for t as $df = (n_1 + n_2 - 2)$, or 119. Since our value is just below the highest value of 120, we will use the value for 120, which is 1.960. Our $t_{critical}$ is greater than our $t_{observed}$ value, indicating that there is no difference in the intelligence of dogs and cats.

CHAPTER 12

1. These values are nominal because the distance between response categories cannot be identified, nor can the categories cannot be ranked.

2. Chi-square = 1133.1

3. There are 6 degrees of freedom.

4. Phi = $\phi = \sqrt{\frac{\chi^2}{n}} = 0.656$, Cramer's $V = \sqrt{\frac{\chi^2}{(n)(\min(r - 1)|(c - 1))}} = 0.464$. It is preferable to use Cramer's V because the table is bigger that 2 by 2.

5. The appropriate statistics to measure the association is phi because the table is 2 by 2. Chi-square = 185.4. Phi = 0.469.

    a) H_0 = People who live in Quebec City are no more likely to identify as Roman Catholic than Church of England.
        H_1 = People who live in Quebec City are more likely to be Roman Catholic than Church of England.

6. H_0 = Male and females believe equally that facial recognition does not constitute an infringement of privacy.
    H_1 = Male and females differ in the belief that facial recognition constitutes an infringement of privacy.

7. First, make two predictions ignoring the independent variable:
    The difference between everyone answering "yes" and the number who actually say "yes" is $2{,}917 - 1{,}075 = 1{,}842$. The difference between everyone answering "no" and the number who actually say "no" is $2{,}917 - 1{,}842 = 1{,}075$. The lowest of these is 1,075, so $E_1 = 1{,}075$.

Second, take account of the sex of respondents:

The difference between all females answering "yes" and those who actually do is $1,699 - 699 = 1,000$. The difference between all females answering "no" and those who actually do is $1,699 - 1,000 = 699$. The difference between all males answering "yes" and those who actually do is $1,218 - 376 = 842$. The difference between all males answering "no" and those who actually do is $1,218 - 842 = 376$.
Add the lowest two values to find $E_2 = 699 + 376 = 1,075$.
Lambda $= (E_1 - E_2)/E_1 = (1,075 - 1,075)/1,075 = 0$

8. Since lambda is zero, knowing if someone is male or female will not allow us to predict that person's views on facial recognition.

9. Chi-square $= 2.13$. Bo and Jonah's hypothesis is not supported because the calculated value is well below the critical value of 3.841 for a 0.05 level of significance.

CHAPTER 13

1. $H_0 =$ Exercising every week does not lead to any changes in self-rated health.
    $H_1 =$ People who exercise every week have a better scores for self-rated health.

2. $N_{same} = 325$ and $N_{diff} = 187$, so gamma $= 0.270$. This value supports Jerry's hypothesis

3. $H_0 =$ Canadian Universities receive the same amount money as they have in the past.
    $H_1 =$ Canadian Universities receive the more money than they have in the past.

4. Spearman's $rho = 0.59$. This value indicates a strong and positive relationship, suggesting that we should reject the null hypothesis.

5. $H_0 =$ the weight of a squirrel does not impact how much food a squirrel will hide away for the winter.
    $H_1 =$ the more a squirrel weights, the more food that a squirrel will hide away for the winter.

6. Somer's $d = 0.339$. The value indicates that there is strong positive relationship between the weight of a squirrel and the amount of food that a squirrel will hide away for the winter. Therefore, we would fail to support the null hypothesis.

7. Kendall's tau-$b = 0.341$. The result of tau-b does not lead us to make a different decision regarding the hypothesis. Because $Ties_x$ and $Ties_y$ are close, there is little effect on the denominator.

CHAPTER 14

1. a) $H_0 =$ There is no relationship between family income and family size.
        $H_1 =$ There is a positive relationship between family income and family size.
        $H_2 =$ There is a negative relationship between family income and family size.

b) $r = -0.2239$

c) We can assess the statistical significance of r by using a t-test:

$$t_{observed} = r\sqrt{\frac{n-2}{1-r^2}}$$

$$= -0.2239\sqrt{\frac{10-2}{1-(-0.2239)^2}}$$

$$= -0.2239\sqrt{\frac{8}{1-0.05}}$$

$$= -0.2239 * 2.902$$

$$= -0.649$$

Since the $t_{observed}$ value of -0.649 is below the $t_{critical}$ value of 2.306, we cannot be 95 per cent confident that the sample r value of -0.2239 did not occur by chance.

d) With $N = 100$, $r = 0.665$. The r-value is higher as the sample size increases. Therefore, we can be more confident that there is no relationship between family income and family size. $t_{critical} = 1.984$. $t_{observed} = 8.8$.

2. The line will slope downwards because of the negative association.

3. H_0 = There is no relationship between how much Chris spends and how much Josie spends when they eat out together
    H_1 = Chris and Josie have a tendency to spend about the same amount as each other when they eat out together.

4. Pearson's $r = 0.281$.

5. We can assess the statistical significance of r by using a t-test:

$$t_{observed} = r\sqrt{\frac{n-2}{1-r^2}}$$

$$= 0.281\sqrt{\frac{8-2}{1-0.281^2}}$$

$$= 0.281\sqrt{\frac{6}{1-0.79}}$$

$$= 0.281 * 2.2825$$

$$= 0.6414$$

Since the $t_{observed}$ value of 0.6414 is below the $t_{critical}$ value of 2.447, we cannot be 95 per cent confident that the sample r value of 0.281 did not occur by chance.

6. Because of the weak correlation of the results, Chris and Josie's concerns are unwarranted and perhaps there is another explanation for why they are spending too much money at restaurants.

CHAPTER 15

1. H_0 = the same amount of calories are burned no matter what type of exercise activity is chosen.

    H_1 = there is a relationship between the amount of calories burned and the type of exercise activity that is chosen.

2. a)

	Bicycling		Cleaning		Health club		Yoga		Tennis	
	X	X²	X	X²	X	X²	X	X²	X	X²
	236	55,696	207	42,849	325	105,625	236	55,696	413	170,569
	321	103,041	249	62,001	401	160,801	312	97,344	599	358,801
	345	119,025	292	85,264	452	204,304	345	119,025	604	364,816
	292	85,264	302	91,204	474	224,676	281	78,961	434	188,356
	301	90,601	222	49,284	353	124,609	301	90,601	477	227,529
Sum	1,495	453,627	1,272	330,602	2,005	820,015	1,475	441,627	2,527	1,310,071
X̄	299		254.4		401		295		505.4	

$N = 25$

Grand mean $= 350.96$

---

b) $SS_{total} = \sum X^2_{total} - N_{total} \overline{X}^2_{total}$

$\qquad = (453627 + 330602 + 820015 + 441627 + 1310071) - 25(350)^2$

$\qquad = 3355942 - 25\,(123172.92)$

$\qquad = 276619$

$SS_{within} = \sum (X - \overline{X}_{group})^2$

$\qquad = 3355942 - [5(299)^2 + 5(254.4)^2 + 5(401)^2 + 5(295)^2 + 5(505.4)^2]$

$\qquad = 3355942 - [447005 + 323596.8 + 804005 + 435125 + 1277145.8]$

$\qquad = 3355942 - 3286877.61$

$\qquad = 69064.39$

$SS_{between} = \sum N_{group} (\overline{X}_{group} - \overline{X})^2$

$\qquad = 3286877.6 - 3079323.04$

$\qquad = 207554.56$

c) $df_{within} = N_{total} - k \qquad\qquad df_{between} = k - 1$

$\qquad = 25 - 5 \qquad\qquad\qquad\quad = 5 - 1$

$\qquad = 20 \qquad\qquad\qquad\qquad\;\; = 4$

d) $MS_{within} = SS_{within}/df_{within} \qquad MS_{between} = SS_{between}/df_{between}$

$\qquad = 69064.39/20 \qquad\qquad\qquad = 207554.56/4$

$\qquad = 3453.22 \qquad\qquad\qquad\qquad = 51888.64$

e) $F = MS_{between}/MS_{within}$

$\quad = 51888.64/3453.22$

$\quad = 15.03$

f) $F_{observed} = 15.03$ and $F_{critical} = 2.87$. So $F_{observed} > F_{critical}$. We can be 95 per cent confident that at least two groups differ significantly in the number of calories burnt per hour.

3. $H_0 =$ there is no relationship between the price of jeans and their durability.

$H_1 =$ there is a relationship between the price of jeans and their durability.

4. a)

	Durabiltiy of Jeans							
	Levi's		People's Liberty		Silvers		Guess	
	X	X²	X	X²	X	X²	X	X²
1	182	33,124	209	43,681	1,040	1,081,600	260	67,600
2	130	16,900	225	50,625	780	608,400	624	389,376
3	91	8,281	156	24,336	520	270,400	416	173,056
4	200	40,000	260	67,600	340	115,600	222	49,284
5	154	23,716	101	10,201	416	173,056	85	7,224
Sum	757	122,021	951	196,443	3,096	2,249,056	1,607	686,541
X	151.4		190.2		619.2		321.4	

$N = 20$

Grand mean = 320.55

$$SS_{total} = \sum X^2_{total} - N_{total}\overline{X}^2_{total}$$
$$= (122021 + 196443 + 2249056 + 686541) - 20(320.55)^2$$
$$= 3254061 - 20(102752.30)$$
$$= 1199015$$

$$SS_{between} = \sum N_{group}(\overline{X}_{group} - \overline{X})^2$$
$$= (122021 + 196443 + 2249056 + 686541) - [5(151.4)^2 + 5(190.2)^2$$
$$+ 5(619.2)^2 + 5(321.4)^2]$$
$$= 3254061 - [114609.8 + 180880.2 + 1917043.2 + 516489.8]$$
$$= 3254061 - 2729023$$
$$= 525038$$

$$SS_{between} = \sum N_{group}(\overline{X}_{group} - \overline{X})^2$$
$$= [5(151.4)^2 + 5(190.2)^2 + 5(619.2)^2 + 5(321.4)^2] - 20(320.55)^2$$
$$= 2729023 - 2055046.05$$
$$= 673976.95$$

$$df_{within} = N_{total} - k \qquad\qquad df_{between} = k - 1$$
$$= 20 - 4 \qquad\qquad\qquad = 4 - 1$$
$$= 16 \qquad\qquad\qquad\qquad = 3$$

$$MS_{within} = SS_{within}/df_{within} \qquad MS_{between} = SS_{between}/df_{between}$$
$$= 525038/16 \qquad\qquad\qquad = 673976.95/3$$
$$= 32814.88 \qquad\qquad\qquad = 224658.98$$

b) $F = MS_{between}/MS_{within}$
$$= 224658.98/32814.88$$
$$= 6.846$$

c) Since the $F_{observed}$ value of 6.846 exceeds the $F_{critical}$ value of 3.24, we know with 95 per cent certainty that at least two of our groups differ significantly in terms of durability. Because $F_{observed} = 6.846$ exceeds $F_{critical}$ of 3.24, there is enough evidence to reject the null hypothesis.

5.

	Kingsway		City Centre		Southgate	
	X	X^2	X	X^2	X	X^2
1	45	2,025	32	1,024	51	2,601
2	32	1,024	47	2,209	55	3,025
3	44	1,936	55	3,025	31	961
4	43	1,849	41	1,681	30	900
Sum	164	6,834	175	7,939	167	7,487
$\bar{X}$	41		43.75		41.75	

$N = 12$

Grand mean = 42.2

$SS_{total} = \sum(X - \bar{X})^2$

$= (45 - 42.2)^2 + (32 - 42.2)^2 + (44 - 42.2)^2 + (43 - 42.2)^2 + (32 - 42.2)^2$
$+ (47 - 42.2)^2 + (55 - 42.2)^2 + (41 - 42.2)^2 + (51 - 42.2)^2 + (55 - 42.2)^2$
$+ (31 - 42.2)^2 + (30 - 42.2)^2$

$= 923.67$

$SS_{within} = \sum(X - \bar{X}_{group})^2$
$= 22260 - [4(41)^2 + 4(43.75)^2 + 4(41.75)^2]$
$= 22260 - [6724 + 7656.25 + 6972.25]$
$= 22260 - 21352.5$
$= 907.52$

$SS_{between} = SS_{total} - SS_{within}$
$= 923.67 - 907.52$
$= 16.15$

$$df_{within} = N_{total} - k$$
$$= 12 - 3$$
$$= 9$$

$$df_{between} = k - 1$$
$$= 3 - 1$$
$$= 2$$

$$MS_{within} = SS_{within}/df_{within}$$
$$= 907.5/9$$
$$= 100.84$$

$$MS_{between} = SS_{between}/df_{between}$$
$$= 16.15/2$$
$$= 8.08$$

$$F_{observed} = MS_{between}/MS_{within}$$
$$= 8.08/100.84$$
$$= 0.080$$

$$F_{critical} = 4.26$$

There is no significant difference between the respective malls in terms of visitors because the value of $F_{observed}$ does not exceed the $F_{critical}$ value.

CHAPTER 16

1. a) $X = 2.33$
       $Y = 771.42$

    b) and c)

X	X − X̄	Y	y − ȳ	(X − X̄)(y − ȳ)	(X − X̄)²	(y − ȳ)²
3	0.67	890	118.58	79.45	0.45	14,061.22
2	−0.33	568	−203.42	67.13	0.11	41,379.70
3	0.67	860	88.58	59.35	0.45	7,846.42
1	−1.33	625	−146.42	194.74	1.77	21,438.82
1	−1.33	775	3.58	−4.76	1.77	12.82
3	0.67	900	128.58	86.15	0.45	16,532.82
3	0.67	1,095	323.58	216.8	0.45	104,704.02
3	0.67	800	28.58	19.15	0.45	816.82
2	−0.33	765	−6.42	2.12	0.11	41.22
3	0.67	629	−142.42	−95.42	0.45	20,283.46
1	−1.33	600	−171.42	227.99	1.77	29,384.82
3	0.67	750	−21.42	−14.35	0.45	458.82
			Σ	838.35	8.68	256,960.96

$SP = 838.35$
$SS_x = 8.68$
$SS_y = 256960.96$

d) $b = \dfrac{SP}{SS_X}$

    $= 838.35/8.68$

    $= 96.58$

e) $a = \bar{Y} - b\bar{X}$

    $= 771.42 - (96.58)(2.33)$

    $= 771.42 - 225.03$

    $= 546.39$

f) $r = \dfrac{SP}{\sqrt{SS_X SS_Y}}$

    $= \dfrac{838.35}{\sqrt{(8.68)(2566960.96)}}$

    $= \dfrac{838.35}{\sqrt{2230421.13}}$

    $= 8.38/1493.46$

    $= 0.56$

g) $r^2 = 0.56 * 0.56$

    $= 0.31$

h) and i) Having found values for a and b, substitute into the following equation to find values for $\hat{Y}$:

$\hat{Y} = a + bX$

$\hat{Y} = 546.39 + 96.58X$

Number of rooms (X)	Monthly rent (Y)	$\hat{Y}$	$Y - \hat{Y}$	$(Y - \hat{Y})^2$
3	890	836.13	53.87	2,901.98
2	568	739.55	−171.55	29,429.40
3	860	836.13	23.87	569.78
1	625	642.97	−17.97	322.92
1	775	642.97	132.03	17,431.92
3	900	836.13	63.87	4,079.38
3	1,095	836.13	258.87	67,013.68
3	800	836.13	−36.13	1,305.38
2	765	739.55	25.45	647.70
3	629	836.13	−207.13	42,902.84
1	600	642.97	−42.97	1,846.42
3	750	836.13	−86.13	7,418.38
			Σ	175,869.78

j)

$$se_b = \frac{\sqrt{\dfrac{(Y - \hat{Y})^2}{n - 2}}}{\sqrt{(X - \hat{X})^2}}$$

$$= \frac{\sqrt{\dfrac{175869.78}{12 - 2}}}{\sqrt{8.68}}$$

$$= \frac{132.6159}{2.9462}$$

$$= 45.01$$

$$t_{observed} = \frac{b}{se_b}$$

$$= \frac{96.58}{45.01}$$

$$= 2.15$$

$$df = n - 2$$
$$= 12 - 2$$
$$= 10$$

$$t_{critical} = 2.228$$

With a confidence interval set at 95%, $t_{observed} < t_{critical}$, providing insufficient evidence to reject the null that there is no relationship between the two variables.

2. a) $X = 2.33$
   $Y = 139.56$

# of people (X)	$X - \bar{X}$	Bills (Y)	$y - \bar{y}$	$(X - \bar{X})(y - \bar{y})$	$(X - \bar{X})^2$	$(Y - \hat{Y})^2$
3	0.67	175	35.44	23.63	0.44	1,256.29
2	-0.33	130	-9.56	3.19	0.11	91.31
3	0.67	231	91.44	60.96	0.44	8,362.04
3	0.67	278	138.44	92.30	0.44	19,166.79
2	0.33	40	-99.56	33.19	0.11	9,911.36
3	0.67	205.83	66.27	44.18	0.44	4,392.27
1	-1.33	0	-139.56	186.07	1.78	19,475.83
1	-1.33	38.41	-101.15	134.86	1.78	10,230.48
1	-1.33	41.23	-98.33	131.10	1.78	9,667.97
3	0.67	44.2	-95.36	-63.57	0.44	9,092.73
3	0.67	176	36.44	24.30	0.44	1,328.18
3	0.67	315	175.44	116.96	0.44	30,780.66
			Σ	787.17	8.67	123,755.90

$$SP = 787.13$$
$$SS_x = 8.68$$
$$SS_y = 123755.87$$

$$b = \frac{SP}{SS_X}$$
$$= 787.17/8.67$$
$$= 90.83$$

$$a = \bar{Y} - b\bar{X}$$
$$= 139.56 - (90.83)(2.33)$$
$$= 139.56 - 211.63$$
$$= -72.07$$

$$r = \frac{SP}{\sqrt{SS_X SS_Y}}$$
$$= \frac{787.17}{\sqrt{(8.67)(123755.90)}}$$
$$= \frac{787.17}{\sqrt{1072963.65}}$$
$$= 787.17/1035.84$$
$$= 0.76$$

$$r^2 = 0.76 * 0.76$$
$$= 0.58$$

b) Standard deviation for $X = 0.89$
Standard deviation of $Y = 106.07$

c) The slope coefficient is 90.83.

d) The estimated monthly charge for a household of four people is $\hat{Y} = -71.72 + 90.68 * 4 = 291$.

e) The standarized value of $b = 0.76$

$$b_{1*} = b_1\left(\frac{s_1}{s_y}\right)$$
$$= 90.68 \, (0.89/106.07)$$
$$= 0.76$$

3. a) $\sum X_1 = 241$
$\sum X_2 = 1135$
$\sum Y = 328$
$\sum (X_1)^2 = 3979$
$\sum (X_2)^2 = 88158$
$\sum Y^2 = 7198.74$

$\sum(X_1 * Y) = 5319$

$\sum(X_2 * Y) = 24785.5$

$\sum(X_1 * X_2) = 18210$

Standard deviation $X_1 = 2.76$

Standard deviation $X_2 = 12.75$

Standard deviation $Y = 1.38$

$$r_{X_1Y} = \frac{N\sum X_1 Y - \left(\sum X_1\right)\left(\sum Y\right)}{\sqrt{\left[N\sum X_1^2 - (X_1)^2\right]\left[N\sum Y^2 - (Y)^2\right]}}$$

$$r_{X_1Y} = \frac{15(5315) - (241)(328)}{\sqrt{\left[15(3979) - 241^2\right]\left[15(7198.75) - 328^2\right]}}$$

$$r_{X_1Y} = \frac{79695 - 79048}{\sqrt{\left[59685 - 58081\right]\left[107981.25 - 107584\right]}}$$

$$r_{X_1Y} = \frac{647}{\sqrt{(1604)(397.25)}}$$

$$r_{X_1Y} = \frac{647}{798.2411916}$$

$$r_{X_1Y} = 0.810531963$$

$$r_{X_2Y} = \frac{N\sum X_2 Y - \left(\sum X_2\right)\left(\sum Y\right)}{\sqrt{\left[N\sum X_2^2 - (X_2)^2\right]\left[N\sum Y^2 - (Y)^2\right]}}$$

$$= \frac{15(24785.5) - (1135)(328)}{\sqrt{\left[15(88159) - 1135^2\right]\left[15(7198.75) - 328^2\right]}}$$

$$= \frac{371782.5 - 372280}{\sqrt{(1322385 - 1288225)(397.25)}}$$

$$= \frac{-497.5}{\sqrt{(34160)(397.25)}}$$

$$= \frac{-497.5}{3683.76}$$

$$= -0.135052229$$

$$r_{X_1X_2} = \frac{N\sum X_1 X_2 - \left(\sum X_1\right)\left(\sum X_2\right)}{\sqrt{\left[N\sum X_1^2 - (X_1)^2\right]\left[N\sum X_2^2 - (X_2)^2\right]}}$$

$$= \frac{15(18210) - (241)(1135)}{\sqrt{\left[15(3979) - 241^2\right]\left[15(88159) - 1135^2\right]}}$$

$$= \frac{273150 - 273535}{\sqrt{(1604)(34160)}}$$

$$= \frac{273150 - 273535}{\sqrt{(1604)(34160)}}$$

$$= \frac{-385}{7402.205077}$$

$$= -0.052011523$$

$$b_1 = \left(\frac{s_Y}{s_{X_1}}\right)\left(\frac{r_{X_1Y} - r_{X_2Y}r_{X_1X_2}}{1 - r_{X_1X_2}^2}\right)$$

$$= \left(\frac{1.38}{2.76}\right)\left(\frac{0.810531963 - (-0.135052229 * -0.052011523)}{1 - (-0.052011523)^2}\right)$$

$$= (0.5)\left(\frac{0.810531963 - 0.00702427}{1 - 0.002520155662}\right)$$

$$= (0.5)\left(\frac{0.803507693}{0.997479845}\right)$$

$$= (0.5)(0.80553777)$$

$$= 0.402768885$$

$$b_2 = \left(\frac{s_Y}{s_{X_2}}\right)\left(\frac{r_{X_2Y} - r_{X_1Y}r_{X_1X_2}}{1 - r_{X_1X_2}^2}\right)$$

$$= \left(\frac{1.38}{12.75}\right)\left(\frac{-0.135052229 - (0.810531963 * -0.052011523)}{1 - (-0.052011523)^2}\right)$$

$$= (0.1082353)\left(\frac{-0.135052229 - (-0.042157001)}{1 - 0.002520155662}\right)$$

$$= (0.1082353)\left(\frac{-0.0928925228}{0.997479845}\right)$$

$$= (0.1082353)(-0.093129929)$$

$$= -0.010079945$$

The partial slope coefficients are $b_1 = 0.40$ and $b_2 = -0.01$

b)

$$b_{1*} = b_1\left(\frac{s_{x1}}{s_y}\right)$$

$$= 0.402768885\left(\frac{2.76}{1.38}\right)$$

$$= 0.402768885\,(2)$$

$$= 0.8055$$

$$b_{2*} = b_2\left(\frac{s_{x2}}{s_y}\right)$$

$$= -0.010079945\left(\frac{12.75}{1.38}\right)$$

$$= -0.010079945\,(9.239130434782609)$$

$$= -0.0931$$

The standardized slope coefficients are b_1 standardized $= 0.8055$

b_2 standardized $= -0.0931$. Since $b_{1*} > b_{2*}$ age is a more important factor than grades.

c) $\hat{Y} = a + b_1X_1 + b_2X_2$

$$= 16.185 + (0.40 * 17) + (-0.01 * 96)$$

$$= 16.185 + (6.8) + (-0.96)$$

$$= 22.025$$

The curfew for 96% grade average and age 17 should be 22.03 or roughly 10:00 PM.

4. As the magnitude of a beta weight increases, r will increase.

CHAPTER 17

1. a) 0.0101
    b) 0.0526
    c) 0.1111
    d) 0.25
    e) 1
    f) 2.003
    g) 3
    h) 7.9286
    i) 999

2. a) 0.3286
    b) 1.2498
    c) 16.119
    d) 1

e) 0.0973

f) 0.0004

CHAPTER 18

1. The mean and standard deviation for the x-variables are 9.00 and 3.32, and for the y-variables they are 7.5 and 2.03, respectively.

2. The slope would be higher and the y-intercept would be lower.

3. This question is a little tricky, because there are only two independent variables, x and $x4$. The r value for x on $x4$ is −0.5, and the r value for $x4$ on x is the same, −0.5. So, we will have the same variance inflation factor (VIF) each time. Cook's distance $= 8.1$.

$$\text{VIF}_X = \frac{1}{1 - R_X^2}$$

$$= \frac{1}{1 - 0.25}$$

$$= 1.333$$

$$\text{VIF}_{X4} = \frac{1}{1 - R_{X4}^2}$$

$$= \frac{1}{1 - 0.25}$$

$$= 1.333$$

4. Cook's Distance for the 11th observation $= 8.1$. Because this is greater than 1, this observation is a cause for concern.

    Cook's Distance for the 9th observation $= 0.14$. Since this is not greater than 1, this observation is not a cause for concern.

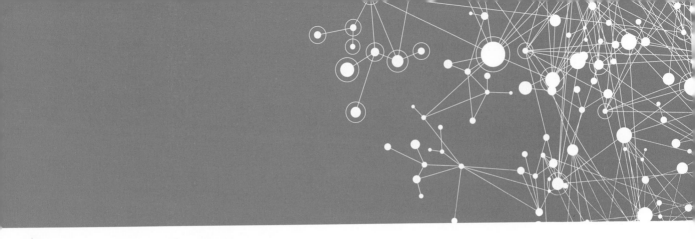

Solution Key for Boxes

BOX 7.1: IT'S YOUR TURN: DETERMINING THE PROPORTION OF OBSERVATIONS AT VARIOUS STANDARD DEVIATION CUT-POINTS

1. 2.5%
2. 0.5%
3. 50%
4. 16%
5. 97.5%

BOX 7.3: IT'S YOUR TURN: CONVERTING STANDARD SCORES TO PERCENTILE RANKS

1. Range of values ±1 standard deviation from the mean.
   We know that z will equal ±1, therefore we solve the standard score equation for X.
   For the lower bound

$$z = \frac{X - \mu}{\sigma}$$
$$-1 = \frac{X - 5.7}{5.1}$$
$$5.1 * -1 = X - 5.7$$
$$-5.1 + 5.7 = X$$
$$0.6 = X$$

For the upper bound

$$z = \frac{X - \mu}{\sigma}$$

$$1 = \frac{X - 5.7}{5.1}$$

$$5.1 * 1 = X - 5.7$$

$$5.1 + 5.7 = X$$

$$10.8 = X$$

Therefore 68% of Canadians between ages 18 and 29 go out to a restaurant, movie, or theatre approximately 1 (0.6) to 11 (10.8) evenings per month.

2. Value that the lowest 10% of all observations fall below.

Because we are looking for a value that extends towards the tail (not from the value to the mean), we look in column C for 0.10 (or column B for 0.40). The z-score value is -1.28 (remember to change from an absolute value to the end of the distribution you are focused on).

$$z = \frac{X - \mu}{\sigma}$$

$$-1.28 = \frac{X - 5.7}{5.1}$$

$$5.1 * -1.28 = X - 5.7$$

$$-6.528 + 5.7 = X$$

$$-0.828 = X$$

Since a person cannot go out less than zero times a month, we can say that the 10% of people who go out least frequently go out about 0 times per month.

3. Value which the highest 40% of all observations are above.

We are looking for a value that extends towards the tail (not from the value to the mean). So we will look in column C for 0.40 (or column B for 0.10). The z-score value is 0.25:

$$z = \frac{X - \bar{X}}{s}$$

$$0.25 = \frac{X - 5.7}{5.1}$$

$$5.1 * +0.25 = X - 5.7$$

$$1.275 + 5.7 = X$$

$$6.975 = X$$

We can say we expect that the 40% of people who go out the most frequently go out at least 7 times per month.

4. The percentage of cases that fall between the values of 4 and 9.

We will need to calculate the z-score for both the upper and lower limits that we have:

Lower limit

$$z = \frac{X - \overline{X}}{s}$$

$$= \frac{4 - 5.7}{5.1}$$

$$= \frac{-1.7}{5.1}$$

$$= -0.333$$

The z-score of −0.333 is equal to 0.129 or 12.9%. Thus 12.9% of people fall between the mean and going out 4 nights per month.

Upper limit

$$z = \frac{X - \overline{X}}{s}$$

$$= \frac{9 - 5.7}{5.1}$$

$$= \frac{3.3}{5.1}$$

$$= 0.647$$

The z-score of 0.647 is equal to 0.242 or 24.2%. Thus 24.2% of people fall between the mean and going out 9 nights per month.

Adding the percentage between the mean and 4, and between the mean and 7 will give the total % of people in this range. 12.9 + 24.2 = 37.1% of people between the ages of 18 and 29 go out between about 4 and 9 nights per month to a restaurant, movie, or theatre.

5. Value which 75% of all observations fall below.

This time we are looking at a value above 50%, or more than half of the distribution. Therefore our value must be above the mean. Since we know that 50% covers from the mean to the lowest value, we know that 25% will fall above the mean (75% – 50%). Therefore we are looking for the z-score at which 25% of cases are between it and the mean.

We are looking for a value towards the mean (column B) for 0.25. The z-score value is 0.67.

$$z = \frac{X - \overline{X}}{s}$$

$$0.67 = \frac{X - 5.7}{5.1}$$

$$5.1 * + 0.67 = X - 5.7$$

$$3.417 + 5.7 = X$$

$$9.12 = X$$

We can expect that 75% of Canadians aged 18 to 29 go out 9 times or less per month.

BOX 10.3: IT'S YOUR TURN: t-TEST FOR THE SAME SAMPLE MEASURED TWICE

Individual	# of partners per year at age 18	# of partners per year at age 21	$d_i = x_{i1} - x_{i2}$	d^2
1	2	1	1	1
2	0	0	0	0
3	3	2	1	1
4	1	2	−1	1
5	8	1	7	49
6	1	1	0	0
7	2	1	1	1
8	0	2	−2	4
9	0	4	−4	16
10	3	1	2	4
	$\overline{X}_1 = 2.00$	$\overline{X}_2 = 1.50$	$\sum d_i = 5$	$\sum d^2 = 77$

1. See table for solutions.

2. See table for solutions.

3. $s_d = \sqrt{\dfrac{\sum d^2}{n-1} - (\overline{X}_1 - \overline{X}_2)^2}$

   $s_d = \sqrt{\dfrac{77}{9} - (2.0 - 1.5)^2}$

   $= \sqrt{8.56 - 0.25}$

   $= 2.88$

4. $s_{\bar{d}} = \dfrac{s_d}{\sqrt{n-1}}$

$= \dfrac{2.88}{\sqrt{9}}$

$= 0.96$

5. $t = \dfrac{\bar{X}_1 - \bar{X}_2}{s_{\bar{d}}}$

$= \dfrac{2.0 - 1.5}{0.96}$

$= 0.52$

6. There is no significant difference between ages, because $t_{observed}$ does not exceed the $t_{critical}$ value of 2.262.

BOX 11.1: IT'S YOUR TURN: THE TWO-SAMPLE t-TEST

1. There will be no difference in feelings of attachment between people who are second generation Canadians versus third generation Canadians.

2. Sophia has asked a question that requires a two-sample t-test (actually, a z-test is what's asked for, but given the large sample size, you could do either).
First, calculate the standard error of the difference between means:

$$s_{\bar{X}_1 - \bar{X}_2} = \sqrt{\left(\dfrac{N_1 s_1^2 + N_2 s_2^2}{N_1 + N_2 - 2}\right)\left(\dfrac{N_1 + N_2}{N_1 N_2}\right)}$$

$$= \sqrt{\left(\dfrac{6799 * 0.776^2 + 23237 * 0.593}{6799 + 23237 - 2}\right)\left(\dfrac{6799 + 23237}{6799 * 23237}\right)}$$

$$= \sqrt{\left(\dfrac{12265.46}{30034}\right)\left(\dfrac{30036}{157988363}\right)}$$

$$= \sqrt{0.408 * 0.00019}$$

$$= 0.0088$$

Then, calculate t:

$$t = \dfrac{\bar{X}_1 - \bar{X}_2}{s_{\bar{X}_1 - \bar{X}_2}}$$

$$= \dfrac{4.59 - 4.78}{0.0088}$$

$$= -21.59$$

The answer may also be -21.56 if no rounding takes place in the previous steps.

3. You would reject the null hypothesis.

BOX 11.2: IT'S YOUR TURN: THE TWO-SAMPLE PROPORTION

1. Calculate P_u the estimate of the proportion of the population in the category of interest (the proportion of somewhat spiritual men and women who use prayer) by using the equation:

$$P_u = \frac{n_1 P_{s1} + n_2 P_{s2}}{n_1 + n_2} = \frac{114734 * 0.381 + 143013 * 0.516}{114734 + 143013} = \frac{43713.65 + 73794.71}{257747} = 0.456$$

2. Use this value to calculate the standard deviation of the difference between sample proportions:

$$\begin{aligned}
s_{\bar{X}_1 - \bar{X}_2} &= \sqrt{P_u * (1 - P_u)\frac{n_1 + n_2}{n_1 n_2}} \\
&= \sqrt{0.456(1 - 0.456)\frac{114734 + 103013}{114734 * 143013}} \\
&= \sqrt{0.257\frac{257747}{16408453542}} \\
&= \sqrt{0.257 * 0.0000157} \\
&= 0.002
\end{aligned}$$

3. Calculate the value of $z_{obtained}$ using

$$z_{obtained} = \frac{(P_{s1} - P_{s2})}{s_{\bar{X}_1 - \bar{X}_2}} = \frac{0.381 - 0.516}{0.002} = -67.5$$

4. As −67.5 is much larger than the one-tailed critical value of −1.65, we can be 95% confident that Aboriginal women who consider themselves very, somewhat, or not very spiritual are more likely to use prayer than Aboriginal men who consider themselves very, somewhat, or not very spiritual to maintain their religion or spirituality.

BOX 12.3: IT'S YOUR TURN: PHI—DRINKING AND DAILY EXERCISE

1.

| | Regularly has more than 12 drinks a week | | |
Exercises daily	Yes	No	Total
Yes	4	2	6
No	5	9	14
Total	9	11	20

2. Upper left $\quad f_e = \dfrac{\Sigma_{column} * \Sigma_{row}}{N} = \dfrac{9 * 6}{20} = \dfrac{54}{20} = 2.7$

Upper right $\quad f_e = \dfrac{\Sigma_{column} * \Sigma_{row}}{N} = \dfrac{11 * 6}{20} = \dfrac{66}{20} = 3.3$

Lower left $\quad f_e = \dfrac{\Sigma_{column} * \Sigma_{row}}{N} = \dfrac{9 * 14}{20} = \dfrac{126}{20} = 6.3$

Lower right $\quad f_e = \dfrac{\Sigma_{column} * \Sigma_{row}}{N} = \dfrac{11 * 14}{20} = \dfrac{154}{20} = 7.7$

| | Regularly has more than 12 drinks a week | | |
Exercises daily	Yes	No	Total
Yes	4 (2.7)	2 (3.3)	6
No	5 (6.3)	9 (7.7)	14
Total	9	11	20

3.

Group	f_o	f_e	$(f_o - f_e)^2$	$\dfrac{(f_o - f_e)^2}{f_e}$
YY	4	2.7	1.69	0.63
YN	2	3.3	1.69	0.51
NY	5	6.3	1.69	0.27
NN	9	7.7	1.69	0.22
Total	20	20		$\chi^2 = 1.63$

4. $\phi = \sqrt{\dfrac{\chi^2}{N}} = \sqrt{\dfrac{1.63}{20}} = 0.285$

There is a moderate association between daily exercise and regularly drinking 12 or more drinks a week.

BOX 12.5: IT'S YOUR TURN: CRAMER'S V

1. We are given the following information:

Work Status in 2000	Marital Status			Total
	Married	Divorced/separated	Single	
Worked mainly full-time weeks	3,485,748 (3,321,615.99)	604,011 (525,916.09)	1,193,175 (1,435,401.92)	5,282,934
Worked mainly part-time weeks	1,291,201 (1,455,333.0)	152,330 (230,424.9)	871,134 (628,907.1)	2,314,665
Total	4,776,949	756,341	2,064,309	7,597,599

In order to calculate chi-square, create a table comparing the variables:

Group	f_o	f_e	$(f_o - f_e)^2$	$\dfrac{(f_o - f_e)^2}{f_e}$
FM	3,485,748	3,321,615.99	164,133.00	8,110.40
FD	604,011	525,916.09	78,094.91	11,596.58
FS	1,193,175	1,435,401.92	−242,226.92	40,875.299
PM	1,291,201	1,455,333.00	−164,132.00	18,510.76
PD	152,330	230,424.90	−78,094.90	26,467.68
PS	871,134	628,907.10	242,226.90	93,294.97
Total	7,597,599	7,597,599.00		198,856.39

Chi-square = 198,856.

2. To calculate Cramer's V:

$$V = \sqrt{\frac{X^2}{(N)(\min{(r-1)|(c-1)})}} = \sqrt{\frac{198856.39}{7597559(2-1)}} = 0.162$$

BOX 12.8: IT'S YOUR TURN: LAMBDA

Wears all protective equipment for in-line skating	Female	Male	Row total
Yes	9	2	11
No	42	47	89
Column total	51	49	100

1. Make the two extreme predictions for the dependent variable.

   Wears protective equipment: $100 - 11 = 89$ misclassifications

   Does not wear protective equipment: $100 - 89 = 11$ misclassifications

   Based on smaller value $E_1 = 11$.

2. Calculate the extreme predictions by using the independent variable; determine E_2.

   Predicting that a female wears protective equipment: $51 - 9 = 42$

   Predicting that a female does not wear protective equipment: $51 - 42 = 9$

   Predicting that a male wears protective equipment: $49 - 2 = 47$

   Predicting that a male does not wear protective equipment: $49 - 47 = 2$

   As lowest classification errors for each sex are for not wearing protective equipment we sum 9 (females) and 2 (males). Thus $E_2 = 11$.

3. Calculate lambda (or the percentage increase in predictive accuracy):

$$\lambda = \frac{E_1 - E_2}{E_1} = \frac{11 - 11}{11} = 0$$

Thus knowing if a person is male or female will not improve our ability to predict whether they will wear protective gear while in-line skating.

BOX 13.2: IT'S YOUR TURN: CALCULATING GAMMA

Counts		Walk alone * Quick justice			
		Courts do good job of quick justice			
		Good	Average	Poor	Total
Walk alone at night	At least once a week	40	77	86	203
	Up to once a month	18	61	51	130
	Never	16	26	38	80
	Total	74	164	175	413

1. Compute N_s and N_D (use tables):

Cell	# of concordant cells	# of concordant observations	Contribution to N_s
a	4 (e,f,h,i)	$61 + 51 + 26 + 38 = 176$	$40 * 176 = 7040$
b	2 (f,i)	$51 + 38 = 89$	$77 * 89 = 6853$
c	0		

(continued)

Cell	# of concordant cells	# of concordant observations	Contribution to N_s
d	2 (h,i)	26 + 38 = 64	18 * 64 = 1152
e	1 (i)	38	61 * 38 = 2318
f	0		
g	0		
h	0		
i	0		N_s = 17363

Cell	# of discordant cells	# of discordant observations	Contribution to N_D
a	0		
b	2 (d,g)	18 + 16 = 34	77 * 34 = 2618
c	4 (d,e,g,h)	18 + 61 + 16 + 26 = 121	86 * 121 = 10406
d	0		
e	1 (g)	16	61 * 16 = 976
f	2 (g,h)	16 + 26 = 42	51 * 42 = 2142
g	0		
h	0		
i	0		N_D = 16142

2. $\gamma = \dfrac{N_{same} - N_{different}}{N_{same} + N_{different}} = \dfrac{17363 - 16142}{17363 + 16142} = \dfrac{1221}{33505} = 0.036$

3. There is a weak relationship between people's views on the efficiency of the courts and walking alone in neighbourhoods after dark.

BOX 13.4: IT'S YOUR TURN: CALCULATING SPEARMAN'S *Rho*

1. Complete table:

Case	Number of drinks a week	Drinks rank	Grade	Grade rank	D	D^2
1	10	2	65	4	−2	4
2	2	5.5	75	2	3.5	12.25
3	2	5.5	52	7	−1.5	2.25
4	0	8	98	1	7	49
5	1	7	45	8	−1	1
6	5	3	55	6	−3	9
7	20	1	70	3	−2	4
8	3	4	60	5	−1	1
					0	82.5

2. $r_s = 1 - \dfrac{6 * \sum D^2}{N(N^2 - 1)}$

    $= 1 - \dfrac{6 * 82.5}{8(64 - 1)}$

    $= 1 - \dfrac{495}{504}$

    $= 0.02$

3. Squared *rho* = 0.0004

4. By knowing the number of drinks a student has, one could reduce their errors of prediction by 0.04%. As this is incredibly low, it doesn't seem that the amount he drinks explains why Andy is doing better than Marianne. Maybe Andy is studying more than he admits?

BOX 13.7: IT'S YOUR TURN: CALCULATING SOMERS' *d*

Hours on unpaid household labour/week	The relationship between educational status and hours spent on unpaid labour per week			
	Educational status			
	Not studying	Part-time student	Full-time student	Total
Less than 5	52 (a)	1 (b)	20 (c)	73
5 to 14	59 (d)	2 (e)	5 (f)	66
15 or more	106 (g)	2 (h)	3 (i)	111
Total	217	5	28	250

Source: 2001 Individual Census

1. Compute N_{same}, $N_{different}$, and $Ties_y$.

$$N_S = a(e + f + h + i) + b(f + i) + d(h + i) + e(i)$$
$$= 52(2 + 5 + 2 + 3) + 1(5 + 3) + 59(2 + 3) + 2(3)$$
$$= 624 + 8 + 295 + 6$$
$$= 933$$

$$N_D = b(d + g) + c(d + e + g + h) + e(g) + f(g + h)$$
$$= 1(59 + 106) + 20(59 + 2 + 106 + 2) + 2(106) + 5(106 + 2)$$
$$= 165 + 3380 + 212 + 540$$
$$= 4297$$

$$Ties_y = a(b + c) + b(c) + d(e + f) + e(f) + g(h + i) + h(i)$$
$$= 52(1 + 20) + 1(20) + 59(2 + 5) + 2(5) + 106(2 + 3) + 2(3)$$
$$= 1092 + 20 + 413 + 10 + 530 + 6$$
$$= 2071$$

2. Calculate Somers' d.

$$d = \frac{N_{same} - N_{different}}{N_{same} + N_{different} + Ties_y} = \frac{933 - 4279}{933 + 4297 + 2071} = \frac{-3364}{7301} = -0.461$$

3. The value of -0.461 indicates that there is a strong relationship between being a student and how many hours you spend on housework. That it is negative means that as you increase one variable (more of a student) you decrease the other (less time on housework).

BOX 13.9: IT'S YOUR TURN: KENDALL'S TAU-*b*

1. Compute the value for $Ties_x$.

$$Ties_x = 52(59 + 106) + 59(106) + 1(2 + 2) + 2(2) + 20(5 + 3) + 5(3)$$
$$= 8580 + 6254 + 4 + 4 + 160 + 15$$
$$= 15017$$

2. Calculate Kendall's tau-b:

$$tau - b = \frac{N_{same} - N_{different}}{(N_{same} + N_{different} + Ties_y)(N_{same} + N_{different} + Ties_x)}$$

$$= \frac{933 - 4297}{\sqrt{(933 + 4297 + 2071)(933 + 4297 + 15017)}}$$

$$= \frac{-3367}{\sqrt{(7301)(20247)}} = \frac{-3367}{12158.3} = -0.277$$

3. By including the ties on the independent variable, $Ties_x$ we can see that the relationship between studying and hours spent on housework is not as strong as it had appeared. There is certainly a moderate (and SPSS tells us significant) relationship, but its strength has decreased.

BOX 14.2: IT'S YOUR TURN: CALCULATING PEARSON'S r

1. The first step is to organize the provided information, as well as the sums and products, into a chart:

obs#	X	Y	X^2	Y^2	XY
1	38	2	1,444	4	76
2	40	2	1,600	4	80
3	60	2	3,600	4	120
4	50	2	2,500	4	100
5	60	2	3,600	4	120
6	50	4	2,500	16	200
7	35	1	1,225	1	35
8	50	2	2,500	4	100
9	36	2	1,296	4	72
10	30	3	900	9	90
11	65	1	4,225	1	65
12	45	1	2,025	1	45
13	48	3	2,304	9	144
14	40	2	1,600	4	80
15	55	3	3,025	9	165
Sum	702	32	34,344	78	1,492

2. Next, we have our equation for r:

$$r = \frac{N\sum XY - (\sum X)(\sum Y)}{\sqrt{\left[N\sum X^2 - (\sum X)^2\right]\left[N\sum Y^2 - (\sum Y)^2\right]}}$$

When we combine the two, we get:

$$r = \frac{15 * 1492 - (702)(32)}{\sqrt{\left[15 * 34,344 - (702)^2\right]\left[15 * 78 - (32)^2\right]}}$$

$$= \frac{-84}{\sqrt{22,356 * 146}}$$

$$= -0.0465$$

3. There is a weak negative correlation between hours of work per week and involvement in organizations.

4. There is now a weak positive correlation in the weighted sample.

REFERENCES

Allison, Paul D. 2000. *Logistic Regression Using the SAS System: Theory and Application.* Cary, NC: The SAS Institute.

Anscombe, F. J. 1973. 'Graphs in Statistical Analysis'. *American Statistician* 27:17–22.

Berk, Richard A. 1983. 'An Introduction to Sample Selection Bias in Sociological Data'. *American Sociological Review,* 48, 3: 386–398.

Campbell, Rachel. 2006. 'Teenage Girls and Cellular Phones: Discourses of Independence, Safety, and "Rebellion"'. *Journal of Youth Studies* 9:195–212.

Canadian Centre for Justice Statistics. 2003. 'Crime Statistics'. *The Daily.* Ottawa: Statistics Canada.

Desrosièrs, A. 1998. *The Politics of Large Numbers: A History of Statistical Reasoning.* C. Naish, trans. Cambridge, MA: Harvard University Press.

Galton, Francis. 1889. *Natural Inheritance.* London: MacMillan & Co.

Gigerenzer, G., Z. Swijtink, T. Porter, L. Daston, J. Beatty, and L. Krüger. 1991. *The Empire of Chance: How Probability Changed Science and Everyday Life.* Cambridge: Cambridge University Press.

Hacking, Ian. 1975. *The Emergence of Probability: A Philosophical Study of Early Ideas about Probability, Induction and Statistical Inference.* London: Cambridge University Press.

Hald, A. 1990. *A History of Probability and Statistics and Their Applications before 1750.* New York: Wiley.

Huff, Darrell. 1954. *How to Lie with Statistics.* New York: Norton.

King, Gary, James Honaker, Anne Joseph, and Kenneth Scheve. 2001. 'Analyzing Incomplete Political Science Data: An Alternative Algorithm for Multiple Imputation'. *American Political Science Review* 95, 1: 49–69.

Kranzler, Gerald, and Janet Moursund. 1999. *Statistics for the Terrified.* Upper Saddle River, NJ: Prentice Hall.

Lorenz, Frederick O. 1987. 'Teaching about Influence in Simple Regression'. *Teaching Sociology* 15:173–177.

Maistrov, L. E. 1974. *Probability Theory: A Historical Sketch.* S. Kotz, trans. New York; London: Academic Press.

Pearson, Karl. 1894. 'Contributions to the Mathematical Theory of Evolution. - I. On the Dissection of Asymmetrical Frequency-curves'. *Philosophical Transactions* (see p. 80) CLXXXV.

Porter, T. 1986. *The Rise of Statistical Thinking, 1820–1900.* Cambridge, MA: Princeton University Press.

Rowntree, Derek. 2000. *Statistics without Tears : An Introduction for Non-Mathematicians.* London: Penguin.

Rubin, D. B. 1987. *Multiple Imputation for Non-response in Surveys.* New York: John Wiley & Sons.

Statistics Canada. 2001. *Aboriginal Peoples Survey (APS), 2001: User's Guide to the Public Use Microdata File.* Catalogue no. 89M0020GPE.

Statistics Canada. 2002. *Ethnic Diversity Survey: User's Guide.* Catalogue no. 89M0019GPE.

Statistics Canada. 2006. 'Income of Individuals'. *The Daily.* Accessed from http://www.statcan.ca/Daily/English/060523/d060523c.htm on January 16, 2007. 23 May 2006.

Stigler, S. M. 1986. *The History of Statistics: The Measurement of Uncertainty Before 1900.* Cambridge, MA: Harvard University Press.

Worswick, C. 2001. *School Performance of the Children of Immigrants, 1994–1998* (No. 178). Ottawa: Statistics Canada.

AN INTRODUCTION
TO STATISTICS FOR
CANADIAN SOCIAL
SCIENTISTS

SPSS LAB
MANUAL

CONTENTS

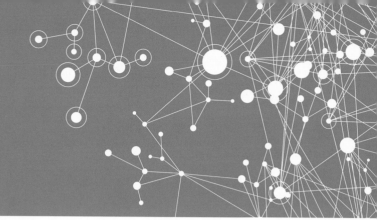

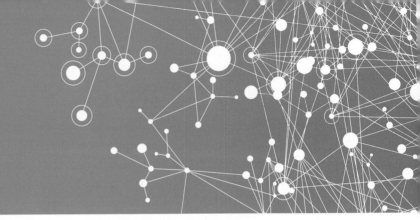

PREFACE

HOW DOES THIS MANUAL WORK?

This manual is intended to give you the opportunity to apply the concepts and principles you learned in each chapter of the text. Through practical examples and step-by-step instructions, this manual seeks to help you improve your understanding of statistical practices and introduce you to SPSS, a key statistical tool used in the social sciences. Often we learn through practice, and by actively engaging with the examples and assignments covered in this lab, your understanding of the course material and the basics of SPSS will be improved.

For nearly all of the chapters in your textbook, there is a corresponding lab exercise. The labs are approached in a workbook style where you will need to participate in each step in order to successfully complete the final assignment. You may find the labs challenging at times, even frustrating. Take a deep breath! Rome wasn't built in a day and neither is an expertise in statistics. To master a skill, one must practise, be challenged, and then try again. It is the intention of the lab manual to challenge you in this way. The knowledge is cumulative, so if you find a particular section tricky, return to earlier sections and brush up on the basics. You may find you need to do this several times before you are able to make sense of the material and the technical aspects of SPSS. Stay with it! By the end of this lab manual, you will have the ability to efficiently use SPSS and apply the concepts and principles taught in this course in a meaningful way.

THE MODEL

Each lab contains three sections:

1. The first section will briefly reintroduce the topic covered by the corresponding chapter and set the learning objectives for the lab.
2. The second section will provide an example to help focus your thinking and help you to understand the key concepts to be covered. The examples are intended to illustrate real-world applications of the concepts.
3. The third section will include a lab assignment to test your understanding of the concepts and skills covered in the lab and corresponding chapter.

WHAT'S COVERED?

This manual is meant to complement the textbook used in this course, not replace it. Through the use of concrete examples, each lab is intended to solidify your understanding of the general concepts and principles taught in each chapter. To help teach you how to analyze data, this lab manual will provide you step-by-step instructions on how to use the spss analysis software.

The labs cover the following key topics:

Lab 1: Introduction to spss
Lab 2: Identifying Types of Variables: Levels of Measures
Lab 3: Univariate Statistics
Lab 4: Introduction to Probability
Lab 5: The Normal Curve
Lab 6: Measures of Central Tendency and Dispersion
Lab 7: Standard Deviations, Standard Scores, and the Normal Distribution
Lab 8: Sampling
Lab 9: Hypothesis Testing: Testing the Significance of the Difference between Two Means
Lab 10: Hypothesis Testing: One- and Two-Tailed Tests
Lab 11: Bivariate Statistics for Nominal Data
Lab 12: Bivariate Statistics for Ordinal Data
Lab 13: Bivariate Statistics for Interval/Ratio Data
Lab 14: Analysis of Variance
Lab 15: ols Regression: Modelling Continuous Outcomes

THE DATASET

The 2009 Alberta Survey (as) is the 20th annual provincial survey administered by the Population Research Laboratory (prl) at the University of Alberta. This annual omnibus survey of households in the province of Alberta enables academic researchers, government departments, and non-profit organizations to explore a wide range of research topics in a structured research framework and environment. Sponsors' research questions are asked together with demographic questions in a telephone interview of Alberta households.

The target population was all persons 18 years of age or older who, at the time of the survey, were living in Alberta and could be contacted by direct dialling. From this population, three samples were drawn to cover Alberta: Edmonton Metropolitan Area, Calgary Metropolitan Area, and the rest of the province. The final dataset contains 1,211 cases.

This dataset is available online as a public-use data file. You can find it on the Population Research Laboratory's website: http://www.uofaweb.ualberta.ca/prl/. Click on "Alberta Survey," then click on the link for "Alberta Survey 2009 Public Release Data." Or the data can be found here: http://www.prl.ualberta.ca/en/AlbertaSurvey/PublicReleaseAlbertaSurveyDatasets2009 .aspx or http://www.ualberta.ca/~prl/easdata/. You will also be able to find some previous Alberta Surveys.

LAB #1: INTRODUCTION TO SPSS

The focus of this lab is to introduce you to SPSS, or "PSAW," as it was called in 2009–2010 (as of January 2010, SPSS became known as "SPSS: an IBM company." To use SPSS to analyze data, you will need to become familiar with the technical components of this software package. This lab will help familiarize you with the SPSS software, including how to access data files, the various base components (i.e., the syntax, data editor, and output), how to define new variables, and how to enter data.

You should be able to find SPSS on many of the computer terminals at your university, but if you can't, your instructor for the course should be able to help you find SPSS.

LEARNING OBJECTIVES

The following lab is directed at helping you understand how to orient SPSS. Specifically, this lab assignment challenges you to clarify your understanding of:

1. The basic components of SPSS
2. How to define variables
3. How to enter data

Part 1: Defining SPSS

What Is SPSS?

SPSS stands for Statistical Package for the Social Sciences and it allows you to analyze and describe data. SPSS is a statistical software package, one of the most commonly used among social scientists.

How Does It Work?

SPSS works by taking a series of commands, supplied by you, and applying them to a set of data, also supplied by you. SPSS will produce output displaying the results of the commands. The commands you supply SPSS will determine your output results. Within SPSS, commands are either given in the form of menu selections and by filling in dialogue boxes, or by writing your own programming syntax. We'll look at both methods here.

The sequence of commands will occur in the following order:

- Enter your data into SPSS, or open already existing data (which is what we'll do here).
- Tell SPSS to apply commands to the data (menus and dialogue boxes).
- SPSS then produces the output.

How Do I Begin an SPSS Session?

To begin, you need to access a computer that contains the SPSS software. Many universities have the SPSS software on their public use computers within computer labs. Once you have found a computer with a copy of the SPSS software, you will need to click on the **Start Menu** (on the bottom left-hand side of your computer screen), find the SPSS program, and open it.

Once you have opened the SPSS program, a pop-up will appear (like the one in Figure 1) asking you what you would like to do. You will have a variety of options, including **open an existing data source, open another type of file, run a tutorial, or type in data**. For the purposes of this lab, you will select **TYPE IN DATA** (we will look at the Alberta Survey later).

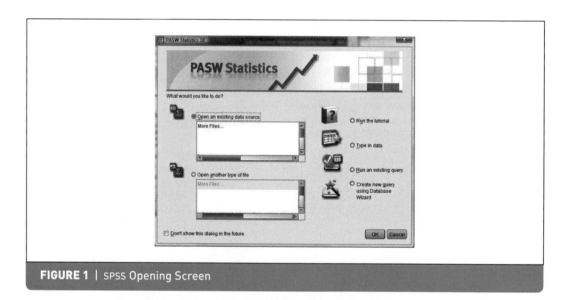

FIGURE 1 | SPSS Opening Screen

Once you click **TYPE IN DATA**, the **data editor screen** will appear (as shown in Figure 2). The data editor window is like a spreadsheet. Within the data editor screen, you can both create and edit pre-existing datasets. The data editor window has two tabs on the bottom left-hand side of the window, one for viewing your data, called the **Data View screen**, the second one for view information about your variables, called the **Variable View screen**. Figure 2 is in **variable view** mode. The current data editor screen has the title, Untitled. To save this file, select **FILE > SAVE AS**. This will allow you to both select a name and location for your file. The saved document will have the suffix ".sav."

Let's take a closer look at the SPSS Data Editor screen. Along the top of the screen you will see the **Menu Bar** that is used to access all the commands available. The menu bar has a number of headings that divide the commands into categories of a similar function (**File, Edit, View, Data, Transform, Analyze, Graphs, Utilities, Window, Help**). Consider browsing through these folders so you can become familiar with their contents. The more familiar you are with what is contained under each heading, the more comfortable you will be with the SPSS software package.

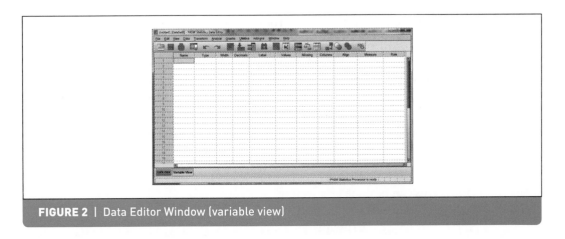

FIGURE 2 | Data Editor Window (variable view)

The second component of SPSS is the **syntax file** (Figure 3). The SPSS syntax file is a very useful tool for organizing your records and analyses. It is a text editor that reads SPSS programming. As mentioned above, there are two approaches to working in SPSS: using a point-and-click approach or manually inputting program commands. In this manual, you will mostly be using the point-and-click approach. Note that the same menu bar that appeared above the data editor screen also appears in the syntax file. To open a new syntax file, select **FILE > OPEN > SYNTAX**. Syntax files can be saved by selecting **FILE > SAVE AS**. The saved document will have the suffix ".sps."

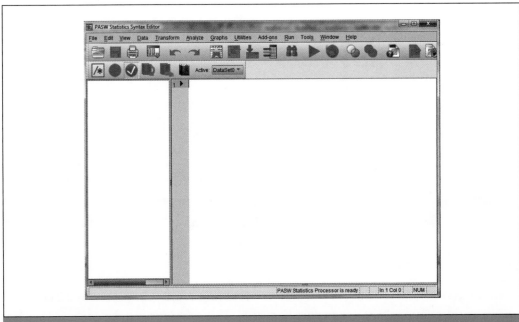

FIGURE 3 | The Syntax File

The third component of spss that is important to familiarize yourself with is the **output window** (Figure 4). The output window displays the output from the statistical analysis you undertake in the data editor window. You will notice a couple of things about this window. First, along the left side of the window is a running log of the commands you have executed during the current session. Second, similar to the **Data Editor** and **Syntax** windows, there is a Menu Bar with a series of headings, dividing the commands into categories of a similar function (**File, Edit, View, Data, Transform, Analyze, Graphs, Utilities, Window, Help**). Third, you will notice within the window itself the commands you ran within your syntax file. This is a particularly useful function when you are analyzing large amounts of data with a series of many commands. This can be done by selecting

EDIT > OPTIONS > VIEWER TAB > DISPLAY COMMANDS IN LOG

To open a new output window, select **FILE > OPEN > OUTPUT**. The Output window can be saved by selecting **FILE > SAVE AS**. The saved document will have the suffix ".spo."

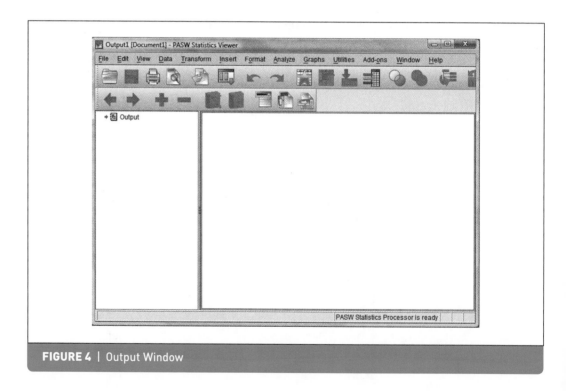

FIGURE 4 | Output Window

Entering spss Commands

There are two ways of entering commands into spss to execute your procedures: The first is known as the point-and-click procedure (Figure 5). This procedure can be done via the Data Editor window, the Output window, or the Syntax window by using the headings in the menu bar.

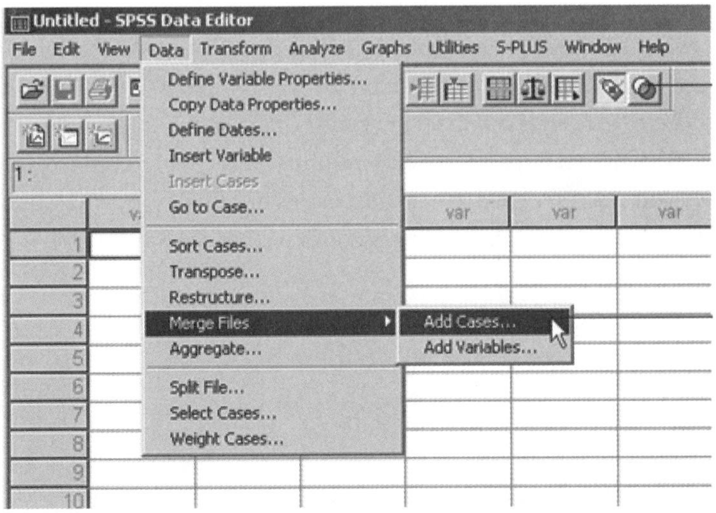

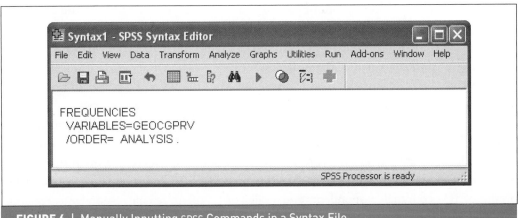

FIGURE 5 | The Point-and-Click Technique

The second way is to enter command programming into the syntax file. This can be done in three ways.

1. Typing them in by yourself.
2. Opening a syntax file that already has the commands written.
3. Using the pull-down menus and pasting the text commands into a syntax file. This method is highly recommended for record keeping. It allows you to save your syntax file (*.sps), so that it can be rerun later if you wish. As your analysis becomes more lengthy and complex, the importance of saving your syntax files will become increasingly obvious (Figure 6).

FIGURE 6 | Manually Inputting SPSS Commands in a Syntax File

Creating a Data File

Although most of the lab exercises in this manual use data from the Alberta Survey, it is important to understand data structure. By understanding how data files are constructed, you will be in a better position to understand what shape and form the variables within your dataset take and how to modify them when you learn how to undertake more advanced analysis.

Imagine that you are interested in whether males or females are more likely to own a cat. You went out onto the street and asked five random people two questions:

1. Are you a male or a female? (Male = 1 and Female = 2)
2. How many cats do you own? (0 to 5)

    Person 1: Male (1) owns 2 cats
    Person 2: Female (2) owns 1 cat
    Person 3: Female (2) owns 0 cats
    Person 4: Male (1) owns 5 cats
    Person 5: Female (2) owns 1 cat

Now that you have your data, you can enter the information into an SPSS data file.

Step 1: Open a new data file.

Step 2: Switch your data file to "Variable View" from "Data View," by clicking on the tab in the bottom left corner of your screen. In this view, notice that several new aspects of your data appear. It is here, for example, where you specify how many decimals your variables have. The rows are going to be your variables (SEX and CATS), the columns are the characteristics of the variables (name of the variable, type of variable, and so on). For this course, we are primarily concerned with the columns entitled, "Name," "Label," "Values," and "Missing."

Step 3: Name your variables. You must first decide on the names of your variables, these names must not have spaces, and they must start with a letter. As good practice, it is useful to keep the number of characters to a minimum where possible. Often, variable names will correspond with the survey question number from which it was derived, such as Q1 or Var01. However, this is not necessary. For our purposes, we will call our variables SEX and CATS.

Step 4: Define your variable labels. Although we have given our variables names that clearly indicate what the variable is measuring, your variable label can help clarify what the variable is measuring, or, if you have named the variable after survey questions (i.e., Q1), it will allow other users to know what information Q1 is measuring. For SEX, we will put "Sex of respondent" and for CATS, we will put "Number of cats owned."

Step 5: Define your value labels. This is done by clicking on the cell for the variable you want under the column "value labels." Often, value labels are attached with ordinal and nominal level variables (concepts you will learn about as you proceed through this course). Without labels, it is difficult to know what the values mean. So, for example, we have attached a value of "1" to our male respondents and a value of "2" to our female respondents. You must specify this under the value label column. To do this, click on the values cell for the variable you are creating. Click on the grey button in the cell. A dialogue box like the one found in Figure 7 will open. Following our example, assign labels male and female to numeric values "1" and "2," respectively, by entering "1" into the **value box** and its label, male, into the **label box**. Click **add** to make the changes for each value of your variable, then click **OK** when you are finished.

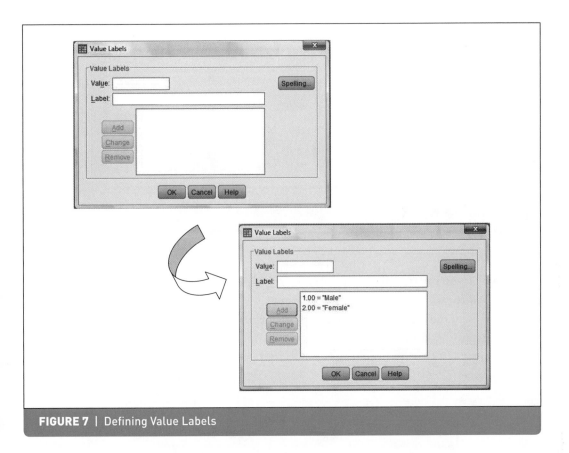

FIGURE 7 | Defining Value Labels

Step 6: Define your missing values. Sometimes when you are collecting data, respondents may not want to provide an answer for a variety of reasons. In such cases, you need to have a way of dealing with **missing data**. In our example, we don't have any such cases but if someone had refused to tell us what their sex was or how many cats they owned, we would have to assign a value to their non-response. While the decision how to code this data is up to the individual researcher creating the database, in the Alberta Survey, in most cases, a value of "0" is associated with "No Response," a –1 for "Not Applicable," and a value of "8" is associated with "Don't Know." To declare missing values, while still in "Variable View," click on the missing cell for the variable you are creating. Click on the grey button in the cell. A dialogue box like the one found in Figure 8 will open. You can assign up to three discrete missing values, such as 0, –1, and 8, as we find in the Alberta Survey 2009, or you can declare a range of values, such as 99 to 199. Click **OK** when you are finished.

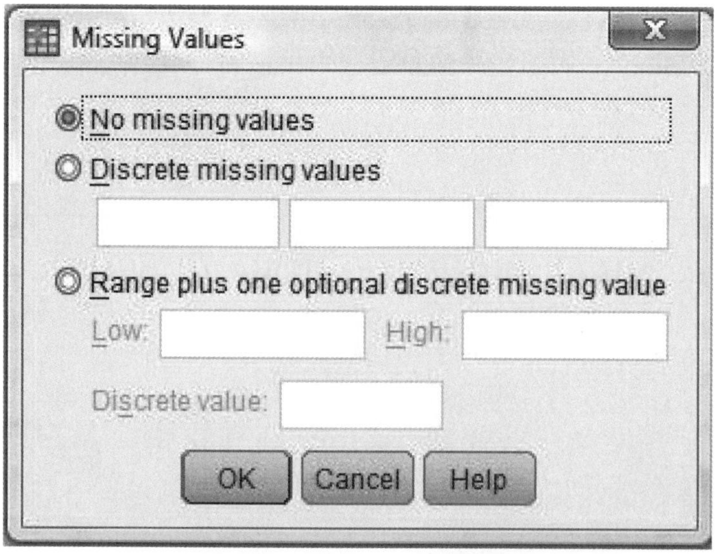

FIGURE 8 | Declaring Missing Values

Now that you have finished creating your variables, you are ready to enter your data. Switch your data editor from "Variable View" to "Data View." Select the first cell under the variable "SEX" and enter the value for your first respondent, who, if you recall, is male and has two cats. Repeat this process for each of your respondents until your data editor screen looks like the one in Figure 9.

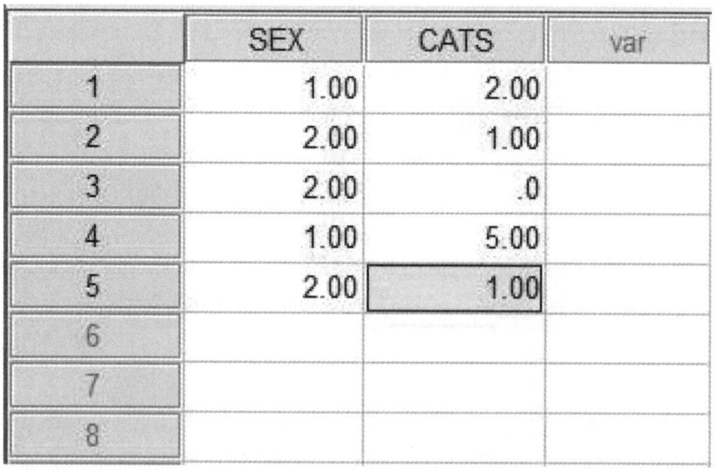

	SEX	CATS	var
1	1.00	2.00	
2	2.00	1.00	
3	2.00	.0	
4	1.00	5.00	
5	2.00	1.00	
6			
7			
8			

FIGURE 9 | Entering Data into the Data Editor Screen

Finally, save your new dataset. It is good practice to save your work regularly so you don't lose information that you have worked to produce. Remember to save files:

FILE > SAVE AS > Lab 1 Practice Example

Now it's your turn!

Putting the Information into Practice

For this lab, you will be required to complete a short survey and input the data into the data editor screen. Although for the remainder of the lab assignments, data will be provided for you, this exercise seeks to make you more familiar with the nature of data organization and storage within the SPSS software package.

The following questions were taken from the Alberta Survey, 2009.

Part 1: Take the time to answer each question as it relates to your life. Then, ask two friends to answer these questions. Pretend a forth respondent refused to give you any answers to your survey. You should have a total of four respondents for your short survey.

1. What is your gender?
   1. Male
   2. Female

2. Do you presently have a paid job or are you self-employed?
   1. Yes, paid job
   2. Yes, self-employed
   3. Yes, paid job and self employed
   4. No, neither

3. What is your CURRENT marital status?
   1. Never Married (Single)
   2. Married
   3. Common-Law Relationship/Live-In Partner
   4. Divorced
   5. Separated
   6. Widowed

4. Do you presently live in . . .
   1. A City
   2. A Town
   3. A Village
   4. A Rural Area

5. How safe do you feel from crime walking alone in your area after dark? Do you feel . . .
   1. Very safe
   2. Reasonably safe
   3. Somewhat unsafe
   4. Very unsafe

Part 2: Create a dataset by using the skills you just learned. Remember to (1) name your variables; (2) define your variable labels; (3) define your value labels; and (4) declare any missing values (hint, this would be the person who refused to answer any of your survey questions). When you have finished creating your dataset, which will include four respondents and five variables, save your file. Congratulations, you have just created your first dataset. Now let's learn what to do next!

LAB #2: IDENTIFYING TYPES OF VARIABLES: LEVELS OF MEASURES

The focus of this lab is to introduce you to the four different levels of variable measurement, how to identify different types of variables within SPSS, and to understand how different levels of measurement are coded and organized within SPSS. This material corresponds with the material presented in Chapter 2.

LEARNING OBJECTIVES

The following lab is directed at helping you understand levels of measurement and how to identify different types of variables within a dataset. Specifically, this lab assignment helps you clarify your understanding of:

1. Variable measurement
2. How variables are organized within SPSS

Part 1: Understanding Levels of Measurement

Variables are measured at four different levels: nominal, ordinal, interval, and ratio. Each of these levels has unique characteristics that define them. For *nominal data*, numeric values are typically used for identification purposes. It is not possible to rank the response categories and there is no quantifiable difference between categories. For *ordinal data*, the numeric values can signify an inherent ordering, because you can rank the response categories but you cannot measure the distance between those categories. For *interval data*, the data can be organized into an order that can be added or subtracted but not multiplied or divided, because there is no true zero value. *Ratio data* are similar to interval data except they have a true zero value.

There are two ways to collect information about the way in which a variable is measured in SPSS. One is to examine the variable values in the data editor screen and the other is to produce a frequency distribution. Using data from the Alberta Survey, this lab will demonstrate the first way to identify variable values. It will then give you a chance to practise identifying variables within SPSS. You will learn how to produce frequency distributions in the next chapter of this lab manual.

To open the Alberta Survey data, simply select file>open>data, then select the Alberta Survey 2009 (AS2009) (your instructor will need to tell you where he/she has placed the file). Or, if you are just opening SPSS, choose the "open existing data" option on the startup screen.

When you have opened the file, take a moment to scroll through the list of variables (be sure to confirm that your data editor screen is on "Variable View"). You will notice that there are 149 variables contained within this dataset. If you change your screen to "'Data View" and scroll to the bottom of the data file, you will see there are 1,211 respondents. OK, now return to the "Variable View" screen. You might notice that the names of the variables don't make a lot of sense without a thorough understanding of the background of this survey (if you want more information about the Alberta Survey, 2009, it can be found on the Population Research Laboratory website). However, in most cases, the variable labels provide key insight into what each of those variables is measuring. For the most part, you will be able to make an informed guess as to what the level of measurement would be for most variables. However, this may not always be accurate.

For example, variable "k12b" has the label "What was your own total individual income for the past year before taxes and deductions?" Given this is an income variable and that a person can feasibly have no income, you might be inclined to guess this is a ratio level variable. However, when you click on the cell in the "values" column, a different story emerges.

As we can see in Figure 1, this variable has been collapsed into discrete categories. Therefore, this variable is actually an **ordinal** level variable, because you can rank the categories but the values associated with the discrete categories (i.e., 1 refers to under $6,000) cannot be meaningfully measured.

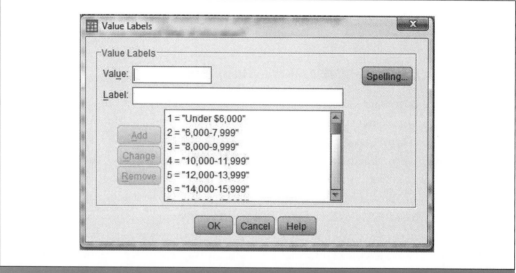

FIGURE 1 | Using Value Labels to Identify a Variable's Level of Measurement, Variable k12b

Let's look at one more example. Find the variable named "ed18" with the label "In the past month, have you done a favour for a neighbour?" Without going to the codebook found on the Population Research Laboratory website, we do not know how this question was to be answered by respondents. This variable might ask for a simple yes or no response or it might ask for the number of times you have done a favour for a neighbour. We cannot be 100 per cent sure unless we check to see how the variable is coded. To do this, again we want to check the "values" by clicking on the cell corresponding to this variable under the "values" column.

As we can see in Figure 2, our first guess was correct: this is a nominal level variable because respondents were simply asked to indicate yes or no.

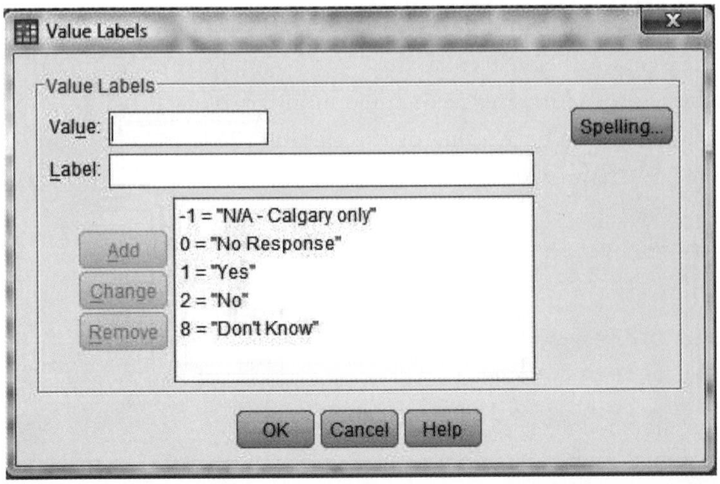

FIGURE 2 | Using Value Labels to Identify a Variable's Level of Measurement, Variable ed18

Now it's your turn!

Putting the Information into Practice

For this lab, you will be asked to fill in the missing information in Table 1. In the space beside each variable name, provide the variable label, the value labels (i.e., 1 = Yes, 2 = No), and try to determine the level of measurement.

TABLE 1

Variable	Variable label	Value label	Level of measurement
sex1			
d2			
e4			
h1			
h12			
k14			
k12a			
respnum$			
e2			

LAB #3: UNIVARIATE STATISTICS

The focus of this lab is to begin to introduce you to analysis with one variable. Generating frequencies is a basic procedure used to obtain a summary of a variable by looking at the number of cases associated with each value of the variable. This material corresponds with the material presented in Chapter 3.

LEARNING OBJECTIVES

The following lab is directed at helping you understand ways of studying the characteristics of data. Specifically, this lab assignment challenges you to clarify your understanding of:

1. How to generate and interpret frequency distributions
2. Data presentation
3. The connection between data presentation and levels of measurement

Part 1: Producing Frequency Distributions

We will first learn to produce a frequency table. Throughout this lab manual, we will use the point-and-click technique through a syntax file. To obtain a frequency distribution, use the following steps.

Step 1: Open a new syntax file, by clicking on

FILE > NEW > SYNTAX FILE

Step 2: Click on:

ANALYZE > DESCRIPTIVE STATISTICS > FREQUENCIES

Step 3: Within the dialogue box that opens, highlight the **gender** variable (SEX1) in the left-hand screen, next click the arrow (this will move the variable into the right-hand screen), then click "paste" (Figure 1).

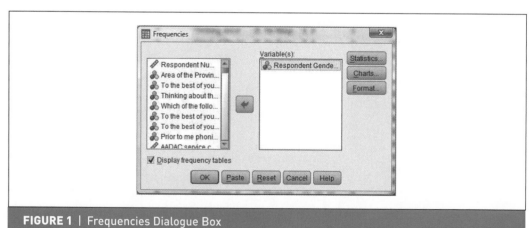

FIGURE 1 | Frequencies Dialogue Box

This will paste the sPSS program coding into your syntax file (Figure 2).

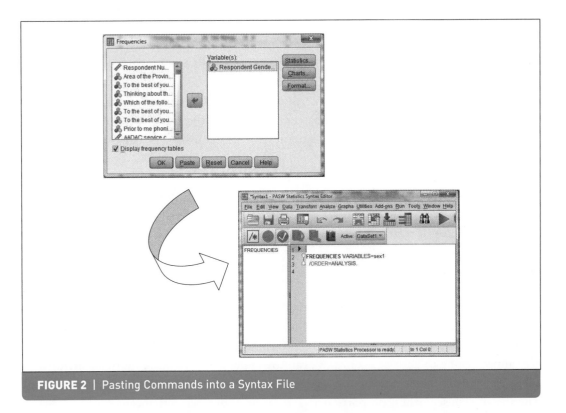

FIGURE 2 | Pasting Commands into a Syntax File

Step 4: In the Menu Bar, click on the **green arrow** to execute the commands. Or, you can put your cursor on the command you want to execute and press **CTRL** and **R** at the same time. This will run the current analysis and bring it up in an SPSS output window.

This may be a good time to save your syntax file. It is good practice to save your work regularly.

The output from the frequencies procedure will contain these two tables:

Statistics

Respondent Gender

N	Valid	1211
	Missing	0

Respondent Gender

		Frequency	Percent	Valid Percent	Cumulative Percent
Valid	Male	603	49.8	49.8	49.8
	Female	608	50.2	50.2	100.0
	Total	1211	100.0	100.0	

What should we note about this output?

1. Under statistics, we can see how many cases are *valid* and how many are *missing*. We have 1,211 valid cases and no missing cases.

2. In the table, we can see the distribution of MALES versus FEMALES by raw frequencies and by percent, valid percent, and cumulative percent. Most often, you will refer to your valid percent. In situations where you have missing cases, there will be differences between your percent and valid percent. The valid percent uses only those cases that are valid answers to the variable you are examining; the percent column incorporates missing values when calculating the percentage breakdown. You can see that there are 603 males and 608 females. Is this the same as what you have on the screen before you?

Part 2: Types of Charts

A **pie chart** is a way of summarizing a set of categorical data. Data are categorical when the values or observations belonging to it can be sorted according to groups but not by values. For example, "sex" is a categorical variable with two categories, "male" and "female," and people cannot belong to both categories. We can then refer to sex as being mutually exclusive. A pie chart is a circle that is divided into segments, each of which represents a particular category. The area of each segment is proportional to the number of cases in that category.

Figure 3 is an example of a pie chart for variable called **STRATA**, which measures which area of Alberta the respondent lives in. Note that in this example we appear to have an equal distribution of respondents from Edmonton, Calgary, and other Alberta.

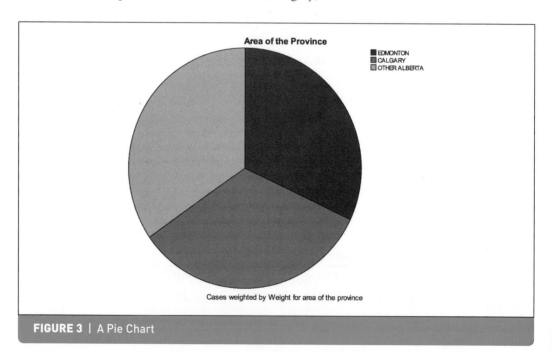

FIGURE 3 | A Pie Chart

How can you create a pie chart by using SPSS?

Step 1: At the top of your screen, click on:

ANALYZE > DESCRIPTIVE STATISTICS > FREQUENCIES

Step 2: Within the dialogue box that opens, highlight the **area of the province** variable (STRATA) in the left-hand screen. Next, click the arrow (this will move the variable into the right-hand screen; see Figure 4).

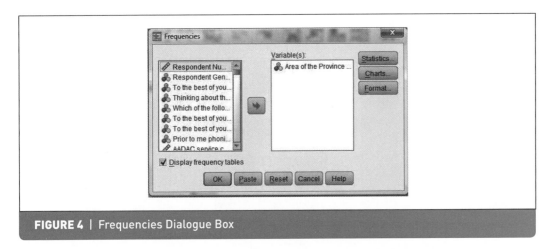

FIGURE 4 | Frequencies Dialogue Box

Step 3: Click on **Charts**. This will open a dialogue box that asks you which chart type you would like to present (Figure 5). Click on **PIE CHARTS > CONTINUE** (this will close the menu screen) > **PASTE**. The paste command is optional but is highly recommended for record keeping purposes and for tracking your progress. However, if you decide not to keep a syntax record, you can simply click on **OK**. For the purposes of this lab manual, we will be pasting all commands into a syntax file.

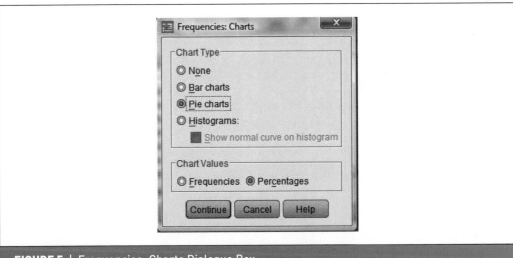

FIGURE 5 | Frequencies: Charts Dialogue Box

Now, after running the commands in your syntax file, you should get an output file containing a pie chart that resembles the one in Figure 3.

Bar Graphs

A **bar graph** is a way of summarizing a set of categorical data. It displays the data by using a number of rectangles of the same width, each of which represents a particular category. The length of each rectangle is proportional to the number of cases in the category it represents. Figure 6 is an example of a bar graph for the question "To the best of your knowledge, what is the leading cause of death for Albertans under the age of 45?" (A1).

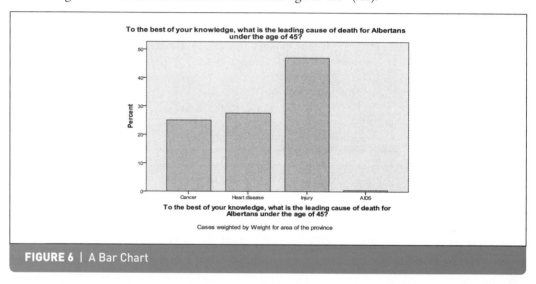

FIGURE 6 | A Bar Chart

Bar graphs are obtained in the same way as pie charts, except that where you selected "pie charts" within the frequency procedure, you will now select "bar charts" (Figure 7).

FIGURE 7 | Frequencies: Charts Dialogue Box

You will also notice that there's an option to produce a "histogram." Since we'll be dealing with histograms later in the course, we'll skip over them for now. They are, however, a very important mode of presentation in statistics.

Which Mode of Presentation Is Best?

Deciding which format to present your data depends on the level of measurement of your selected variable and the clarity of the presentation. For example, if you have a categorical variable, but a large number of categories, a pie chart may make the presentation crowded and confusing, so selecting a bar graph may be more appropriate.

There are some general suggestions you may want to consider:

- Use tables to display data details that would be lost in graphs or charts.
- Opt for a bar graph to compare data.
- Consider a pie chart to show how percentages relate to each other within a whole.
- Focus on the main point and consider your audience.
- Non-technical audiences often appreciate visual representations of data, so try to use pie and bar charts when you think your audience would prefer them.

Summary

In this section, you were introduced to the basics of data presentation. You explored three methods of data presentation: frequency tables, pie charts, and bar graphs. Specifically, you learned how to generate and interpret frequency distributions, how to create three types of modes of presentation, and the connection between data presentation and levels of measurement.

Now it's your turn!

Putting Information into Practice

1. Using what you've learned about interpreting frequency tables, fill in the blanks of the following paragraph. Use the appropriate variables from the lesson above.

   In AS2009's sample of 1,211 respondents, _____% are males and _____% are females. When asked about the different health problems facing Albertans today, _____% felt that injuries were an extremely serious health problem and _____% felt they were not serious. Respondents were varied in guessing what their chances of visiting the emergency room in the next year because of an injury. In fact, _____% felt it would be one in 500 compared to _____% who felt it would be one in ten. Interestingly, a higher percentage of people thought they would be more likely to go the emergency room because of a motor vehicle collision. Specifically, _____% felt the chances of going to the emergency room because of a motor vehicle collision were one in 500.

2. Produce the specified graphs for the following variables:
    a) "d2":   Bar Chart
    b) "k14":   Pie Chart
    c) "k16a":   Bar Chart
    d) "h10":   Frequency Table

3. Choose one of the variables from Question 2 and provide an interpretation. Specifically, what is the percentage distribution of the categories? What is the total number of respondents who answered the question? How many, if any, missing values are there?

LAB #4: INTRODUCTION TO PROBABILITY

The focus of this lab is to review what you have already learned and to introduce you to the concept of recoding variables. Recoding variables is an important component in conducting analysis because the categories of a variable, as they were asked in the questionnaire, may not work for your specific needs. For example, if you are interested in individuals who have a high school education or less compared with those who have a post-secondary education, you may not require a level of detail that looks at all the specific types of post-secondary education available. This lab will show you how to manipulate variables.

We will also look at how to calculate probabilities from SPSS output. This material corresponds with the material presented in Chapter 4.

LEARNING OBJECTIVES

The following lab is directed at helping you understand how to manipulate variables. Specifically, this lab assignment challenges you to clarify your understanding of:

1. Why you might want to recode variables
2. How to use SPSS to recode variables
3. How to use SPSS output to calculate probability

Part 1: Recoding Variables

Let's assume you are interested in the opinions Albertans have regarding whether people with intellectual disabilities are able to be parents. Within the current dataset, we have a variable that asks, "Indicate how much you agree or disagree with the following statement: People with intellectual disabilities are not fit to be parents" (d10). After obtaining a frequency distribution (Figure 1) of the variable, you realize you do not require this level of detail. You are only interested in whether people disagree, neither agree nor disagree, or agree. Therefore, you realize that you will need to collapse the first two categories together (Strongly Disagree and Somewhat Disagree) and the last two categories together (Somewhat Agree and Strongly Agree).

Step 1: To change the coding of this variable to suit your needs, click on:

TRANSFORM > RECODE INTO DIFFERENT VARIABLES

It is important to select this option because you are interested in creating a new variable from your original variable rather than altering the existing variable. Although it is possible to recode into the same variable, the original information on the AS2009 will be overwritten, **so always choose to recode into different variables!**

People with intellectual disabilities are not fit to be parents.

		Frequency	Percent	Valid Percent	Cumulative Percent
Valid	Strongly Disagree	297	24.5	26.7	26.7
	Somewhat Disagree	316	26.1	28.4	55.2
	Neither Disagree nor Agree	166	13.7	14.9	70.1
	Somewhat Agree	221	18.2	19.9	90.0
	Strongly Agree	111	9.2	10.0	100.0
	Total	1111	91.7	100.0	
Missing	No Response	58	4.8		
	Don't Know	42	3.5		
	Total	100	8.3		
Total		1211	100.0		

FIGURE 1 | Frequency Distribution for Variable D10

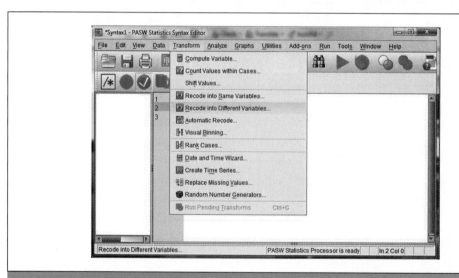

FIGURE 2 | Transforming into Different Variables

Step 2: The **Recode into Different Variables** dialogue box will appear (Figure 2). First, you need to specify the variable you are interested in working with, in this example, Recode: People with disabilities are not fit to be parents (D10). Bring that variable into the **numeric variable > output variable box**. This can either be done by dragging and dropping the variable, or by using the little arrow between the two boxes.

Now, decide on a name and variable label for your new variable and type them into the **output variable** box. As you can see from Figure 3, I chose "d10_recode." You can call your variable whatever you'd like, but make sure that the name is intuitive. Once you've done this, click on **Change**.

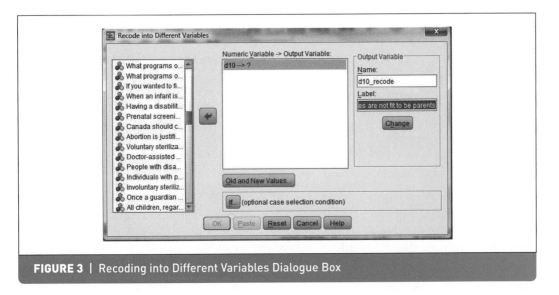

FIGURE 3 | Recoding into Different Variables Dialogue Box

Step 3: You now want to define the categories within your new variable, using the old variable values as a basis. So, you need to click on **Old and New Values**. Since you are interested in creating a variable where Strongly Disagree and Disagree are in one category and Agree and Strongly Agree are in another, you will need to tell SPSS this is what you want.

Recall from the first lab that you can use your data editor screen to determine what values were assigned to particular categories within a variable. In **Variable View**, go to the row with your variable of interest and click on the cell corresponding with the **Values Column**. You can also use the codebook located on the Population Research Lab's website for the Alberta Survey (http://www.uofaweb.ualberta.ca/prl/).

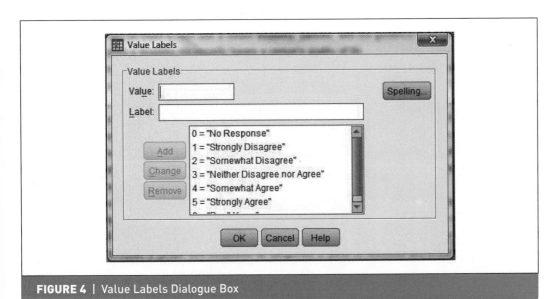

FIGURE 4 | Value Labels Dialogue Box

Step 4: By clicking on the **Values Column** for variable D10, we see that 1 and 2 correspond with Strongly Disagree and Somewhat Disagree and 4 and 5 correspond with Somewhat Agree and Agree (Figure 4). Therefore, we will need to recode our new variable in the following way:

Old Value > New Value
1, 2 > 1 (Disagree)
3 > 2 (Neither disagree nor agree)
4, 5 > 3 (Agree)

Step 5: Within the dialogue box you opened when you clicked on **Old and New Values**, you will transform the values in the original D10 variable into the new D10_recode. In Figure 5, you can see that 1 and 2 have been coded into 1, 3 has been coded into 2, and 4 has been coded into 3, and 5 is being coded into 3. Once you have finished defining your new variable, click on **Continue**.

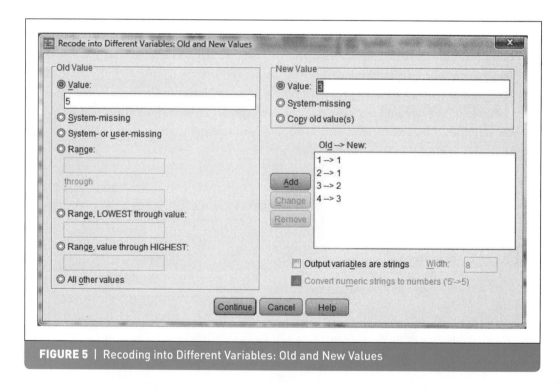

FIGURE 5 | Recoding into Different Variables: Old and New Values

Step 6: Click on **Paste** to display the commands in your syntax file. Then click on the **green arrow** to execute the commands. Or, you can hit **Continue** at the bottom of the screen, and **OK** on the next screen. Either way, your syntax file should look like Figure 6.

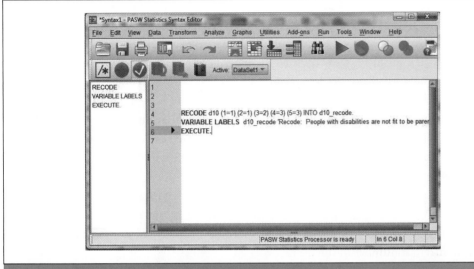

FIGURE 6 | Syntax File with Recode Commands

Now, as a final check, run a frequency distribution on the new variable, D10_recode, and the original variable, D10, to confirm that your new values add up to the values in the original variable (Figure 7). For example, the values of Strongly Disagree + Somewhat Disagree (297 + 316) should sum the total of the first category of the new variable (613).

People with intellectual disabilities are not fit to be parents.

		Frequency	Percent	Valid Percent	Cumulative Percent
Valid	Strongly Disagree	297	24.5	26.7	26.7
	Somewhat Disagree	316	26.1	28.4	55.2
	Neither Disagree nor Agree	166	13.7	14.9	70.1
	Somewhat Agree	221	18.2	19.9	90.0
	Strongly Agree	111	9.2	10.0	100.0
	Total	1111	91.7	100.0	
Missing	No Response	58	4.8		
	Don't Know	42	3.5		
	Total	100	8.3		
Total		1211	100.0		

Recode: People with disabilities are not fit to be parents

		Frequency	Percent	Valid Percent	Cumulative Percent
Valid	1.00	613	50.6	55.2	55.2
	2.00	166	13.7	14.9	70.1
	3.00	332	27.4	29.9	100.0
	Total	1111	91.7	100.0	
Missing	System	100	8.3		
Total		1211	100.0		

FIGURE 7 | Frequency Distribution of Variables D10 and D10_recode

Naturally, you'd want to go back and use the information in Lab #2 to attach value labels to your new variable.

You can test your recode by determining if the appropriate number of observations are in each category. For example, we combined Strongly Disagree and Somewhat Disagree from D10, and these categories had 297 and 316 observations. So, the recoded category 1 should have 297 + 316, or 613, observations.

Chapter 4 discusses probabilities and simply requires that you know the number of observations in each category to be able to calculate probabilities. So, if you wanted to know the probability that someone chosen at random in your sample would disagree with the statement about whether people with intellectual disabilities should be parents, you would only need to know the frequency of people in the disagree category (613) over the total number of people in the sample (1,211). This yields a probability of roughly 51 per cent (613/1211). Calculating the probability of the other outcomes would proceed in a similar way, except that you'd have a different number in the numerator.

Putting Information into Practice

1. Using the techniques that you have just been taught, recode variable H8, "I feel pressure from friends to drink alcohol during parties and celebrations." Create a three-category variable where the categories are 1 Infrequent/No Pressure 2 Sometimes Feel Pressure and 3 Frequent/Always Feel Pressure.

2. Interpret your recoded variable. Specifically, what is the percentage distribution of the categories? What is the total number of respondents who answered the question?

3. Based on the frequency distribution of your recoded variable, what is the probability that an individual will always or frequently feel pressure to drink?

4. Based on the frequency distribution of the original variable, what is the probability that an individual will never feel pressure to drink?

5. Based on the frequency distribution of your recoded variable, what is the probability a person will sometimes feel pressure to drink?

LAB #5: THE NORMAL CURVE

The focus of this lab is to introduce you to the concept of the normal curve. The distribution of data can take on different shapes. Understanding how data are distributed is important for more complex analysis that you will learn as this course progresses. This lab corresponds with the material presented in Chapter 5.

LEARNING OBJECTIVES

The following lab is directed at helping you understand how to manipulate variables. Specifically, this lab assignment challenges you to clarify your understanding of:

1. How to produce histograms in SPSS, and how to use them to see how data are distributed
2. How to describe and identify distributions

Part 1: Creating a Histogram in SPSS

Step 1: Within your syntax file, click on:

ANALYZE > DESCRIPTIVE STATISTICS > FREQUENCIES

Step 2: Within the dialogue box that opens (Figure 1), highlight the **how many years of schooling do you have** variable (K7) in the left-hand screen. Next click the arrow (this will move the variable into the right-hand screen).

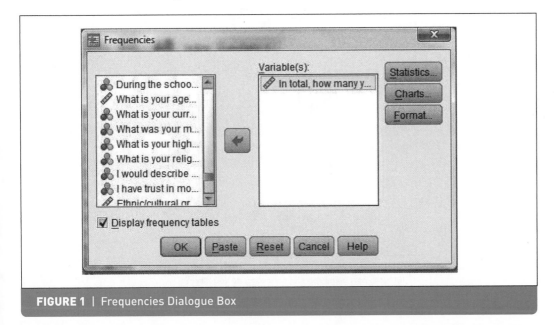

FIGURE 1 | Frequencies Dialogue Box

Step 3: Click on **Charts**. This will open a dialogue box that asks you which chart type you would like to present (Figure 2). Click on **HISTOGRAMS > SHOW NORMAL CURVE > CONTINUE** (this will close the menu screen) > **PASTE**. The paste command is optional but is highly recommended for record keeping purposes and for tracking your progress. However, if you decide not to keep a syntax record, you can simply click on **OK**. For the purposes of this lab manual, we will be pasting all commands into a syntax file.

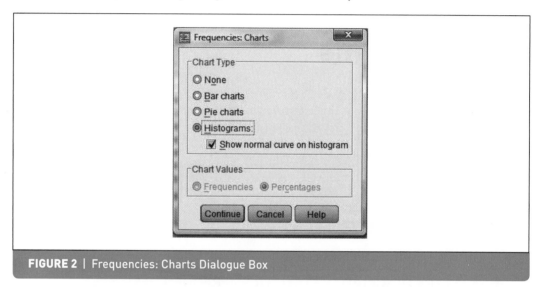

FIGURE 2 | Frequencies: Charts Dialogue Box

Now, after running the commands in your syntax file, you should get an output file containing a histogram that resembles the one in Figure 3.

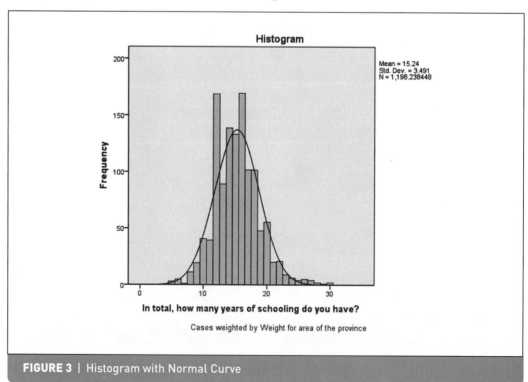

FIGURE 3 | Histogram with Normal Curve

Now, what can we say about this distribution? Well, it is **bimodal** because there are two spikes, one at the 12 years of schooling mark and the other at the 16 years of schooling mark. The curve has a slight **positive** or **right skew** because there are more people with higher levels of education than lower levels. The curve is a little more "peaked" than normal. This is hard to know from seeing a distribution, but having two peaks that are higher, and none that are dramatically lower than the rest of the distribution, provides a clue that the distribution has positive kurtosis.

OK, now it's your turn.

Putting Information into Practice

1. Obtain a histogram for the following variables:
   a) "age"
   b) "k3b"
   c) "h14"

2. For each variable, describe the symmetry of the distribution, the skewness of the distribution, its type of kurtosis, and whether it is unimodal, bimodal, or multimodal. For now, you can only do this visually, but we'll learn how to do more than this in the coming chapters.

LAB #6: MEASURES OF CENTRAL TENDENCY AND DISPERSION

The focus of this lab is to introduce you to various measures of central tendency. Measures of central tendency allow you to further understand the distribution of a variable. In this lab, you will learn how to generate various measures of central tendency within SPSS. This lab corresponds with the material presented in Chapter 6.

LEARNING OBJECTIVES

The following lab is directed at helping you understand how to generate measures of central tendency. Specifically, this lab assignment challenges you to clarify your understanding of:

1. The differences between the mean, median, and mode
2. The relationship between levels of measurement and the mean, median, and mode
3. How to generate measures of central tendency within SPSS

Generating Measures of Central Tendency in SPSS

Step 1: Within your syntax file, click on:

ANALYZE > DESCRIPTIVE STATISTICS > FREQUENCIES

Step 2: Within the dialogue box that opens (Figure 1), highlight the **how many years of schooling do you have** variable (K7) in the left-hand screen, next click the arrow (this will move the variable into the right-hand screen).

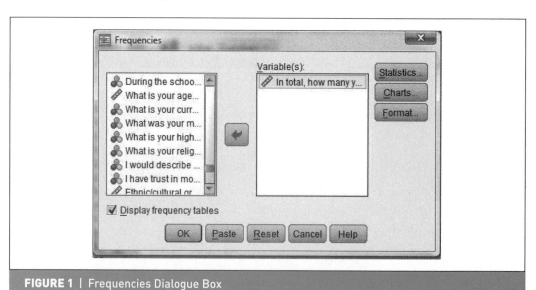

FIGURE 1 | Frequencies Dialogue Box

Step 3: Click on **Statistics**. This will open a dialogue box that asks you which statistics you are interested in obtaining (Figure 2). Under **Central** Tendency, click on **Mean, Median, and Mode**. Then, under **Dispersion,** select **Std. deviation, Variance, and Range**. Notice too that it's possible to obtain skewness and kurtosis statistics here. Let's leave these unchecked for now, however, and click on **CONTINUE** (this will close the menu screen) ♦ **PASTE**.

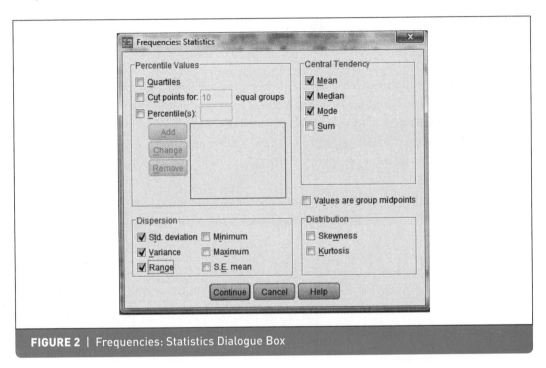

FIGURE 2 | Frequencies: Statistics Dialogue Box

Now, after running the commands in your syntax file, you should get an output file containing the table shown in Figure 3:

Statistics	
In total, how many years of schooling do you have?	
N Valid	1198
Missing	13
Mean	15.24
Median	15.00
Mode	16
Std. Deviation	3.491
Variance	12.186
Range	25

FIGURE 3 | Statistics Box

Now, before we continue, we need to ask ourselves if these numbers make sense. In other words, do these measures of central tendency make sense in relation to the level of measurement of our variable? Years of schooling is a ratio level variable because we have a true zero value: individuals can obtain no years of schooling.

This table tells us that, on average, our respondents have 15.24 years of schooling. The median tells us that if we were to line up all our respondents, from the lowest level of schooling to the highest, the middle score would be 15 years of schooling. The mode, or most frequently occurring score, is 16 years of school.

We have a standard deviation of 3.491 and a variance of 12.186. What does this mean? As you progress through this course, the meaning of these statistics will become clearer. However, for now, knowing how to generate these statistics in SPSS is sufficient. We also see that we have a range of 25. This means that the distance between the highest level of education and the lowest level of education is 25 years. Since this number is plausible, we should have faith that the data have no errors, or that we didn't do anything wrong (not trivial occurrences in statistics!).

Let's look at one more example to illustrate the difference between mean, median, and mode. Figure 4 shows the frequency distribution for the variable "If an election were held today, how would you vote federally?" (k16a).

If an election were held today, how would you vote federally?

		Frequency	Percent	Valid Percent	Cumulative Percent
Valid	Liberal Party of Canada	206	17.0	22.9	22.9
	Conservative Party of Canada	536	44.3	59.7	82.6
	Canada's NDP	51	4.3	5.7	88.3
	Green Party of Canada	45	3.7	5.0	93.3
	Other	19	1.6	2.1	95.4
	Would not vote	41	3.4	4.6	100.0
	Total	899	74.2	100.0	
Missing	Not Eligible	23	1.9		
	Don't Know	182	15.1		
	No Response/Refused	107	8.9		
	Total	313	25.8		
Total		1211	100.0		

FIGURE 4 | Frequency Distribution of Variable k16a

This variable is a nominal level variable because the categories cannot be ranked. Referring back to the material presented in Chapter 6, we know that the mode is most commonly used for nominal or ordinal level data. Though this is a good rule to memorize, here is the reason. When we look at the mean (Figure 5), we have a value of 2.18. If we were to translate a value of 2.18 into words, it would mean that on average, people would vote for the Conservative Party of Canada with a slight component of Canada's NDP. If you have ever voted in a federal election, you know you have to pick one, and only one, party or your ballot will be deemed invalid. Therefore, the mathematical mean does not make sense for nominal level data. Instead, we should pick the mode, which tells us that the most frequently selected category is "2," the Conservative Party of Canada. Can you see why this is the case?

Statistics

If an election were held today, how would you vote federally?

N	Valid	899
	Missing	313
Mean		2.18
Median		2.00
Mode		2
Std. Deviation		1.175
Variance		1.382
Range		5

FIGURE 5 | Statistics Box

Now it's your turn!

Putting Information into Practice

1. For each variable, identify the level of measurement of the variable.
   a) "e22"
   b) "age"
   c) "k10"
   d) "k6"
   e) "k3b"
   f) "k8a"
   g) "d13"
   h) "d6"
   i) "e"
   j) "h15"

2. For each of the ten variables, run both a frequency distribution and *appropriate* measures of central tendency and dispersion (i.e., mean, median, mode, standard deviation, variance, and/or range).

3. Based on your analysis of your output, complete the following table by writing in the values of the *appropriate* measures of central tendency and dispersion. Leave the boxes blank where the statistic is inappropriate.

Variable	Mean	Median	Mode	Standard Deviation	Variance	Range
e22						
age						
k10						
k6						
k3b						
k8a						
d13						
d6						
e9						
h15						

LAB #7: STANDARD DEVIATIONS, STANDARD SCORES, AND THE NORMAL DISTRIBUTION

The focus of this lab is to introduce you to z-scores and help you further understand how the standard deviation relates to the normal curve. Z-scores are the most commonly used standard score and are a measure of the relative location in a distribution. Specifically, in standard deviation units, z-scores give the distance a particular score is from the mean. In this lab, you will learn how to generate various z-scores within SPSS. This lab corresponds with material presented in Chapter 7.

LEARNING OBJECTIVES

The following lab is directed at helping you understand how **z**-scores relate to the normal curve and the standard deviation. Specifically, this lab assignment challenges you to clarify your understanding of:

1. The shape of distributions and the normal curve
2. The relationship between **z**-scores and the normal curve
3. How to use **z**-scores to mathematically calculate the percentage of cases that fall between two values.

Part 1: Reviewing the Shape and Characteristics of Distributions

Before learning to calculate z-scores, first refresh our memories on the shape and characteristics of distributions.

In Figure 1, we see a histogram for the variable "In total, how many years of schooling do you have?"

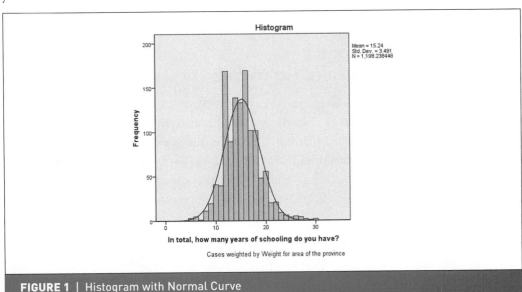

FIGURE 1 | Histogram with Normal Curve

Now, what can we say about this distribution? It is **bimodal** because there are two spikes, one at the 12 years of schooling mark and the other at the 16 years of schooling mark. The curve has a slight **negative skew** because there are more people with higher levels of education than lower levels. The two peaks of the distribution are higher than the rest of the distribution, suggesting that the distribution has positive kurtosis.

When we look at the statistics box in Figure 2, we see that on average, respondents have 15.24 years of school with a standard deviation of 3.491.

Statistics		
In total, how many years of schooling do you have?		
N	Valid	1198
	Missing	13
Mean		15.24
Median		15.00
Mode		16
Std. Deviation		3.491
Variance		12.186
Range		25

FIGURE 2 | Statistics for 'In total, how many years of schooling do you have?'

All right, so now we have refreshed our memory regarding the shape and characteristics of distributions. Keeping these elements in mind will help us to further understand z-scores and what it means to standardize a distribution.

Part 2: Calculating Z-Scores

Calculating a z-score is very similar to other commands you have learned up to this point.

Step 1: Within your syntax file, click on:

ANALYZE > DESCRIPTIVE STATISTICS > DESCRIPTIVES

Step 2: Within the dialogue box that opens (Figure 3), highlight the **how many years of schooling do you have** variable (K7) in the left-hand screen. Nex, click the arrow (this will move the variable into the right-hand screen). The key to this step is to **click the box that says, "Save standardized values as variables**." This will create a new variable at the bottom of your data editor screen called "ZK7" where all the values of the original K7 variable are now standardized scores, or z-scores. Then, click **Paste** and **run your syntax commands**.

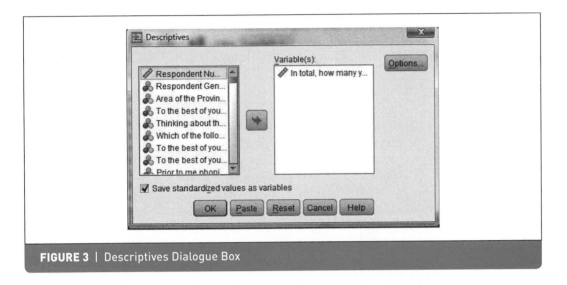

FIGURE 3 | Descriptives Dialogue Box

Step 3: Run a frequency distribution on your new variable "zk7." Be sure to include the mean, standard deviation, and variance.

In our statistics box in Figure 4, you will first notice that we have a mean of 0, a standard deviation of 1 and a variance of 1.

To convince yourself of the accuracy of the calculations, feel free to manually calculate the z-score for an observation, using the equation presented below (and taken from Chapter 7). Remember that you need to use the standard deviation from the actual variable, not the z-score variable.

$$z = \frac{X - \mu}{\sigma}$$

Statistics

Zscore: In total, how many years of schooling do you have?

N	Valid	1198
	Missing	13
Mean		.0000000
Std. Deviation		1.00000000
Variance		1.000

FIGURE 4 | Statistics Box for Z-scores of Variable K7

In Figure 5, you will notice that some of the scores are negative numbers. These scores now measure the distance of each original value (years of education) from the mean.

Zscore: In total, how many years of schooling do you have?				
		Frequency	Percent	Valid Percent	Cumulative Percent
Valid	-2.93298	3	.3	.3	.3
	-2.64652	5	.4	.4	.7
	-2.36006	1	.1	.1	.8
	-2.07359	11	.9	.9	1.7
	-1.78713	19	1.6	1.6	3.3
	-1.50067	41	3.4	3.4	6.7
	-1.21421	39	3.3	3.3	10.0
	-.92774	169	13.9	14.1	24.1
	-.64128	89	7.4	7.4	31.5
	-.35482	139	11.4	11.6	43.1
	-.06836	133	11.0	11.1	54.2
	.21811	169	14.0	14.1	68.3
	.50457	102	8.4	8.5	76.8
	.79103	101	8.4	8.5	85.2
	1.07750	48	3.9	4.0	89.2
	1.36396	55	4.6	4.6	93.9
	1.65042	20	1.6	1.7	95.5
	1.93688	21	1.7	1.7	97.3
	2.22335	9	.7	.7	98.0
	2.50981	6	.5	.5	98.5
	2.79627	4	.3	.3	98.8
	3.08274	5	.4	.4	99.3
	3.36920	4	.3	.3	99.6
	3.65566	2	.2	.2	99.8
	3.94212	1	.1	.1	99.8
	4.22859	2	.2	.2	100.0
	Total	1198	98.9	100.0	
Missing	System	13	1.1		
Total		1211	100.0		

FIGURE 5 | Frequency Table for Z-scores of Variable K7

Now it's your turn!

Putting Information into Practice

1. Run a frequency distribution for "age." Be sure to include a histogram, the mean, standard deviation, and variance.

    a) Are your respondents' ages normally distributed? What evidence supports your answer (consider the shape and characteristics of your distribution)?

2. Create a new variable called "zage."

3. In your data editor window, on data view, find respondent #7. (Hint: Use the variable called "respnum$." This variable assigns a number that is unique for each respondent who participated in the survey.) What are respondent #7's values for "age" and "zage"?

4. In your data editor window, on data view, find respondent #32. What are respondent #32's values for "age" and "zage"?

5. What percentage of respondents are older than respondent #7?

6. What percentage of respondents are younger than respondent #32?

7. What percentage of respondents are older than respondent #7 but younger than respondent #82?

LAB #8: SAMPLING

The focus of this lab is to introduce you to the select cases function within SPSS and to help you to further understand how larger sampling distributions improve data accuracy. A sample that is accurately and carefully selected without a lot of sampling error allows for a more precise analysis without including the full population. Because we are often unable to survey every individual, we make decisions about how much of the population to include based on our knowledge of the population parameter. In this lab, we are going to pretend that the total number of respondents who participated in this survey represent the entire population of Alberta (as though the survey was a census). This lab corresponds with the material presented in Chapters 8 and 9.

LEARNING OBJECTIVES

The following lab is directed at helping you understand what effect sample size has on the accuracy of sample values. Specifically, this lab assignment challenges you to clarify your understanding of:

1. The relationship between samples and populations
2. How increasing a sample size will reduce sampling error

Part 1: How to Select Cases in SPSS

Before we begin, run a frequency distribution on the sex variable.

Respondent Gender

		Frequency	Percent	Valid Percent	Cumulative Percent
Valid	Male	603	49.8	49.8	49.8
	Female	608	50.2	50.2	100.0
	Total	1211	100.0	100.0	

Note that we have 603 males and 608 females. This will be the basis of our population parameters. However, remember that these numbers, in reality, do not represent the true population of Alberta. We are only using this as a population for illustrative purposes.

Step 1: Within your syntax file, click on:

DATA → SELECT CASES

Under this window, you have a variety of options (Figure 1). For our purposes, you are going to select the option, "**Random Sample of Cases**."

FIGURE 1 | Select Cases Dialogue Window

Step 2: Click on:

Random Sample of Cases → SAMPLE

A dialogue box like the one in Figure 2 will appear. Here you will decide what percentage of cases you are interested in selecting. For this example, we will select 5 per cent of the cases. To do so, type "5" into the box next to the words "% of all cases." Notice that an option at the bottom-right corner of the box now illuminates, asking what you'd like to do with the cases you don't select. Typically, the best thing to do is to filter out the cases, because otherwise you won't be able to draw the unselected cases back in if you delete.

Once you have taken a look at the options and are satisfied with what you are doing, click **Continue**, then **Paste**. Next, run these commands in your syntax file.

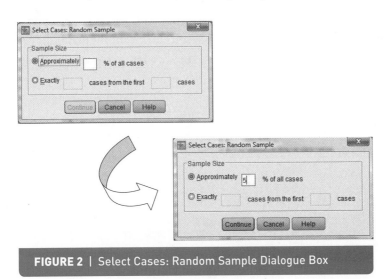

FIGURE 2 | Select Cases: Random Sample Dialogue Box

Now, run a frequency distribution on the sex variable.

Respondent Gender

		Frequency	Percent	Valid Percent	Cumulative Percent
Valid	Male	29	44.2	44.2	44.2
	Female	37	55.8	55.8	100.0
	Total	66	100.0	100.0	

Can you see how your sample size is much smaller than what's in the full dataset? What's more, given that the sample is randomly drawn each and every time, it is possible that your frequencies differ from those above. Can you see why this might be the case? If you'd like to generate another sample, you can go to **Transform > Select cases > Reset**, then generate another sample. Is this sample different yet again? It might be, because once again you've created another random sample.

Standard Error of a Sample Mean

The next thing we're going to do is use SPSS to help us calculate the standard error of a sample mean. Recall from Chapter 9 that the equation is

$$s_{\bar{X}} = \frac{s_X}{\sqrt{n-1}}$$

Using this, it is possible to estimate the distance that your sample is likely to be from a population mean. You can do this even though you don't know what the population mean actually is, using statistical theory and what we know about the normal distribution (which is how we're assuming the data from the Alberta Survey are distributed).

Suppose that you wanted to know the average age of your 5 per cent sample, remember that you would do this by selecting **Analyze > descriptives**, then selecting your variable of interest ("Age"). The resulting output will give you the mean, the standard deviation, and the number of observations necessary to calculate the standard error.

Now it's your turn!

Putting Information into Practice

Run a frequency distribution for the "Area of the Province" variable (STRATA) for the population.

Use the select cases procedure to take a random sample of 2 per cent of the cases from the "population."

Run a frequency distribution on "STRATA" and record the percentage of respondents living in Edmonton. Calculate the standard error of the sample mean, using the standard deviation estimates generated by SPSS.

Repeat this process to complete the following table.

%	% in Edmonton	Sampling error
5%		
10%		
25%		
50%		
75%		

1. Which percentage of cases would you choose if you were under budget and time constraints to complete your survey? In other words, which percentage begins to most closely resemble your population and at what point does your distribution start to level off?

LAB #9: HYPOTHESIS TESTING: TESTING THE SIGNIFICANCE OF THE DIFFERENCE BETWEEN TWO MEANS

The focus of this lab is to introduce you to the **one sample *t*-tests** function within SPSS and help you to further understand how we use confidence intervals to determine generalizability of our samples to populations. This lab corresponds with material presented in Chapter 10.

LEARNING OBJECTIVES

The following lab is directed at helping you understand what effect sample size has on the accuracy of sample values. Specifically, this lab assignment challenges you to clarify your understanding of:

1. How to use a *t*-test to approximate the mean for a population from your sample
2. The relationship between confidence intervals and statistical significance

Part 1: Calculating a One Sample *t*-Test in SPSS

Let's pretend we are interested in knowing whether the average years of schooling of our sample differs significantly from the population mean of 16 years (high school plus an undergraduate degree) at the 95 per cent confidence level. Suppose that we got this number from the Canadian census, and that it accurately represents the entire population.

Step 1: Within your syntax file, click on:

ANALYZE → COMPARE MEANS → ONE SAMPLE T TEST

Step 2: Within the dialogue box that opens (Figure 1), highlight the **how many years of schooling do you have** variable (K7) in the left-hand screen, next click the arrow (this will move the variable into the right-hand screen).

Step 3: Insert the population mean in the test value box. This option is very useful because it allows you to construct confidence intervals from *any* number, not just a population mean.

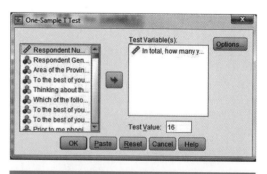

FIGURE 1 | One-Sample *t*-Test Dialogue Box

Step 4: Click on **OPTIONS**. In this dialogue box (Figure 2), you want your **Confidence Interval** Percentage to equal 95 per cent. This way, you can be 95 per cent confident your sample mean is generalizable to the population mean. Then click **Continue**, **Paste** and **run your syntax commands**.

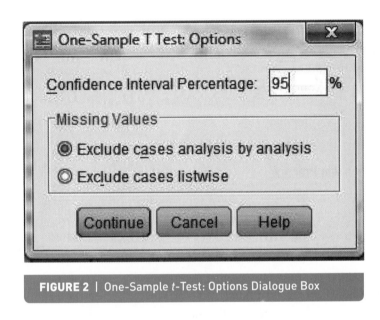

FIGURE 2 | One-Sample *t*-Test: Options Dialogue Box

The following tables should come up in your output file:

One-Sample Statistics

	N	Mean	Std. Deviation	Std. Error Mean
In total, how many years of schooling do you have?	1198	15.24	3.491	.101

One-Sample Test

	Test Value = 16					
					95% Confidence Interval of the Difference	
	t	df	Sig. (2-tailed)	Mean Difference	Lower	Upper
In total, how many years of schooling do you have?	-7.550	1197	.000	-.761	-.96	-.56

First, we can note that we have 1,198 cases and a mean of 15.24 years of schooling. The standard deviation is 3.491. In the next piece of output, we see we have a *t* value of −7.550 with 1,197 degrees of freedom. This is the equivalent of our *t*-obtained value. By looking at the Sig.

(2-tailed), we can see that we have a significance level of .000. This means that we can be more than 99 per cent confident that the average of our sample is significantly different from a sample with a mean of 16 years of schooling. Can you use these numbers to do the *t*-test manually, by looking at the student's *t*-table in Appendix B of your textbook?

Don't despair if you can't, because SPSS does the work for you. If you go to the far right-hand side of your output, you can see at the 95 per cent confidence interval that our lower boundary is –.96 and our upper boundary is –.56. This means that 95 times out of 100, our sample mean difference will be between –0.96 and –0.56.

If you wanted to (and who wouldn't want to?), you could use the information in the SPSS output to calculate the confidence intervals yourself, and compare them to the numbers that SPSS generated.

OK, now it's your turn!

Putting Information into Practice

1. Let's imagine that the average age of someone living in Alberta is 27 years old. We want to know if the average age of our sample differs significantly from the average age of someone living in Alberta at the 95 per cent confidence level. Conduct a one-sample *t*-test.

2. Can you be 95 per cent confident that the average age of our respondents differs significantly from the average age of someone living in Alberta?

3. What is your confidence interval? What does this mean?

LAB #10: HYPOTHESIS TESTING: ONE- AND TWO-TAILED TESTS

The focus of this lab is to introduce you to the **t-tests with two samples** function within SPSS. For this type of analysis, you need to have a dichotomous independent variable and a interval/scale for your dependent variable. This lab corresponds with material presented in Chapter 11.

LEARNING OBJECTIVES

The following lab is directed at helping you understand how you can use a t-test to compare the means of two independent samples. Specifically, this lab assignment challenges you to clarify your understanding of:

1. Stating the null and research hypotheses
2. Establishing a sampling distribution and critical region

Part 1: Calculating a t-Test with Two Samples in SPSS

Let's pretend we are interested in knowing whether the average years of schooling of our sample differs significantly between males and females. Since both are samples and scores on the outcome of interest are independent of each other (presumably, the education level of women has nothing to do with the education level of men), it is most appropriate to conduct a t-test on independent samples.

Step 1: State the null and research hypotheses.

In this case, we are going to make the claim that because Alberta is an industry-driven economy where a significant proportion of the male population pursues employment in the oil sands, that men and women will differ in the amount of years of education they obtain.

Therefore, we are claiming that,

> H_0: **In the population, the mean level of education for men and women does not differ.** ($\mu_{MEN} = \mu_{WOMEN}$)
>
> H_1: **In the population, the mean level of education for men is not equally to that of women.** ($\mu_{MEN} \neq \mu_{WOMEN}$)

Step 2: Select the sampling distribution and establish the critical region.

On a z-score distribution, the critical region, which corresponds to a p-value < 0.05, will be represented by a t-score of +/−1.96 (Figure 1).

Should our test statistic be found in the 5 per cent of the distribution that is bounded by the two critical regions of our t-score distribution, we can be 95 per cent confident that we can reject our null hypothesis. Since we are only hypothesizing that there will be a difference in H_1, without saying anything about the direction of the difference (such as $\mu_{MEN} < \mu_{WOMEN}$), we're conducting a two-tailed test. If we were conducting a one-tailed test (and we were hypothesizing a direction of the relationship,), remember from Chapter 10 that we'd have a critical t-score of $+/-1.65$.

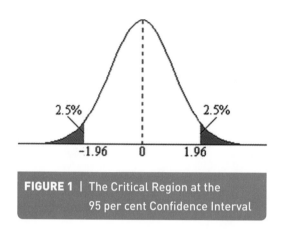

FIGURE 1 | The Critical Region at the 95 per cent Confidence Interval

Step 3: Using the data editor screen, check to see how the two groups of your independent variable are coded in the codebook. In this case, males are coded as "1" and females are coded as "2."

Now, you are ready to run your **Independent Samples *T*-Test**:

Step 4: In your syntax file, click on:

ANALYZE → COMPARE MEANS → INDEPENDENT SAMPLES T-TEST

Our test variable will be "**how many years of schooling do you have**?" and our Grouping Variable will be **sex of respondent**.

Click **Define Groups** and indicate to SPSS which value you would like associated with each group. For right now, leave males as "1" and females as "2." Then click **Continue** and **Paste** and **run your syntax commands**.

You should get the following output:

Group Statistics

	Respondent Gender	N	Mean	Std. Deviation	Std. Error Mean
In total, how many years of schooling do you have?	Male	595	15.31	3.525	.145
	Female	603	15.16	3.458	.141

Independent Samples Test

		Levene's Test for Equality of Variances		t-test for Equality of Means					95% Confidence Interval of the Difference	
		F	Sig.	t	df	Sig. (2-tailed)	Mean Difference	Std. Error Difference	Lower	Upper
In total, how many years of schooling do you have?	Equal variances assumed	.509	.476	.747	1196	.455	.151	.202	-.245	.547
	Equal variances not assumed			.747	1194.944	.455	.151	.202	-.245	.547

Table 1: Group Statistics: Looking at Table 1, we can see that our groups both had approximately the same sample size, 595 males and 603 females.

Already we can see that the mean values of years of education are quite similar, although men are slightly higher, as hypothesized. However, this difference in means may be due to chance, so we have to check the *t*-tests in the next table.

Table 2: Independent Samples Test: The first two columns pertain to the Levene's Test of equal variances between our two groups (one of the assumptions). THESE TWO COLUMNS ARE NOT INDICATORS OF SIGNIFICANCE THAT YOU'RE INTERESTED IN. This refers to something else, which is beyond our focus here. Focus on the "Sig. (2-tailed)" column.

Earlier, we said that we needed a *t*-score of > +/−1.96. Here we see that we have a *t*-value of 0.747. Since this score falls outside our lower critical region, we can conclude that the mean years of education for our two sample groups (males and females) are not significantly different. Therefore, we can fail to reject the null hypothesis of no differences between groups. Similarly, if we were conducting a one-tailed test, we would also fail to reject the null hypothesis.

Now it's your turn!

Putting Information into Practice

Let's pretend we are interested in knowing whether the average number of children under the age of 18 differs significantly between those who live on a farm and those who do not.

We will use variables "Do you live on a farm?" (k15) and "How many children under the age of 18 live at this number?" (k3b).

1. Identify your dependent and independent variable.

2. State your null and research hypotheses.

3. Run an independent samples *t*-test.

4. What is the average number of children under the age of 18 living on a farm?

5. What is the average number of children under the age of 18 not living on a farm?

6. Using a *t*-test, do you accept or reject the null hypothesis? Why?

LAB #11: BIVARIATE STATISTICS FOR NOMINAL DATA

The focus of this lab is to introduce you to the **association or relationship between nominal variables**. Specifically, this lab will help clarify your understanding of independent and dependent variables and how to interpret the chi-square test of statistical significance. This lab corresponds with the material presented in Chapter 12.

LEARNING OBJECTIVES

The following lab is directed at helping you understand how to interpret the relationship between two nominal variables (bivariate relationships). Specifically, this lab assignment challenges you to clarify your understanding of:

1. Dependent and independent variables
2. How to create a cross-tabulation or a contingency table
3. How to interpret your findings and determine statistical significance

Part 1: Creating Contingency Tables within SPSS

Now, let's learn how to create contingency tables in SPSS. For this example, we will ask the question, who is more likely to have driven while impaired, males or females?

Step 1: Identify your dependent and independent variables.

An independent variable can be thought of as the modifying outcome, the dependent variable can be thought of as the outcome of interest. In this situation, we are interested in seeing if gender will modify patterns of impaired driving; therefore, it is our independent variable. The outcome we are interested in is impaired driving; therefore, it is our dependent variable.

Step 2: Using the syntax file, click on:

ANALYZE → DESCRIPTIVE STATISTICS → CROSSTABS

Step 3: Select the dependent and independent variable.

This will bring up the crosstabs dialogue screen (Figure 1). Once you are in that screen, bring your dependent variable, "In the past 12 months, have you driven while impaired?" (h1), into the **row(s) box,** and bring your independent variable, sex, into the **column(s) box**. When you have finished doing that, click on **statistics icon**.

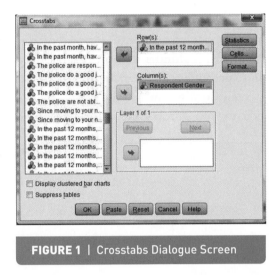

FIGURE 1 | Crosstabs Dialogue Screen

Step 4: Select your statistics.

Within this screen, select **chi-square** (Figure 2). We will be using a chi-square test to measure the statistical significance of the relationship between gender. Also notice that there's an option to select different measures of association for nominal variables. Select **Phi and Cramer's V**, one of the nominal measures of association covered in Chapter 12 of your text. Then click **Continue**.

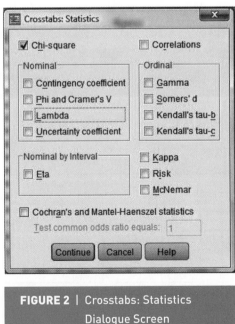

FIGURE 2 | Crosstabs: Statistics Dialogue Screen

Step 5: Percentage your columns.

You will return to the crosstabs screen. Once there, select the **cells button** (Figure 3). Within this screen, you will select **columns under the percentages** list. You are selecting columns because you want to percentage along males and females so you can compare the differences across gender. Then hit **Continue**, which will return you to the crosstabs screen. Then click **Continue**, **Paste**, and **run your syntax commands**.

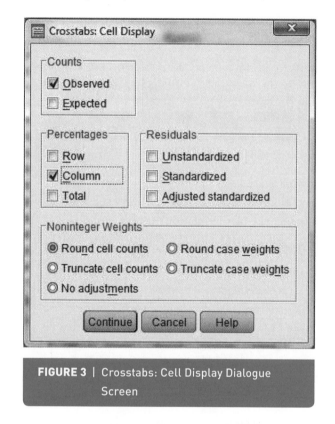

FIGURE 3 | Crosstabs: Cell Display Dialogue Screen

You should get the following output:

Case Processing Summary

	Cases					
	Valid		Missing		Total	
	N	Percent	N	Percent	N	Percent
In the past 12 months, have you driven while impaired? * Respondent Gender	1203.279[a]	99.3%	7.960	.7%	1211.239	100.0%

a. Number of valid cases is different from the total count in the crosstabulation table because the cell counts have been rounded.

The **Case Processing Summary** tells you the number of respondents, 1,203.279, and the percentage that are valid, 99.3 per cent. Valid cases are those that are meaningful to your analysis.

In this example, it would be those respondents who indicated being male or female, not those who did not give an applicable response or did not answer. This is followed by the number of missing cases, 7.960, and the total number of cases, including both valid and missing cases, 1,211.239.

Following the case summary report is the contingency table, cross-tabulating gender by whether or not the respondent has driven while impaired in the past 12 months. You will notice that you obtain both raw frequencies and percentages. Let's start to interpret these results. There do appear to be differences between men and women in their opinions of their weight. In particular, we find that females are less likely to report having driven while impaired than males, 1.8 per cent compared to 6.2 per cent respectively. However, how do we know if these differences are statistically significant? That is, how do we know if the differences seen in the sample also exist within the population?

In the past 12 months, have you driven while impaired? * Respondent Gender Crosstabulation

			Respondent Gender		Total
			Male	Female	
In the past 12 months, have you driven while impaired?	Yes	Count	37	11	48
		% within Respondent Gender	6.2%	1.8%	4.0%
	No	Count	560	595	1155
		% within Respondent Gender	93.8%	98.2%	96.0%
Total		Count	597	606	1203
		% within Respondent Gender	100.0%	100.0%	100.0%

One way to test this is to use a chi-square test. A **chi-square test**, as discussed in Chapter 8 of the textbook, is a hypothesis test that measures whether or not a relationship exists. This measure is suitable for all levels of measurement and all distributions. It tests the **null hypothesis** and measures the discrepancy between observed and expected events. The events are assumed to be independent and have the same distribution, and the outcomes of each event must be mutually exclusive.

Chi-Square Tests

	Value	df	Asymp. Sig. (2-sided)	Exact Sig. (2-sided)	Exact Sig. (1-sided)
Pearson Chi-Square	15.077[a]	1	.000		
Continuity Correction[b]	13.955	1	.000		
Likelihood Ratio	15.862	1	.000		
Fisher's Exact Test				.000	.000
Linear-by-Linear Association	15.065	1	.000		
N of Valid Cases	1203				

a. 0 cells (.0%) have expected count less than 5. The minimum expected count is 23.82.

b. Computed only for a 2x2 table

To evaluate whether we will reject the null hypothesis that no differences exist between males and females, we need to determine the degrees of freedom, which can be found in the SPSS output. For our results, the degrees of freedom equal 1. Since chi-square has a known distribution, the critical chi-square value for 2 degrees of freedom equals 3.841 at the 0.05 level of statistical significance, and our chi-square value is 15.077. Therefore, since our chi-square value exceeds the critical chi-square value, we can reject the null hypothesis and conclude that there are statistically significant differences between males and females with whether or not they have driven while impaired in the past 12 months.

Sometimes, you are interested in identifying the *strength* of a relationship (not just the existence), and this is what measures of association are for. Remember that above we selected Phi and Cramer's *V* when we were setting up our analysis. Let's turn to this table now:

Symmetric measures			
		Value	Approx. Sig.
Nominal by Nominal	Phi	.112	.000
	Cramer's *V*	.112	.000
N of Valid Cases		1203	

There are a number of relevant pieces of information here. First, notice that phi and Cramer's *V* values are identical. This will always be the case in a 2 by 2 table, which makes the calculation of phi somewhat unnecessary (this is why it's included alongside Cramer's *V* in SPSS). Second, since these are chi-square based measures of association, you will notice that SPSS reports the significance of the measures. Chi-square is used to calculate significance here, so you needn't check the box for chi-square if you don't want to. The number of valid cases is also reported, and this number should coincide with the number of cases in the database (it does). Sometimes, if people do not answer a question, this number will go down because of missing values.

Remembering the classification criteria covered in Chapter 12, you can see that since the value is below 0.3, the relationship is weak but significant.

Now's it's your turn!

Putting Information into Practice

Continuing with the theme of this chapter, we are going to ask the question, who is more likely to act as a designated driver, males or females?

1. Answer the following questions:
    a) What is your null hypothesis?
    b) What is your research hypothesis?
    c) What is your dependent variable?
    d) What is your independent variable?
    e) What are the levels of measurement of your variables?

2. Produce a contingency table. Be sure to include percentages, the chi-square statistic, and phi and Cramer's *V*.

3. Based on your output, answer the following questions:
    a) What is the total valid sample size for this table?
    b) How many missing cases do you have?
    c) What percentage of females indicate they have been a designated driver in the past 12 months? What percentage of males indicate the same?
    d) How much difference (variance) is there between males and females with respect to the percentage that have been a designated driver in the past 12 months?
    e) What is the value of your chi-square statistic?
    f) How many degrees of freedom do you have?
    g) What is the critical chi-square value for this table?
    h) Are your findings statistically significant? Why?
    i) What is the nature of the relationship? Why?

LAB #12: BIVARIATE STATISTICS FOR ORDINAL DATA

The focus of this lab is to introduce you to the **association or relationship between ordinal variables**. Specifically, this lab will help clarify your understanding of independent and dependent variables, how to interpret the chi-square test of statistical significance, as well as other measures of association (i.e., gamma and Somer's *d*). This lab corresponds with material presented in Chapter 13.

LEARNING OBJECTIVES

The following lab is directed at helping you understand how to interpret the relationship between two variables (bivariate relationships). Specifically, this lab assignment challenges you to clarify your understanding of:

1. Dependent and independent variables
2. How to create a cross-tabulation or a contingency table
3. How to interpret your findings and determine statistical significance

Part 1: Establishing Your Research Question and Identifying Your Variables

In this example, we will ask the question, does level of education affect an individual's opinion on whether having a disability lowers an individual's quality of life (d2).

Step 1: Identify your dependent and independent variables.

An independent variable can be thought of as the modifying outcome; the dependent variable can be thought of as the outcome of interest. In this situation, we are interested in seeing if highest level of education will modify opinions on quality of life among those who have disabilities; therefore, it is our independent variable. The outcome we are interested in is opinions on quality of life among those with disabilities; therefore it is our dependent variable.

Step 2: Recode your independent variable.

In this example, we are going to recode our independent variable from a 15 category variable into a 4 category variable measuring highest level of education. In Lab #4, you were introduced to the recode function. Let's review by recoding our highest level of education variable (k6).

Step 1: Click on:

TRANSFORM → RECODE INTO DIFFERENT VARIABLES

It is important to select this option because you are interested in creating a new variable from your original variable rather than altering the existing variable (Figure 1).

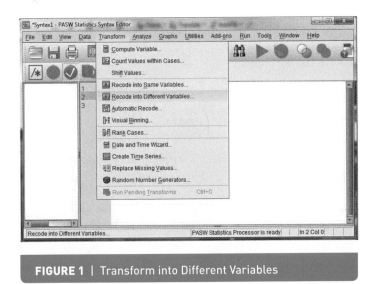

FIGURE 1 | Transform into Different Variables

Step 2: The **Recode into Different Variables** dialogue box will appear (Figure 2). First, you need to specify the variable you are interested in working with, in this example, Recode: What is your highest level of education? (k6). Bring that variable into the **numeric variable →output variable box**. Now, decide on a name and variable label for your new variable and type them into the **output variable** box. Then click on **Change**.

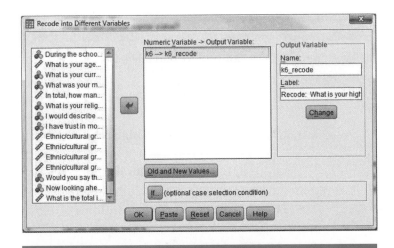

FIGURE 2 | Recode into Different Variables Dialogue Box

Step 3: You now want to define the categories within your variable. So, you need to click on **Old and New Values** (Figure 3). Since you are interested in creating a variable where you want to collapse your variable into 4 categories:

1. Less than high school
2. High school
3. College/Certificate/Diploma
4. University degree or higher

You will need to tell SPSS that this is what you want.

Recall from the first lab that you can use your data editor screen to determine what values were assigned to particular categories within a variable. In **Variable View**, go to the row with your variable of interest and click on the cell corresponding with the **Values Column**.

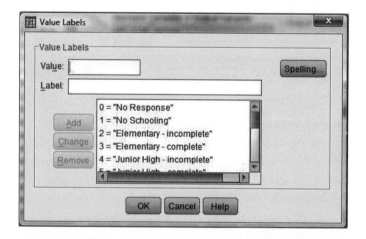

FIGURE 3 | Value Labels Dialogue Box

Step 4: By clicking on the **Values Column** for variable k6, we will need to recode our new variable in the following way:

Old Value → New Value

1, 2, 3, 4, 5, 6 → 1 (less than high school)

7, 8, 10 → 2 (high school)

9, 11 → 3 (College, certificate, diploma)

12, 13, 14, 15 → 4 (University degree or higher)

Step 5: Within the dialogue box you opened when you clicked on **Old and New Values**, you will transform the values in the original k6 variable into the new k6_recode. In Figure 4, you can see that 1 and 2 have been coded into 1, 3 has been coded into 2, and 4 has been coded into 3, and 5 is being coded into 3. Once you have finished defining your new variable, click on **Continue**.

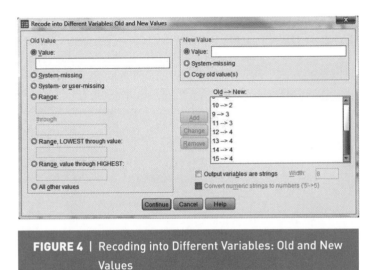

FIGURE 4 | Recoding into Different Variables: Old and New Values

Step 6: Click on **Paste** to display the commands in your syntax file. Then click on the **green arrow** to execute the commands.

In your data editor screen, on variable view, you can add value labels to your new variable, k6_recode, so you can recall what the numeric values you assigned to each category mean (Figure 5). Locate your new variable and click on the cell in the **values** column. Then, name the values accordingly.

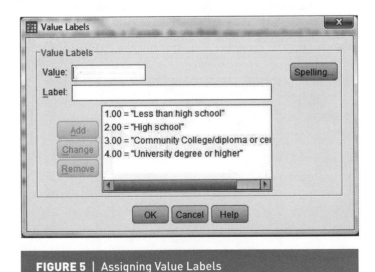

FIGURE 5 | Assigning Value Labels

Now, as a final check, run a frequency distribution on the new variable, k6_recode and the original variable, k6 to confirm your new values add up to the values in the original variable.

Part 2: Creating Contingency Tables within SPSS

Now let's learn how to create contingency tables in SPSS.

Step 1: Using the syntax file, click on:

ANALYZE → DESCRIPTIVE STATISTICS → CROSSTABS

Step 2: Select the dependent and independent variable.

This will bring up the crosstabs dialogue screen (Figure 6). Once you are in that screen, bring your dependent variable, "Having a disability necessarily lowers a person's quality of life" (d2), into the **row(s) box,** and bring your independent variable, "Recode: Highest level of education," into the **column(s) box**. When you have finished doing that, click on **statistics icon**.

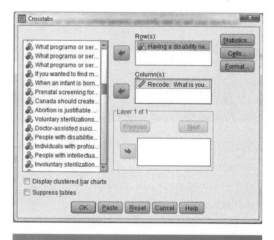

FIGURE 6 | Crosstabs Dialogue Screen

Step 3: Select your statistics.

Within this screen (Figure 7), select **chi-square**, **gamma**, and **Somer's _d_**. Then click **Continue**.

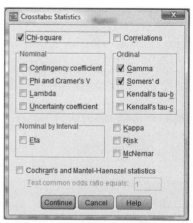

FIGURE 7 | Crosstabs: Statistics Dialogue Screen

Step 4: Percentage your columns.

You will return to the crosstabs screen (Figure 8). Once there, select the **cells button**. Within this screen, you will select **columns under the percentages** list. You are selecting columns because you want to percentage along males and females so you can compare the differences across education levels. Then hit **Continue,** which will return you to the crosstabs screen. Then click **Continue**, **Paste** and **run your syntax commands**.

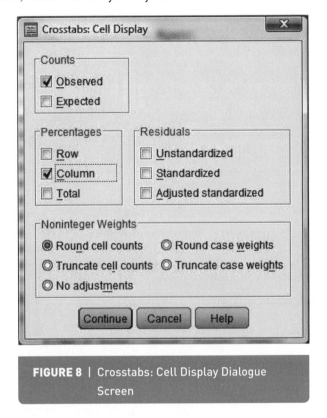

FIGURE 8 | Crosstabs: Cell Display Dialogue Screen

You should get the following output:

Case Processing Summary

	Cases					
	Valid		Missing		Total	
	N	Percent	N	Percent	N	Percent
Having a disability necessarily lowers a person's quality of life. * Recode: What is your highest level of education?	1171.154[a]	96.7%	40.085	3.3%	1211.239	100.0%

a. Number of valid cases is different from the total count in the crosstabulation table because the cell counts have been rounded.

The **Case Processing Summary** tells you the number of respondents, 1,171.154, and the percentage that are valid, 96.7 per cent. This is followed by the number of missing cases, 40.085, and the total number of cases, including both valid and missing cases, 1,211.239.

Following the case summary report is the contingency table, cross-tabulating highest level of education by opinion on whether having a disability lowers a person's quality of life. Let's start to interpret these results. There do appear to be differences between levels of education and people's opinions. In particular, we find that those with less than a high school education are less likely to strongly disagree that having a disability lowers quality of life than those with a university degree or higher, 3.8 per cent compared with 2 per cent respectively. Take a minute to look at the other cells within this table. What else do you notice?

Now we need to determine if the differences seen in the sample also exist within the population. In other words, are these differences statistically significant?

Having a disability necessarily lowers a person's quality of life. * Recode: What is your highest level of education? Crosstabulation

| | | | Recode: What is your highest level of education? | | | | |
			Less than high school	High school	Community College/diploma or certificate	University degree or higher	Total
Having a disability necessarily lowers a person's quality of life.	Strongly Disagree	Count	4	70	59	88	221
		% within Recode: What is your highest level of education?	3.8%	21.6%	18.3%	21.0%	18.9%
	Somewhat Disagree	Count	16	52	74	92	234
		% within Recode: What is your highest level of education?	15.2%	16.0%	22.9%	22.0%	20.0%
	Neither Disagree nor Agree	Count	10	26	40	53	129
		% within Recode: What is your highest level of education?	9.5%	8.0%	12.4%	12.6%	11.0%
	Somewhat Agree	Count	42	111	91	110	354
		% within Recode: What is your highest level of education?	40.0%	34.3%	28.2%	26.3%	30.2%
	Strongly Agree	Count	33	65	59	76	233
		% within Recode: What is your highest level of education?	31.4%	20.1%	18.3%	18.1%	19.9%
Total		Count	105	324	323	419	1171
		% within Recode: What is your highest level of education?	100.0%	100.0%	100.0%	100.0%	100.0%

One way to test this is to use a chi-square test. To evaluate whether we will reject the null hypothesis that no differences exist between the various levels of education, we need to determine the degrees of freedom, which can be found in the SPSS output. For our results, the degrees of freedom equal 12. Since chi-square has a known distribution, the critical chi-square value for 12 degrees of freedom equals 21.026 at the 0.05 level of statistical significance, and our chi-square value is 41.080. Therefore, since our chi-square value exceeds the critical chi-square value, we can reject the null hypothesis and conclude that there are statistically significant differences between highest level of education and opinion on whether having a disability lowers a person's quality of life.

Chi-Square Tests

	Value	df	Asymp. Sig. (2-sided)
Pearson Chi-Square	41.080[a]	12	.000
Likelihood Ratio	46.318	12	.000
Linear-by-Linear Association	18.571	1	.000
N of Valid Cases	1171		

a. 0 cells (.0%) have expected count less than 5. The minimum expected count is 11.57.

The following two tables contain our Somers' *d* statistic and the gamma statistic. We can see we have a Somers' *d* value of −.095. The negative value means that we have a discordant relationship between our independent and dependent variable where, for example, a value of "high school" on the independent value (higher levels of education) results in a lower expected score on our dependent variable (Strongly Disagree). The value of .095 means we are 9.5 per cent better at predicting the score on the dependent variable when we know the value of our independent variable. Furthermore, a score of .095 means that the association between our dependent and independent value is weak.

Directional Measures

			Value	Asymp. Std. Error[a]	Approx. T[b]	Approx. Sig.
Ordinal by Ordinal	Somers' d	Symmetric	-.095	.024	-3.970	.000
		Having a disability necessarily lowers a person's quality of life. Dependent	-.100	.025	-3.970	.000
		Recode: What is your highest level of education? Dependent	-.091	.023	-3.970	.000

a. Not assuming the null hypothesis.

b. Using the asymptotic standard error assuming the null hypothesis.

We find a similar story with our gamma value. The negative value means we have a discordant relationship between our independent and dependent variable in which high school on the independent value (higher levels of education) result in a lower score on our dependent variable (strongly disagree). The value of .128 means we are 12.8 per cent better at predicting the score on the dependent variable when we know the value of our independent variable. Furthermore, a score of .128 means the association between our dependent and independent values is moderate. Recall from Chapter 13 that the gamma statistic is more liberal in its calculation. If you want to err on the side of caution, it is recommended you use the Somers' *d*.

Symmetric Measures

		Value	Asymp. Std. Error[a]	Approx. T[b]	Approx. Sig.
Ordinal by Ordinal	Gamma	-.128	.032	-3.970	.000
N of Valid Cases		1171			

a. Not assuming the null hypothesis.

b. Using the asymptotic standard error assuming the null hypothesis.

Now's it's your turn!

Putting Information into Practice

Continuing with the theme of this chapter, we are going to ask the question, does level of education affect an individual's opinion on whether involuntary sterilization is justifiable for people with chronic mental or intellectual disabilities who rely on government support?

1. Answer the following questions:
    a) What is your null hypothesis?
    b) What is your research hypothesis?
    c) What is your dependent variable?
    d) What is your independent variable?
    e) What are the levels of measurement of your variables?

2. Produce a contingency table. Be sure to include percentages and the chi-square statistic, gamma and Somers' *d*.

3. Based on your output, answer the following questions:
    a) What is the total valid sample size for this table?
    b) How many missing cases do you have?
    c) What percentage of individuals with less than a high school education indicate they strongly disagree? What percentage of individuals with a university degree or higher indicate the same?
    d) How much difference (variance) is there between those with less than a high school education and those with a university degree or higher with respect to the percentage that strongly agree that people with chronic mental or intellectual disabilities who rely on government support should be involuntary sterilized?
    e) What is the value of your chi-square statistic?
    f) How many degrees of freedom do you have?
    g) What is the critical chi-square value for this table?
    h) Are your findings statistically significant? Why?
    i) What is the value of your gamma and your Somers' *d*? What do these statistics tell you?

LAB #13: BIVARIATE STATISTICS FOR INTERVAL/RATIO DATA

The focus of this lab is to introduce you to the **association or relationship between interval/ratio level variables**. Specifically, this lab will help clarify your understanding of Pearson's r and explained variance. This lab corresponds with the material presented in Chapter 14.

LEARNING OBJECTIVES

The following lab is directed at helping you understand how to interpret the relationship between two variables (bivariate relationships). Specifically, this lab assignment challenges you to clarify your understanding of:

1. Dependent and independent variables
2. How to calculate and interpret Pearson's r
3. How to interpret explained variance

Part 1: Calculating Pearson's r in SPSS

When calculating Pearson's r, we make the assumption that the two variables we are correlating (evaluation the extent to which the variables are related) have a linear relationship. That is, the relationship between the two variables is the same, regardless of what the value of either of these variables is. So, the first step in calculating Pearson's r is to evaluate whether the relationship between the two variables is linear.

In this example, we are interested in whether an individual's age is correlated with the number of years of education they have obtained. In this case, our dependent variable is years of educational attainment and our independent variable is an individual's age.

Step 1: Evaluate for linearity.

To evaluate for linearity, we will use a scatterplot. To create a scatterplot in SPSS, click on

GRAPHS → LEGACY DIALOGS → SCATTER/DOT . . .

Select **SIMPLE SCATTER**, then click on **Define** (Figure 1). Place your dependent variable in the Y-axis and your independent variable in your X-axis. Then click **Paste** and **run your syntax commands**.

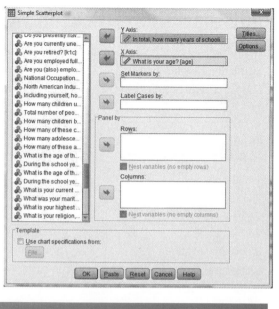

FIGURE 1 | Simple Scatterplot Dialogue Screen

This is the scatterplot that should have been produced:

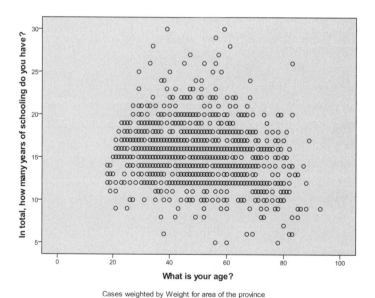

Cases weighted by Weight for area of the province

Here are a few observations we could make about this scatterplot:

1. While not as strong as we might have liked to have obtained, the dots appear to be arranged in a linear fashion, thus, for our purposes, satisfying the linear assumption of the Pearson correlation.

2. There are a few outliers both above and below the line . . .

Now that we are confident that our variables do meet the linear assumption, we are ready to calculate Pearson's r in SPSS.

The computation of our Pearson's r is done "behind the scenes" by SPSS, and is quite complex. In a nutshell, it considers the amount of covariation between your X variable (independent variable) and your Y variable (dependent variable).

Pearson's r ranges from −1.00 to +1.00

−1.0 = a perfect negative relationship or association
−0.5 = a moderate negative relationship or association
 0.0 = no correlation between two variables
+0.5 = a moderate positive relationship or association
+1.0 = a perfect positive relationship or association

Step 2: In your syntax file, click on:

ANALYZE → CORRELATE → BIVARIATE

You should see a screen that looks like the one in Figure 2. Bring both your dependent and independent variables into the variable list. Be sure to select **Pearson** under the Correlation Coefficients.

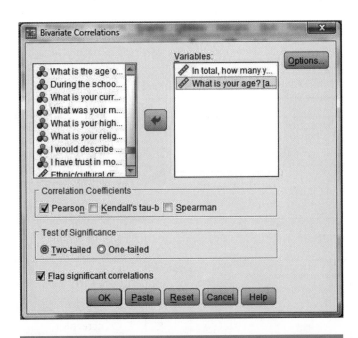

FIGURE 2 | Bivariate Correlations Dialogue Screen

Now click on Options . . . and select Means and Standard Deviations (Figure 3). Then click Continue, Paste and run your syntax commands.

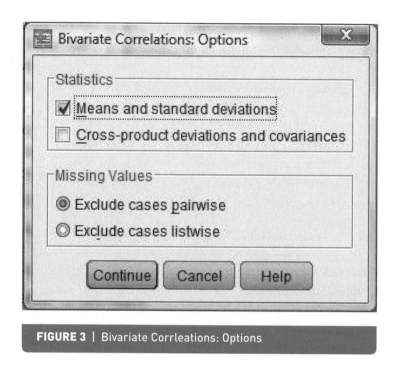

FIGURE 3 | Bivariate Corrleations: Options

You should see two tables that looks like these ones:

Descriptive Statistics

	Mean	Std. Deviation	N
In total, how many years of schooling do you have?	15.24	3.491	1198
What is your age?	49.37	15.856	1168

Correlations

		In total, how many years of schooling do you have?	What is your age?
In total, how many years of schooling do you have?	Pearson Correlation	1	-.180[**]
	Sig. (2-tailed)		.000
	N	1198	1158
What is your age?	Pearson Correlation	-.180[**]	1
	Sig. (2-tailed)	.000	
	N	1158	1168

[**]. Correlation is significant at the 0.01 level (2-tailed).

Looking at the first table, we observe that 1,198 people answered the schooling question whereas only 1,168 reported their age. We can see that, on average, respondents have 15.24 years of schooling and the average respondent age is 49.37 years.

Now look at the second table. This table is called a **correlation matrix**. Refering to the upper-right hand cell, we see we get a Pearson's r of $-.180$. This means that the relationship between our two variables is negative but weak, because it falls below 0.5. However, looking at the value immediately below our Pearson's r coefficient, we see that our results are statistically significant at the .000 level.

Now it's your turn!

Putting the Information into Practice

In this example, we are interested in whether the number of children in the household (k3c) is correlated with the number of years of education they have obtained (k7).

1. Answer the following questions:
    a) What is your null hypothesis?
    b) What is your research hypothesis?
    c) What is your dependent variable?
    d) What is your independent variable?
    e) What are the levels of measurement of your variables?

2. Produce a scatter plot.
    a) Does the relationship between your two variables meet the assumption of linearity?

3. Calculate Pearson's r. Be sure to include the mean and standard deviation of your variables.
    a) What sample size did SPSS use to calculate the Pearson correlation coefficient between k7 and k3c?
    b) What is the mean value of k7? What is the mean value of k3c?
    c) What is the Pearson correlation coefficient? Is it significant? Is it small, large?
    d) In terms of our two variables, what does the Pearson correlation coefficient mean? (Hint: Is the Pearson correlation coefficient positive or negative?)

LAB #14: ANALYSIS OF VARIANCE

The focus of this lab is to introduce you to a procedure known as ANOVA, or **analysis of variance**. Specifically, this lab will help clarify your understanding of when this procedure should be used, how to calculate within-group sum of squares, between-group sum of squares, and the total sum of squares, which are the three major components of ANOVA. Finally, this lab will teach you how to interpret the *F*-distribution with ANOVA. This lab corresponds with the material presented in Chapter 15.

LEARNING OBJECTIVES

The following lab is directed at helping you understand how to interpret the relationship between two variables by using a procedure called ANOVA. Specifically, this lab assignment challenges you to clarify your understanding of:

1. Dependent and independent variables
2. Null and research hypotheses
3. How to interpret your findings and determine statistical significance

Analysis of variance, or ANOVA, is like a *t*-test but allows us to compare more than two groups. Conceptually, ANOVA compares three things:

1. Differences between means
2. Differences in values within samples
3. Differences in values across samples

Essentially, ANOVA is used to compare the variation caused by the independent variable and the variation that occurs at random, around the mean within groups to the variation across groups.

Part 1: Calculating ANOVA with SPSS

In this example, we will ask the question: Are there significant differences in years of schooling (k7) by city, village, town or rural residence (k14)?

Step 1: Recode into different variables.

Recode variables k7 and k14, eliminating missing and reserve values.

> **For k7, recode −6, −5, and 98 as system missing**
> **For k14, recode 0 as missing.**

Step 2: Request a one-way ANOVA.

In a new syntax file, click on:

ANALYZE → COMPARE MEANS → ONE-WAY ANOVA

Step 3: From the left-hand screen**, bring over your recoded dependent variable**, "How many years of schooling do you have?" variable, into the **dependent list** (Figure 1). Next, **bring your recoded independent variable** into the **factor list**, "Do you live in a city, village, town or rural residence."

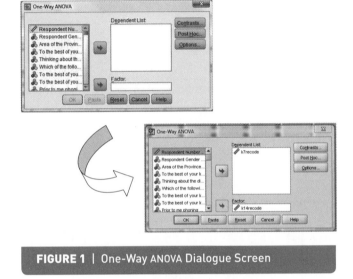

FIGURE 1 | One-Way ANOVA Dialogue Screen

Select **OPTIONS**. Within Options, click on **descriptive** (Figure 2).

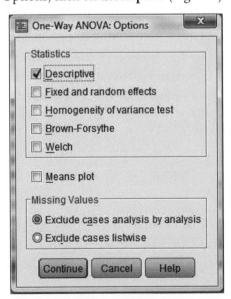

FIGURE 2 | One-Way ANOVA Options Dialogue Screen

Now, select **Continue** and **Paste** and **run your syntax commands**.

You will get the following results in your output file.

Descriptives

k7recode

	N	Mean	Std. Deviation	Std. Error	95% Confidence Interval for Mean		Minimum	Maximum
					Lower Bound	Upper Bound		
1.00	792	15.7425	3.59682	.12783	15.4916	15.9935	-2.00	30.00
2.00	185	14.3125	3.47256	.25542	13.8086	14.8165	-2.00	26.00
3.00	36	12.9438	4.66123	.78138	11.3568	14.5307	-2.00	27.00
4.00	189	13.9396	3.48195	.25325	13.4401	14.4392	5.00	30.00
Total	1201	15.1558	3.68928	.10645	14.9470	15.3647	-2.00	30.00

There are a few things to note here. First, let's look at the means. You will notice that those in category 1 (lives in a city) on k14recode have, on average, 15.7 years of schooling. On the opposite end of the spectrum, those in a rural part of the province (k14recode=4) have, on average, 13.9 years of schooling. Although differences are observed, are they meaningful? In other words, can we expect to see them in our population?

ANOVA

k7recode

	Sum of Squares	df	Mean Square	F	Sig.
Between Groups	857.735	3	285.912	22.111	.000
Within Groups	15477.869	1197	12.931		
Total	16335.604	1200			

To determine this, we need to look at the ANOVA table. For our between-group sum of squares we can see that we have three degrees of freedom and a value of 857.735. For our within-group sum of squares, we have 1,197 degrees of freedom and a value of 15,477.869. If we go to Appendix, D at the back of the textbook, we find that the critical F-distribution score for four degrees of freedom for the between-groups score and for more than 120 degrees of freedom for the within-group value is less than 2.45. We can see in our table that our F-score (F-observed) is 22.111. Because this number exceeds the critical F-score of 2.45, we can conclude with 95 per cent confidence that there are significant differences between at least two groups.

Now it's your turn!

Putting the Information into Practice

In this assignment, we will ask the question: Do urban Albertans have different incomes than rural Albertans. Use K12b to measure income (pretend that the variable is suitable for ANOVA, even though it technically is not) and k14 to measure how urban a person is. Be sure to handle all missing values appropriately.

1. Answer the following questions:
   a) What is your null hypothesis?
   b) What is your research hypothesis?
   c) What is your dependent variable?
   d) What is your independent variable?
   e) What are the levels of measurement of your variables?

2. Calculate ANOVA (remember to include your descriptive statistics).

3. In your output, using the table called descriptives, calculate the difference between mean income for
   a) Those who live in a city and those who live in a rural area: _____
   b) Those who live in a town and those who live in a village: _____
   c) Those who live in a village and those who live in a rural area: _____

4. What do these data suggest about the relationship between the degree of rurality and income?

5. State the value of the total sum of squares, the within-groups sum of squares, and the between-groups sum of squares.

6. What is the value of your F-statistic?
   a) Does this mean your results are statistically significant?
   b) Do you accept or reject your null hypothesis? Why?

LAB #15: OLS REGRESSION: MODELLING CONTINUOUS OUTCOMES

The focus of this lab is to introduce you to a form of multivariate analysis called **regression analysis**. Specifically, this lab will help clarify your understanding of when this procedure should be used, how to calculate and interpret ordinary least squares (OLS) regression, and how to compute dummy variables. This lab corresponds with the material presented in Chapter 16.

LEARNING OBJECTIVES

The following lab is directed at helping you understand how to interpret the relationship between multiple variables using OLS regression. Specifically, this lab assignment challenges you to clarify your understanding of:

1. Dummy variables
2. Standardized partial slopes
3. How to interpret your findings and determine statistical significance

Part 1: Calculating OLS Regression with SPSS

In this example, we are interested in which variables might affect the number of years of education an individual has obtained? For various reasons, we think that the number of years of education an individual has obtained may vary by gender (sex1) and by what part of Alberta they live in (STRATA).

Step 1: Code your variables.

Because one of the conditions of OLS regression states that all variables must be interval, ratio, or dummy variables, we will need to recode our variables to meet these conditions.

First, gender is a nominal level variable where the values are coded 1 "male" and 2 "female." We will need to recode this variable into a dummy variable where the response categories are 1 "male" and 0 "female."

Recall from earlier labs, to recode a variable, click on:

TRANSFORM → RECODE INTO DIFFERENT VARIABLES

When the dialogue box appears, select the original gender variable (sex1) and place it in the box labelled "Numeric Variable → Output Variable." Then, name your new variable under the box labelled "Output Variable." Since we will be making males equal to a value of one, we will call our new variable "male," as we have done in Figure 1. Once you have done that, select the button **Change**.

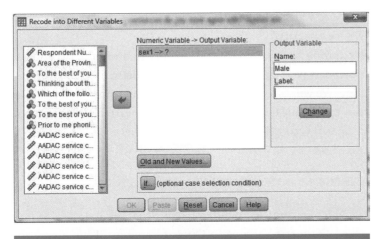

FIGURE 1 | Recode into Different Variables Dialogue Screen

Next, click the button **Old and New Values**. In this screen you will want to make the **old value** of "1" into **new value** "1." In other words, the male value of "1" will remain as "1." Next, make the old value "2" into new value "0." Now, the female value of "2" will become "0." Select **Continue** to return to the **Recode into different variables** dialogue screen (Figure 2).

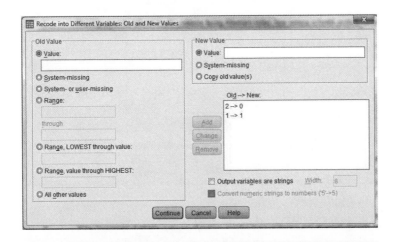

FIGURE 2 | Recode into Different Variables: Old and New Values Dialogue Screen

Now, select **Paste** and **run your syntax commands**.

To double check to make sure your new dummy variable for gender matches the original variable for gender, run a frequency distribution on both variables.

Next, we will need to create a series of dummy variables for our area of the province variable (STRATA). As you recall from Chapter 16, you need to leave out one category of your independent variable (STRATA) as a reference category. As we are most interested in the differences between Edmonton and Calgary, as compared to the rest of the province, we will make "Other Alberta" our reference category.

To create two dummy variables from our one original variable, you will follow the same steps as when you coded your gender variable, except you will be creating two new variables rather than just one. We will call these new variables "Edmonton" and "Calgary." We know by clicking the **values** tab in our data editor screen for the variable STRATA that "Edmonton" is coded as a "1," "Calgary" is coded as a "2," and "Other Alberta" is coded as a "3."

First, click on:

TRANSFORM → RECODE INTO DIFFERENT VARIABLES

When the dialogue box appears (Figure 3), select the original variable (STRATA) and place it in the box labelled "Numeric Variable → Output Variable." Then, name your new variable under the box labelled "Output Variable." Since our first dummy variable corresponds with Edmonton, we will be making Edmonton equal to a value of "1" and everyone else equal to "0," we will call our new variable "Edmonton," as we have done in Figure 1. Once you have done that, select the button **Change**.

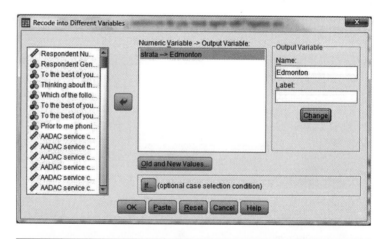

FIGURE 3 | Recode into Different Variables Dialogue Screen

Next, click the button **Old and New Values**. In this screen, you will want to make the **old value** of "1" into **new value** "1." In other words, the "Edmonton" value of "1" will remain as "1." Next, make the old value "2" into new value "0" and old value "3" into new value "0." Now, the "Calgary" value of "2" will become "0" and the "Other Alberta" value of "3" will become "0." Select **Continue** to return to the **Recode into different variables** dialogue screen (Figure 4).

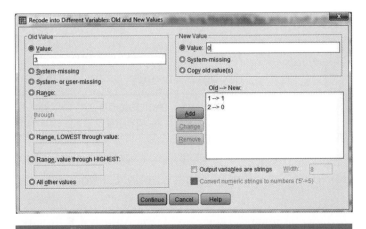

FIGURE 4 | Recode into Different Variables: Old and New Values Dialogue Screen

Now, select **Paste** and **run your syntax commands**. Repeat this process for "Calgary," making a new variable named "Calgary," where the old value of "2" becomes the new value of "1," and both other old values have a new value of "0."

Step 2: Conduct an OLS regression in SPSS.

First, click on:

ANALYZE → REGRESSION → LINEAR

Bring your dependent variable, "In total, how many years of schooling do you have?" (k7) into the **Dependent** box (Figure 5). Then, bring your independent variables (male, Edmonton, Calgary) into the **Independent(s)** box.

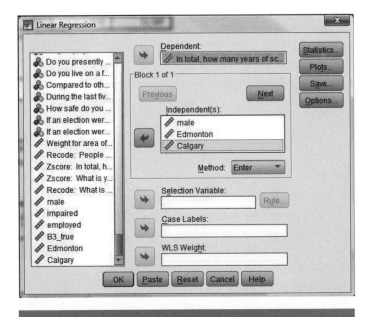

FIGURE 5 Linear Regression Dialogue Screen

Now, select **Paste** and **run your syntax commands**.
You should get the following output.

Model Summary

Model	R	R Square	Adjusted R Square	Std. Error of the Estimate
1	.252[a]	.063	.061	3.383

a. Predictors: (Constant), Calgary, male, Edmonton

First, look at the "Model Summary" Table. Notice the **Adjusted R Square** value. *R*-squared measure how well the model fits your data; it tells you how much of the variation in the dependent variable can be explained by all the independent variables. In our example, we have explained about 6.1 per cent of the variation in educational attainment.

ANOVA[b]

Model		Sum of Squares	df	Mean Square	F	Sig.
1	Regression	925.165	3	308.388	26.952	.000[a]
	Residual	13664.467	1194	11.442		
	Total	14589.632	1197			

a. Predictors: (Constant), Calgary, male, Edmonton

b. Dependent Variable: In total, how many years of schooling do you have?

The ANOVA table displays information on the variation, whether random or caused by the independent variables, around the mean within groups and across groups. We find that the differences in variation between and across groups is statistically significant (F = 26.952, Sig. = .000, which is less than .05).

Finally, we have the piece of output that quantifies our regression equation, the coefficients table. Now, if you recall, the regression equation is as follows:

$$y = a + bx + \varepsilon$$

A **regression equation** expresses the relationship between two or more variables. The variable *a* is the constant term, the intercept value when all independent values are set to zero, and it equals 14.042. This means that our respondents in the reference category (females, other Alberta) have, on average, 14.042 years of schooling, a finding that is statistically significant at the .000 level. The *bx* term in the equation above represents the coefficients (*b*) and the independent variables (*x*), and their values are listed below in the column labelled "B." We can see from the output that men have .152 years more schooling that females, however this finding is not statistically significant (*p* = .438, which is greater than .05). Next, individuals living in Edmonton have 1.334 more years of schooling than those living in "Other Alberta," and this finding is statistically significant at the .000 level. Finally, individuals living in Calgary have

2.094 more years of schooling than those living in "Other Alberta," and this finding is statistically significant at the .000 level.

Coefficients[a]

Model		Unstandardized Coefficients		Standardized Coefficients	t	Sig.
		B	Std. Error	Beta		
1	(Constant)	14.042	.192		73.181	.000
	male	.152	.195	.022	.776	.438
	Edmonton	1.334	.239	.178	5.572	.000
	Calgary	2.094	.237	.283	8.834	.000

a. Dependent Variable: In total, how many years of schooling do you have?

Now it's your turn!

Putting the Information into Practice

In this assignment, we are interested in whether age affects behaviours surrounding alcohol consumption. Specifically, we are interested in whether an individual has driven while impaired (h1), whether an individual has consumed alcohol while driving a motor vehicle (h4), and whether an individual has been involved in a traffic accident because of an impaired driver (h7).

1. Answer the following questions:
   a) What is your null hypothesis?
   b) What is your research hypothesis?
   c) What is your dependent variable?
   d) What is your independent variable?

2. Recode h1, h4, and h7 into dummy variables (make "yes" your reference category, i.e., equal to "1").

3. Conduct an OLS regression analysis using SPSS.

4. What is the value of your R-squared? What does this mean?

5. Write the equation for your regression equation.

6. What is the average age of someone who has driven while impaired? Is this finding statistically significant?

7. What is the average age of someone who has consumed alcohol while driving a motor vehicle? Is this finding statistically significant?

8. What is the average age of someone who has been involved in a traffic accident because of an impaired driver? Is this finding statistically significant?

AN INTRODUCTION
TO STATISTICS FOR
CANADIAN SOCIAL
SCIENTISTS

STATA LAB
MANUAL

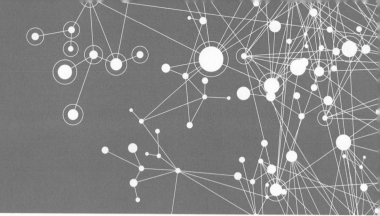

CONTENTS

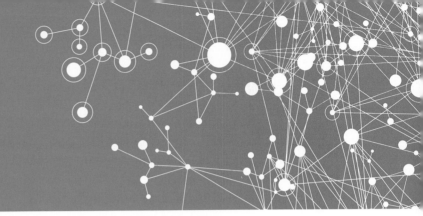

PREFACE

HOW DOES THIS MANUAL WORK?

This manual is intended to give you the opportunity to apply the concepts and principles you learn in each chapter of the text. Through practical examples and step-by-step instructions, this manual seeks to help you improve your understanding of statistical practices and introduce you to STATA, a key statistical tool used in the social sciences. Often we learn through practice, and by actively engaging with the examples and assignments covered in this lab, you will improve your understanding of the course material and the basics of STATA.

For nearly all of the chapters in your textbook, there is a corresponding lab exercise. The labs are approached in a workbook style where you will need to participate in each step to successfully complete the final assignment. You may find the labs challenging at times, even frustrating. Take a deep breath! Rome wasn't built in a day and neither is expertise in statistics. To master a skill, one must practise, be challenged, and then try again. It is the intention of the lab manual to challenge you in this way. The knowledge is cumulative, so if you find a particular section tricky, return to earlier sections and brush up on the basics. You may find you need to do this several times before you are able to make sense of the material and the technical aspects of STATA. Stay with it! By the end of this lab manual, you will have the ability to use STATA efficiently and apply the concepts and principles taught in this course in a meaningful way.

THE MODEL

Each lab contains three sections:

The first section will briefly reintroduce the topic covered by the corresponding chapter and set the learning objectives for the lab.

The second section will provide an example to help focus your thinking and help you to understand the key concepts to be covered. The examples are intended to illustrate the real-world applications of the concepts.

The third section will include a lab assignment to test your understanding of the concepts and skills covered in the lab and corresponding chapter.

WHAT'S COVERED?

This manual is meant to complement the textbook used in this course, not replace it. Through the use of concrete examples, each lab is intended to solidify your understanding of the general concepts and principles taught in each chapter. To help teach you how to analyze data, this lab manual will provide step-by-step instructions on how to use the STATA analysis software.

The labs cover the following key topics:

Lab 1: Introduction to STATA
Lab 2: Identifying Types of Variables: Levels of Measurement
Lab 3: Univariate Statistics
Lab 4: Introduction to Probability
Lab 5: The Normal Curve
Lab 6: Measures of Central Tendency and Dispersion
Lab 7: Standard Deviations, Standard Scores, and the Normal Distribution
Lab 8: Sampling
Lab 9: Hypothesis Testing: Testing the Significance of the Difference between Two Means
Lab 10: Hypothesis Testing: One- and Two-Tailed Tests
Lab 11: Bivariate Statistics for Nominal Data
Lab 12: Bivariate Statistics for Ordinal Data
Lab 13: Bivariate Statistics for Interval/Ratio Data
Lab 14: Analysis of Variance
Lab 15: OLS Regression: Modelling Continuous Outcomes

THE DATASET

The 2009 Alberta Survey (AS) is the 20th annual provincial survey administered by the Population Research Laboratory (PRL) at the University of Alberta. This annual omnibus survey of households in the province of Alberta enables academic researchers, government departments, and non-profit organizations to explore a wide range of research topics in a structured research framework and environment. Sponsors' research questions are asked together with demographic questions in a telephone interview of Alberta households.

The target population was all persons 18 years of age or older who, at the time of the survey, were living in Alberta and could be contacted by direct dialling. From this population, three samples were drawn to cover Alberta: Edmonton Metropolitan Area, Calgary Metropolitan Area, and the rest of the province. The final dataset contains 1,211 cases.

This dataset is available online as a public-use data file. You can find it on the Population Research Laboratory's website: http://www.uofaweb.ualberta.ca/prl/. Click on "Alberta Survey," then click on the link for "Alberta Survey 2009 Public Release Data." The data can also be found here: http://www.prl.ualberta.ca/en/AlbertaSurvey/PublicReleaseAlberta SurveyDatasets2009.aspx or http://www.ualberta.ca/~prl/easdata/. You will also be able to find some previous Alberta surveys.

LAB #1: INTRODUCTION TO STATA

The focus of this lab is to introduce you to STATA. To use STATA to analyze data, you will need to become familiar with the technical components of this software package. This lab will help familiarize you with the STATA software, including how to access data files, the various base components (i.e., the syntax, data editor, and output), how to define new variables, and how to enter data.

You should be able to find STATA on many of the computer terminals at your university, but if you can't, your instructor for the course should be able to help you find STATA.

LEARNING OBJECTIVES

The following lab is directed at helping you understand how to orient STATA. Specifically, this lab assignment challenges you to clarify your understanding of:

1. The basic components of STATA
2. How to define variables
3. How to enter data

Part 1: Defining STATA

What Is STATA and How Does It Work?

STATA is a statistical software package commonly used by social scientists. It works by taking a series of commands, supplied by you, and applying them to a set of data, also supplied by you. STATA will produce output displaying the results of the commands. The commands you supply STATA will determine your output results. Within STATA, commands are either given in the form of menu selections and by filling in dialogue boxes, or by writing your own programming syntax. We'll look at both methods here.

The sequence of commands will occur in the following order:

- Enter your data into STATA, or open already existing data (which is what we'll do here).
- Tell STATA to apply commands to the data (menus and dialogue boxes).
- STATA then produces the output.

How Do I Begin a STATA Session?

To begin, you need to access a computer that contains the STATA software. Many universities have the STATA software inside computer labs on their public use computers. Once you have found a computer with a copy of the STATA software, you will need to click on the **Start Menu** (on the bottom left-hand side of your computer screen), find the STATA program, and open it.

Once you have opened the STATA program, you should see a screen that looks something like the one in Figure 1.

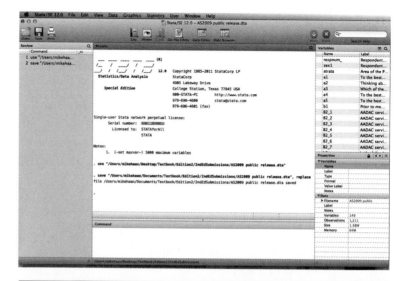

FIGURE 1 | STATA Opening Screen

To open your data, select **File > Open > My Computer**. Find your data in **My Computer** and double click on the file. For the examples in this manual, you will be using CCHS2-1.dta. All the variables in the CCHS2-l.dta data set are listed along the left side of the screen in the box labelled **Variables**.

The Various Components of STATA

The STATA desktop contains several components:

- The menu bar
- The command window
- The STATA results window
- The variables window
- The review window

In addition, STATA has other windows that you will be using:

- The data editor
- The data browser
- The log
- The do-file editor

The Menu Bar

Along the top of the screen you will see the menu bar, which gives you access to all the available commands. The menu bar has a number of headings, dividing the commands into categories with similar functions (**File, Edit, Prefs, Data, Graphics, Statistics, User, Window**, and **Help**). Browse through these pull-down menus to become familiar with their contents.

The Command Window

To conduct an analysis within STATA, type the commands into the command window. For instance, to open the 2009 Alberta Survey data set in the folder N:\courses folder\ SOC. 210, type

Use "N:\courses folder\ SOC. 210/AS2009 public release.dta", clear

The path will vary according to where your data is stored. Remember that you can also execute this command by clicking **File > Open > My Computer**, finding your data file, and double clicking on it. "Clear" closes any data files that are already open and, although it is not necessary here since there are no open files, it is a good habit to have when opening new data.

The Results Window

The results window displays the output from the statistical analysis you perform.

The Variables Window

The variables window lists the variables contained in your data set. Double click on any variable to bring it over to the commands window.

The Review Window

The review window lists all of the commands that have been executed in the current session. You can repeat these commands by double clicking on them, clicking anywhere in the command window, and hitting enter.

The Do-file (.do)*

The do-file is a text file containing a list of STATA commands. You can run it by entering the STATA prompt **do filename.do**, where "filename" is the name of your do-file. This will save your syntax with a *.do extension, and you can give the file any name.

The Log File (.smcl)*

The log file is an output file—it records whatever appears in your STATA results window. You can ask STATA to keep a log of your session by typing **log using filename.smcl**, and STATA will name the log file filename.smcl. When you are done, type **log close**, and the log file will then be ready for you to view, edit, or print. You can ask STATA to open and close your log file within your do-file.

Saving Your STATA Files

To save your STATA files, click on **File > Save As**. Move to the directory in which you want to save the file and give your document a name. If you have previously saved your file and you have merely modified it, select **Save** from the **File** menu or click the icon in the menu bar that looks like a floppy disk.

You will have a variety of options, including **open an existing data source**, **open another type of file**, **run a tutorial**, or **type in data**. For the purposes of this lab, you will select **TYPE IN DATA** (we will look at the Alberta Survey later).

If you want to enter your own data, simply click the "data editor" button on the top of the screen. The data editor window is like a spreadsheet (as shown in Figure 2). Within the data editor screen, you can both create and edit pre-existing datasets. The current data editor screen has the title Untitled. To save this file, select **FILE ➔ SAVE AS**. This will allow you to select both a name and a location for your file. The saved document will have the suffix '.sav.'

Let's take a closer look at the STATA Data Editor screen. Along the top of the screen you will see the **Menu Bar** that is used to access all the commands available. The menu bar has a number of headings, dividing the commands into categories of a similar function (**File**, **Edit**, **View**, **Data**, **Graphics**, **Statistics**, **User**, **Window**, **Help**). Consider browsing through these options so you can become familiar with their contents. The more familiar you are with what is contained under each heading, the more comfortable you will be with the STATA software package.

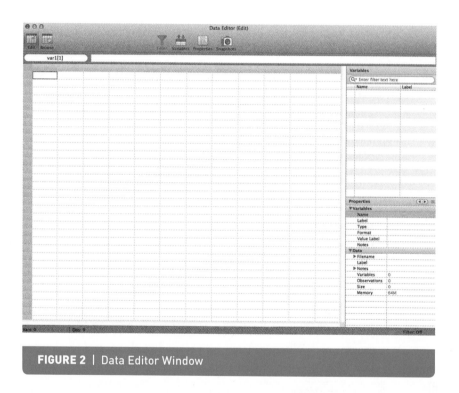

FIGURE 2 | Data Editor Window

The second component of STATA is the *.**do file** (Figure 3). The STATA syntax file is a very useful tool for organizing your records and analyses. It is a text editor that reads STATA programming. As mentioned above, there are two approaches to working in STATA: using a point-and-click approach or manually inputting program commands. In this manual, you will mostly be using the point-and-click approach. Note that the same menu bar that appeared above the data editor screen also appears in the syntax file. To open a new syntax file, select **FILE ➔ OPEN ➔ SYNTAX**. Syntax files can be saved by slecting **FILE ➔ SAVE AS**. The saved document will have the suffix .do.

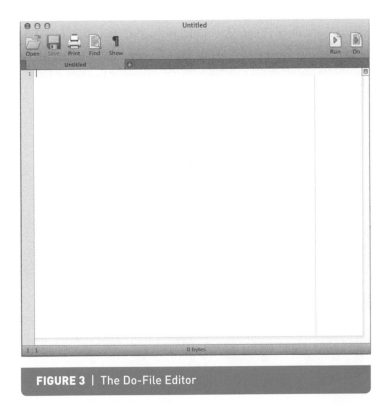

FIGURE 3 | The Do-File Editor

The do-file editor allows you to execute a long list of commands and modifications to your dataset. If you plan only to execute a few quick commands, it is also possible to use the command window at the bottom of the main STATA interface screen (Figure 4):

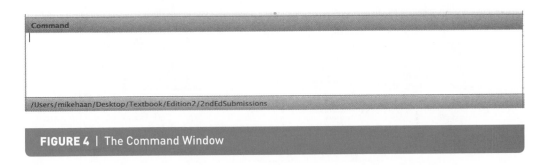

FIGURE 4 | The Command Window

The next component of STATA that is important to familiarize yourself with is the **results window** (Figure 5). The results window displays the output from the statistical analysis you undertake in the do-file editor window. You will notice a couple of things about this window. First, along the left side of the window is a running log of the commands you have executed during the current session. Second, similar to the **Data Editor** and **do-file** windows, you have a Menu Bar with a series of headings, dividing the commands into categories of a similar function (**File**, **Edit**, **View**, **Data**, **Transform**, **Analyze**, **Graphs**, **Utilities**, **Window**, **Help**).

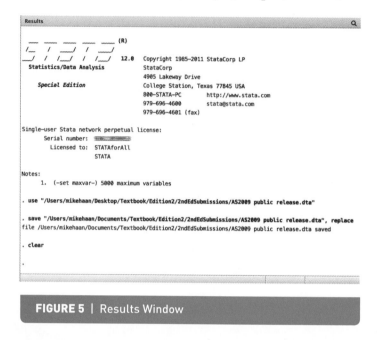

FIGURE 5 | Results Window

Entering STATA Commands

There are three ways of entering commands into STATA to execute your procedures: The first is known as the point-and-click procedure. This procedure can be done via the buttons along the top of the main interface.

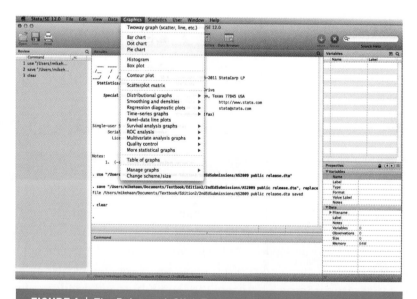

FIGURE 6 | The Point-and-Click Technique

The second way is to enter syntax in the command window (the example in Figure 7 asks for a tabulation of the variable sex1):

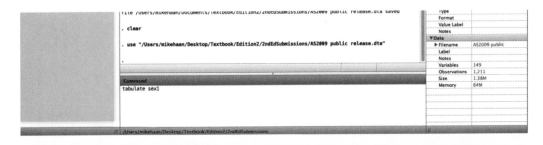

FIGURE 7 | Using the Command Window to Enter Commands in STATA

The third way is to enter command programming into the syntax file (Figure 8).

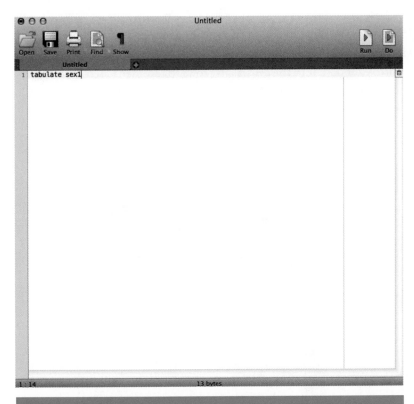

FIGURE 8 | Using the Do-file Editor to Enter Commands in STATA

Creating a Data File

Although most of the lab exercises in this manual use data from the Alberta Survey, it is important to understand data structure. By understanding how data files are constructed, you will be in a better position to understand what shape and form the variables within your data-set take and how to modify them when you learn how to undertake more advanced analysis.

Imagine you are interested in whether males or females are more likely to own a cat. You went out onto the street and asked five random people two questions:

1.   Are you a male or a female? (Male = 1 and Female = 2)
2.   How many cats do you own? (0 to 5)

Person 1: Male (1) owns 2 cats
Person 2: Female (2) owns 1 cat
Person 3: Female (2) owns 0 cats
Person 4: Male (1) owns 5 cats
Person 5: Female (2) owns 1 cat

Now that you have your data, you can enter the information into an STATA data file.

Step 1: Open a new data editor window (remember that this is on the top of the main interface window).

Step 2: Enter your data into the cells, using rows to represent each observation (there are 5), and columns to contain a piece of information about each individual (sex of respondents and # of cats they own). Once you are done, you should have a small data matrix that looks like Figure 9:

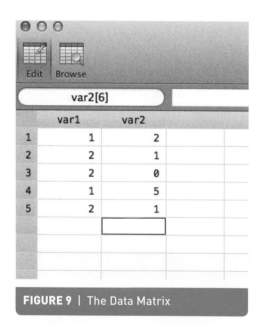

FIGURE 9 | The Data Matrix

Step 3: Name your variables by using the properties button on the top of the screen. You must first decide on the names of your variables, these names must not have spaces and must start with a letter. As good practice, it is useful to keep the number of characters to a minimum where possible. Often variable names will correspond with the survey question number from which it was derived, such as Q1 or Var01, however, this is not necessary here. For our purposes, we will call our variables SEX and CATS.

Step 4: Define your variable labels ("Label" under the variable heading), also within the properties screen. Although we have given our variables names that clearly indicate what the variable is measuring, your variable label can help clarify what the variable is measuring, or, if you have named the variable after survey questions (i.e., Q1), it will allow other users to know what information Q1 is measuring. For SEX, we will put, "Sex of respondent" and for CATS, we will put, "Number of cats owned."

Step 5: Define your value labels ("Value Label" under the variable heading) within the properties screen. Often value labels are attached with ordinal and nominal level variables (concepts you will learn about as you proceed through this course). Without labels, it is difficult to know what the values mean. So, for example, we have attached a value of "1" to our male respondents and a value of "2" to our female respondents. You must specify this under the value label column. To do this, click on value label when you have the variable of interest highlighted. Click on the grey button with 3 dots in the cell. A dialogue box will open. Following our example, assign labels male and female to numeric values "1" and "2," respectively, by entering "1" into the **value box** and its label, male, into the **label box**. Click **add** to make the changes for each value of your variable, then click **OK** when you are finished.

Finally, don't forget to close the data editor and save your new dataset. It is good practice to save your work regularly so you don't lose information that you have worked to produce. Remember to save files:

FILE → SAVE AS → Lab 1 Practice Example

Now, it's your turn!

Putting the Information into Practice

For this lab, you will be required to complete a short survey and input the data into the data editor screen. For the remainder of the lab assignments, data will be provided for you, but this exercise seeks to make you more familiar with the nature of data organization and storage within the STATA software package.

The following questions were taken from the Alberta Survey, 2009.
Part 1: Take the time to answer each question as it relates to your life. Then, ask two friends to answer these questions. Pretend a fourth respondent refused to give you any answers to your survey. You should have a total of four respondents for your short survey.

1. What is your gender?
    1. Male
    2. Female

2. Do you presently have a paid job or are you self-employed?
    1. Yes, paid job
    2. Yes, self-employed
    3. Yes, paid job and self-employed
    4. No, neither

3. What is your CURRENT marital status?
    1. Never Married (Single)
    2. Married
    3. Common-Law Relationship/Live-In Partner
    4. Divorced
    5. Separated
    6. Widowed

4. Do you presently live in . . .
    1. A City
    2. A Town
    3. A Village
    4. A Rural Area

5. How safe do you feel from crime walking alone in your area after dark? Do you feel . . .
    1. Very safe
    2. Reasonably safe
    3. Somewhat unsafe
    4. Very unsafe

Part 2: Create a dataset by using the skills you just learned. Remember to (1) name your variables; (2) define your variable labels; (3) define your value labels; and (4) declare any missing values (hint, this would be the person who refused to answer any of your survey questions). When you have finished creating your dataset, which will include four respondents and five variables, save your file. Congratulations, you have just created your first dataset. Now, let's learn what to do next!

LAB #2: IDENTIFYING TYPES OF VARIABLES: LEVELS OF MEASUREMENT

The focus of this lab is to introduce you to the four different levels of variable measurement, how to identify different types of variables within STATA, and how different levels of measurement are coded and organized within STATA. This material corresponds with the material presented in Chapter 2.

LEARNING OBJECTIVES

The following lab is directed at helping you understand levels of measurement and how to identify different types of variables within a dataset. Specifically, this lab assignment helps you clarify your understanding of:

1. Variable measurement
2. How variables are organized within STATA

Part 1: Understanding Levels of Measurement

Variables are measured at four different levels: nominal, ordinal, interval, and ratio. Each of these levels has unique characteristics that define them. For *nominal data*, numeric values are typically used for identification purposes. It is not possible to rank the response categories and there is not a quantifiable difference between categories. For *ordinal data*, the numeric values can signify an inherent ordering because you can rank the response categories but you cannot measure the distance between those categories. For *interval data*, the data can be organized into an order that can be added or subtracted but not multiplied or divided, because there is no true zero value. *Ratio data* are similar to interval data except they have a true zero value.

There are two ways to collect information about how a variable is measured in STATA. One is to examine the variable values in the data editor screen and the other is to produce a frequency distribution. Using data from the Alberta Survey, this lab will demonstrate the first way to identify variable values, then give you a chance to practise identifying variables within STATA. In the next chapter of this lab manual, you will learn how to produce frequency distributions.

To open the Alberta Survey data, simply select file>open>data, then select the Alberta Survey 2009 (AS2009) (your instructor will need to tell you where he/she has placed the file).

When you have opened the file, take a moment to scroll through the list of variables and observations in data editor. You will notice there are many variables (149 to be exact) contained within this dataset. If you scroll down the observations, you will see that there are 1,211 respondents. Return to the main interface screen. You might notice that the names of the variables don't make a lot of sense without a thorough understanding of the background of this survey (if you want more information about the Alberta Survey, 2009, the codebook is at the end of this text). However, in most cases, the variable labels provide key insight into what each of those variables is measuring. For the most part, you will be able to make an informed guess as to what the level of measurement would be for most variables. However, this may not always be accurate.

For example, variable 'k12b' has the label "What was your own total individual income for the past year before taxes and deductions?" Given that this is an income variable and a person can feasibly have no income, you might be inclined to guess this is a ratio level variable. However, when you click on the cell in the 'values' column, a different story emerges.

As we can see if we look at page 518 of the codebook (Figure 1), the response categories for this variable are grouped into discrete categories. Therefore, this variable is actually an *ordinal* level variable, because you can rank the categories but the values associated with the discrete categories (i.e., 1 refers to under $6,000) cannot be meaningfully measured.

K12b
What was your own total INDIVIDUAL income for the past year BEFORE taxes and deductions?
Again, we're just looking for a ballpark figure.

[NOTE: PROBE WITH CATEGORIES AS EXAMPLES IF NEEDED]

1	Under $6,000	16	34,000-35,999	31	100,000-124,999
2	6,000-7,999	17	36,000-37,999	32	125,000-149,999
3	8,000-9,999	18	38,000-39,999	33	150,000+
4	10,000-11,999	19	40,000-44,999	34	Don't Know **[DO NOT READ]**
5	12,000-13,999	20	45,000-49,999	35	No Response **[DO NOT READ]**
6	14,000-15,999	21	50,000-54,999		
7	16,000-17,999	22	55,000-59,999		
8	18,000-19,999	23	60,000-64,999		
9	20,000-21,999	24	65,000-69,999		
10	22,000-23,999	25	70,000-74,999		
11	24,000-25,999	26	75,000-79,999		
12	26,000-27,999	27	80,000-84,999		
13	28,000-29,999	28	85,000-89,999		
14	30,000-31,999	29	90,000-94,999		
15	32,000-33,999	30	95,000-99,999		

FIGURE 1 | Coding Details for Variable K12b

Let's look at one more example. Find the variable named "e18" with the label "In the past month, have you done a favour for a neighbour?" (codebook p. 503). Without going to the codebook, we do not know how this question was to be answered by respondents. This variable might ask for a simple yes or no response or it might ask for the number of times you have done a favour for a neighbour. We cannot be 100 per cent sure unless we check to see how the variable is coded. To do this, again we want to check the "values" by clicking on the cell corresponding to this variable under the "values" column.

As we can see from the codebook, our first guess was correct: this is a nominal level variable because respondents were simply asked to indicate yes or no.

Now it's your turn!

Putting the Information into Practice

For this lab, you will be asked to fill in the missing information in Table 1. In the space beside each variable name, provide the variable label, the value labels (i.e., 1 = Yes, 2 = No), and try to determine the level of measurement.

TABLE 1			
Variable	**Variable label**	**Value label**	**Level of measurement**
sex1			
d2			
e4			
h1			
h12			
k14			
k12a			
respnum$			
e2			

LAB #3: UNIVARIATE STATISTICS

The focus of this lab is to begin to introduce you to analysis with one variable. Generating frequencies is a basic procedure used to obtain a summary of a variable by looking at the number of cases associated with each value of the variable. This material corresponds with the material presented in Chapter 3.

LEARNING OBJECTIVES

The following lab is directed at helping you understand ways of studying the characteristics of data. Specifically, this lab assignment challenges you to clarify your understanding of:

1. How to generate and interpret frequency distributions
2. Data presentation
3. The connection between data presentation and levels of measurement

Part 1: Producing Frequency Distributions

We will first learn to produce a frequency table. Throughout this lab manual, we will use the command prompts. To obtain a frequency distribution, use the following steps.

Step 1: Open the Alberta Survey by either using the open button on the toolbar or typing.

use "<<enter the path for your data here>>/AS2009_public_ release.dta", clear

Step 2: Type the following in the command box:

tabulate sex1 or tab sex1

You should get output that looks like Figure 1:

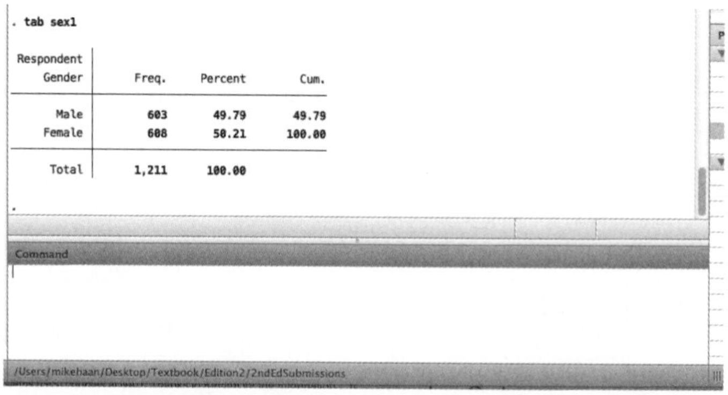

FIGURE 1 | A Basic Frequency in STATA

What should we note about this output?

1. We can see that we have 1,211 total cases.
2. In the table, we can see the distribution of MALE versus FEMALE by frequencies, per cent, and cumulative per cent. You can see that there are 603 males and 608 females. Is this the same as what you have on the screen before you?

Part 2: Types of Charts

A **pie chart** is a way of summarizing a set of categorical data. Data are categorical when the values or observations belonging to it can be sorted according to groups but not by values. For example, "sex" is a categorical variable with two categories, "male" and "female," and people cannot belong to both categories. We can then refer to sex as being mutually exclusive. A pie chart is a circle that is divided into segments, with each segment representing a particular category. The area of each segment is proportional to the number of cases in that category.

The following is an example of a pie chart for a variable called STRATA that measures in which area of Alberta the respondent lives. Note that in this example we appear to have an equal distribution of respondents from Edmonton, Calgary, and other Alberta.

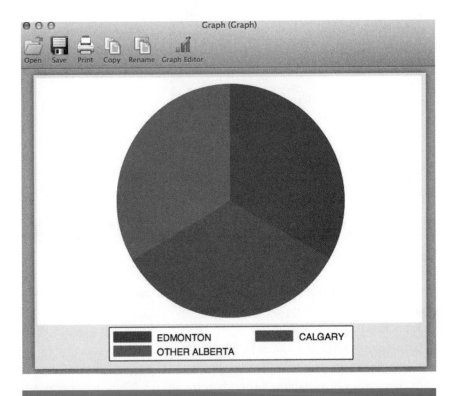

FIGURE 2 | A Pie Chart

How can you create a pie chart using STATA?

    Step 1: Type "tabulate strata, generate(f)

    Step 2: Type "graph pie f1 f2 f3"

Bar Graphs

A **bar graph** is a way of summarizing a set of categorical data. It displays the data using a number of rectangles of the same width, each of which represents a particular category. The length of each rectangle is proportional to the number of cases in the category it represents. Figure 3 is an example of a bar graph for the question, "To the best of your knowledge, what is the leading cause of death for Albertans under the age of 45?" (A1).

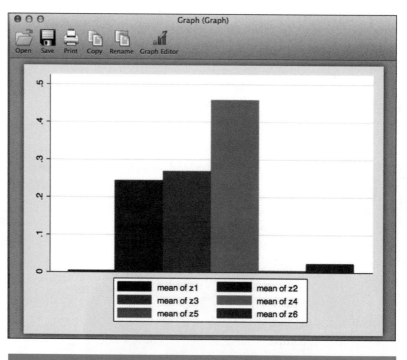

FIGURE 3 | A Bar Chart

    Bar graphs are created through the same two-step process, except that you must specify "bar" instead of "pie" as the chart type.

    Step 1: Tabulate a1, generate (z).

    Step 2: Graph bar z1 z2 z3 z4 z5 z6 or graph bar z*.

    This two-step process is necessary because STATA needs to be told that you want to plot the counts or frequencies of variables, rather than the means. Thus, it is necessary to create new variables in step 1 from which the means can be taken. When creating these new variables, ensure that the root ("z" in the example above) is not already in use by other variables in the dataset.

Which Mode of Presentation Is Best?

Deciding which format to use to present your data depends on the level of measurement of your selected variable and the clarity of the presentation. For example, if you have a categorical variable, but a large number of categories, a pie chart may make the presentation crowded and confusing. Selecting a bar graph may be more appropriate.

Here are some general suggestions you may want to consider:

- Use tables to display data details that would be lost in graphs or charts.
- Opt for a bar graph to compare data.
- Consider a pie chart to show how percentages relate to each other within a whole.
- Focus on the main point and consider your audience.
- Non-technical audiences often appreciate visual representations of data, so try to use pie and bar charts when you think your audience would prefer them.

Summary

In this section, you were introduced to the basics of data presentation. You explored three methods of data presentation: frequency tables, pie charts, and bar graphs. Specifically, you learned how to generate and interpret frequency distributions, how to create three types of modes of presentation, and the connection between data presentation and levels of measurement.

Now it's your turn!

Putting Information into Practice

1. Using what you've learned about interpreting frequency tables, fill in the blanks of the following paragraph. Use the appropriate variables from the lesson above.

   In AS2009's sample of 1,211 respondents, _____% are males and _____% are females. When asked the different health problems facing Albertans today, _____% felt that injuries were an extremely serious health problem and _____% felt they were not serious. Respondents were varied in guessing what their chances of visiting the emergency room in the next year because of an injury. In fact, _____% felt it would be one in 500, compared to _____% who felt it would be one in ten. Interestingly, a higher percentage of people thought they would be more likely to go the emergency room because of a motor vehicle collision. Specifically, _____% felt the chances of going to the emergency room because of a motor vehicle collision were one in 500.

2. Produce the specified graphs for the following variables:
   a) d2:   Bar Chart
   b) k14:   Pie Chart
   c) k16a: Bar Chart
   d) h10:   Frequency Table

3. Choose one of the variables from Question 2 and provide an interpretation. Specifically, what is the percentage distribution of the categories? What is the total number of respondents who answered the question? How many, if any, missing values are there?

LAB #4: INTRODUCTION TO PROBABILITY

The focus of this lab is to review what you have already learned and to introduce you to the concept of recoding variables. Recoding variables is an important component in conducting analysis because the categories of a variable as they were asked in the questionnaire might not work for your specific needs. For example, if you are interested in comparing individuals who have a high school education or less with those who have a post-secondary education, you may not require a level of detail that looks at all the specific types of post-secondary education available. This lab will show you how to manipulate variables.

We will also look at how to calculate probabilities from STATA output. This material corresponds with the material presented in Chapter 4.

LEARNING OBJECTIVES

The following lab is directed at helping you understand how to manipulate variables. Specifically, this lab assignment challenges you to clarify your understanding of:

1. Why you might want to recode variables
2. How to use STATA to recode variables
3. How to use STATA output to calculate probability

Part 1: Recoding Variables

Let's assume you are interested in the opinions Albertans have regarding whether people with intellectual disabilities are able to be parents. Within the current dataset, we have a variable that asks, "Indicate how much you agree or disagree with the following statement: People with intellectual disabilities are not fit to be parents" (d10). After obtaining a frequency distribution (Figure 1) of the variable, you realize that you do not require this level of detail. You are interested in whether people disagree, neither agree nor disagree, or agree. Therefore, you realize you will need to collapse the first two categories together (Strongly Disagree and Somewhat Disagree) and the last two categories (Somewhat Agree and Strongly Agree).

Step 1: To change the coding of this variable to suit your needs, it is easiest in STATA to create a new variable and transform the new variable. It is important to select this option because you are interested in creating a new variable from your original variable rather than altering the existing variable. Although it is possible to recode into the same variable, the original information on the AS2009 will be overwritten, **so always choose to create a new variable!**

Step 1: Create a new variable by typing:

generate newvar = oldvar

where "newvar" is the variable you want to create, and "oldvar" is the variable you are using as a base. For our purposes, we will use d10 as the old variable and d10_recode as the new variable.

```
. tab d10
```

People with intellectual disabilities are not fit to be parents.	Freq.	Percent	Cum.
No Response	58	4.79	4.79
Strongly Disagree	298	24.61	29.40
Somewhat Disagree	316	26.09	55.49
Neither Disagree nor Agree	166	13.71	69.20
Somewhat Agree	220	18.17	87.37
Strongly Agree	111	9.17	96.53
Don't Know	42	3.47	100.00
Total	1,211	100.00	

FIGURE 1 | Frequency Distribution for Variable D10

Step 2: Decide on how you want the new variable to be coded. Use the codebook here to guide you.

D10
People with intellectual disabilities are not fit to be parents.

1 Strongly Disagree
2 Disagree Somewhat
3 Neither Disagree nor Agree
4 Agree Somewhat
5 Strongly Agree

0 Don't Know
8 No Response

Suppose that we are interested in creating a variable where Strongly Disagree and Disagree are in one category and Agree and Strongly Agree are in another. You will need to tell STATA that this is what you want. You will also want to recode no response, and don't know to be missing. For our purposes here, the table below demonstrates how we will recode.

Old value	New value
1, 2	1
3	2
4, 5	3
0, 8	.

STATA (and all other software packages) typically recognize "." to represent a missing value.

Step 3: Now, to recode the variable, remember to use your new variable:

recode d10_recode (1 2 = 1) (3 = 2) (4 5 = 3) (0 8 = .)

We did the recode in two separate steps above, first creating a new variable, then recoding that variable. STATA allows multiple shortcuts, including the ability to recode and create a new variable in one step. The syntax below demonstrates how to do that:

recode d10 (1 2 = 1) (3 = 2) (4 5 = 3) (0 8 = .), gen (d10__recode)

If you want to practise the syntax above, please remember to drop the new variable you created earlier by typing "drop d10_recode").

Now, as a final check, run a frequency distribution on the new variable, D10_recode, and the original variable, D10, to confirm that your new values add up to the values in the original variable (Figure 2). For example, the values of Strongly Disagree + Somewhat Disagree (297 + 316) should sum the total of the first category of the new variable (613).

```
. tab d10
```

People with intellectual disabilities are not fit to be parents.	Freq.	Percent	Cum.
No Response	58	4.79	4.79
Strongly Disagree	298	24.61	29.40
Somewhat Disagree	316	26.09	55.49
Neither Disagree nor Agree	166	13.71	69.20
Somewhat Agree	220	18.17	87.37
Strongly Agree	111	9.17	96.53
Don't Know	42	3.47	100.00
Total	1,211	100.00	

```
. tab d10_recode
```

RECODE of d10 (People with intellectual disabilities are not fit to be parents.)	Freq.	Percent	Cum.
1	614	55.27	55.27
2	166	14.94	70.21
3	331	29.79	100.00
Total	1,111	100.00	

FIGURE 2 | Frequency Distribution of Variables D10 and D10_recode

Naturally, you'd want to go back and use the information in Lab 2 to attach value labels to your new variable.

You can test your recode by determining if the appropriate number of observations are in each category. For example, we combined Strongly Disagree and Somewhat Disagree from D10, and these categories had 298 and 316 observations. So, for the recoded category 1 should have 298 + 316, or 614, observations.

Chapter 4 discusses probabilities, and simply requires that you know the number of observations in each category to be able to calculate probabilities. So, if you wanted to know the probability that someone chosen at random in your sample would disagree with the statement about whether people with intellectual disabilities should be parents, you would only need to know the frequency of people in the disagree category (613) over the total number of people in the sample (1,211). This yields a probability of roughly 51 per cent (613/1,211). Calculating the probability of the other outcomes would proceed in a similar way, except that you'd have a different number in the numerator.

Putting Information into Practice

1. Using the techniques that you have just been taught, recode variable H8, "I feel pressure from friends to drink alcohol during parties and celebrations." Create a three-category variable in which the categories are 1 Infrequent/No Pressure 2 Sometimes Feel Pressure and 3 Frequent/Always Feel Pressure.

2. Interpret your recoded variable. Specifically, what is the percentage distribution of the categories? What is the total number of respondents who answered the question?

3. Based on the frequency distribution of your recoded variable, what is the probability that an individual will always or frequently feel pressure to drink?

4. Based on the frequency distribution of the original variable, what is the probability that an individual will never feel pressure to drink?

5. Based on the frequency distribution of your recoded variable, what is the probability that a person will sometimes feel pressure to drink?

LAB #5: THE NORMAL CURVE

The focus of this lab is to introduce you to the concept of the normal curve. The distribution of data can take on different forms. Understanding how data are distributed is important for more complex analysis, which you will learn as this course progresses. This lab corresponds with the material presented in Chapter 5.

LEARNING OBJECTIVES

The following lab is directed at helping you understand how to manipulate variables. Specifically, this lab assignment challenges you to clarify your understanding of:

1. How to produce histograms in STATA, and how to use them to see how data are distributed
2. How to describe and identify distributions

Part 1: Creating a Histogram in STATA

Step 1: In the command window, type

hist k7

You should get output that looks like this:

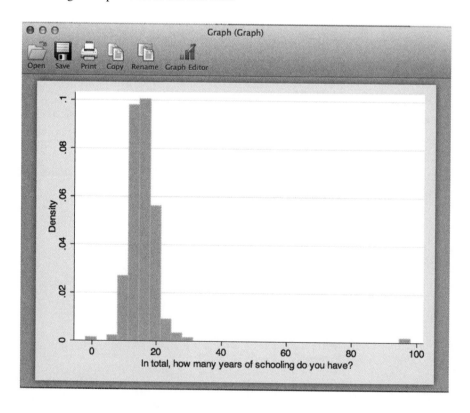

There are a few problems with this output. First, there appear to be either extreme outliers or missing values on the right side of the distribution. Second, there is no overlaid normal curve.

Both of these problems are easy to fix. To figure out the valid values for k7, consult the codebook. There you will see that there are missing value codes of −5, −6, and 98. So, we only have to eliminate them.

To do this, modify the code above to read:

hist k7 if k7> −1 & k7<40

That tells STATA that you are interested only in values that are greater than −1 and less than 40. Although this is more restrictive than the −5 low value and 98 high value in the codebook, my recommendation is to restrict your values only to those that are reasonable, in case there are data entry errors in the dataset. This helps reduce the likelihood of such an occurrence.

To overlay the normal curve, you need to add the following:

hist k7 if k7> −1 & k7<40, normal

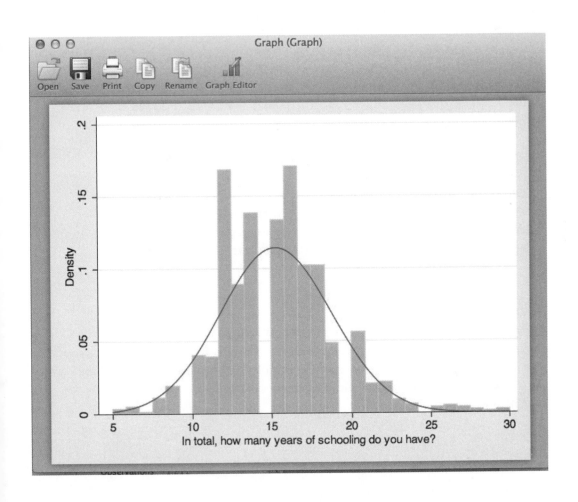

Now, what can we say about this distribution? Well, it is **bimodal** because there are two spikes, one at the 12 years of schooling mark and the other at the 16 years of schooling mark. The curve has a slight **positive** or **right skew** as there are more people with higher levels of education than lower levels. The curve is a little more "peaked" than normal. This is hard to know from seeing a distribution, but having two peaks that are higher, and none that are dramatically lower than the rest of the distribution provides a clue that the distribution has positive kurtosis.

To get an even better sense of the distribution of k7, you might choose to ask STATA for a summary of the variable. This can be done by entering the following command:

sum k7 if k7> −1 & k7<40, detail

This will give you output that looks like the following:

```
. sum k7 if k7> −1 & k7<40, detail

        In total, how many years of schooling do you have?

        Percentiles      Smallest
 1%           8               5
 5%          10               5
10%          12               5       Obs              1198
25%          13               6       Sum of Wgt.      1198

50%          15                       Mean          15.2571
                          Largest     Std. Dev.    3.490387
75%          17              28
90%          20              29       Variance      12.1828
95%          21              30       Skewness     .5225816
99%          26              30       Kurtosis     4.156461
```

There is quite a bit of information here in the summary output, most of which we'll learn about in the next lab. For our purposes here, only skewness and kurtosis are of interest. The skewness value of 0.52 confirms our earlier hunch of a slightly positive skew, and the kurtosis value of 4.16 tells us that the distribution is more peaked than normal.

OK, now it's your turn.

Putting Information into Practice

1. Obtain a histogram for the following variables:
   a) "age"
   b) "k3b"
   c) "h14"

2. For each variable, describe the symmetry of the distribution, the skewness of the distribution, its type of kurtosis, and whether it is unimodal, bimodal, or multimodal. For now, you can only do this visually, but we'll learn how to do more than this in the coming chapters.

LAB #6: MEASURES OF CENTRAL TENDENCY AND DISPERSION

The focus of this lab is to introduce you to various measures of central tendency. Measures of central tendency allow you to further understand the distribution of a variable. In this lab, you will learn how to generate various measures of central tendency within STATA. This lab corresponds with the material presented in Chapter 6.

LEARNING OBJECTIVES

The following lab is directed at helping you understand how to measures of central tendency. Specifically, this lab assignment challenges you to clarify your understanding of:

1. The differences between the mean, median, and mode
2. The relationship between levels of measurement and the mean, median, and mode
3. How to generate measures of central tendency within STATA

Part 1: Generating Measures of Central Tendency in STATA

Step 1: Ensure that you have the 2009 Alberta Survey file open.

Step 2: Within the command box, type the following:

sum k7

This will allow you to get basic information on central tendency, and will produce output that resembles Figure 1 for the variable k7, which is the total years of schooling variable used in the previous lab:

```
. sum k7
```

Variable	Obs	Mean	Std. Dev.	Min	Max
k7	1211	15.64988	7.278835	-2	98

FIGURE 1 | Summary Statistics for Variable k7

Now, before we continue, we need to ask ourselves if these numbers make sense, in other words do the measures of central tendency make sense in relation to the level of measurement of our variable? Years of schooling is a ratio level variable because we have a true zero value: individuals can obtain no years of schooling.

We should also notice that the minimum and maximum values seem unreasonably low and high, respectively. Also, it would be nice to have more information than what this output provides.

In lab 5, we learned about how to remove observations with missing values, and how to ask for greater detail in STATA within **sum**. Here's a reminder of the syntax:

sum k7 if k7> −1 & k7<40, detail

```
. sum k7 if k7> -1 & k7<40, detail

        In total, how many years of schooling do you have?

          Percentiles      Smallest
   1%           8               5
   5%          10               5
  10%          12               5       Obs            1198
  25%          13               6       Sum of Wgt.    1198

  50%          15                       Mean        15.2571
                           Largest      Std. Dev.   3.490387
  75%          17              28
  90%          20              29       Variance    12.1828
  95%          21              30       Skewness    .5225816
  99%          26              30       Kurtosis    4.156461
```

FIGURE 2 | Detailed Summary Statistics for Variable k7

The table in Figure 2 tells us that, on average, our respondents have 15.26 years of schooling. The median tells us that if we were to line up all our respondents from the lowest level of schooling to the highest, the middle score, or that of the 50th percentile, we would have 15 years of schooling. Oddly, STATA doesn't report the mode in this procedure. This number must be retrieved by plotting a histogram and looking for the highest bar, or running a frequency and picking the largest category (Figure 3).

```
. tab k7 if k7> -1 & k7<40
```

In total, how many years of schooling do you have?	Freq.	Percent	Cum.
5	3	0.25	0.25
6	5	0.42	0.67
7	1	0.08	0.75
8	11	0.92	1.67
9	19	1.59	3.26
10	40	3.34	6.59
11	39	3.26	9.85
12	168	14.02	23.87
13	89	7.43	31.30
14	138	11.52	42.82
15	133	11.10	53.92
16	170	14.19	68.11
17	102	8.51	76.63
18	102	8.51	85.14
19	48	4.01	89.15
20	56	4.67	93.82
21	20	1.67	95.49
22	21	1.75	97.25
23	9	0.75	98.00
24	6	0.50	98.50
25	4	0.33	98.83
26	5	0.42	99.25
27	4	0.33	99.58
28	2	0.17	99.75
29	1	0.08	99.83
30	2	0.17	100.00
Total	1,198	100.00	

FIGURE 3 | Frequencies of Variable k7

We see now that the mode is 16 years of schooling.

Returning to Figure 2, we have a standard deviation of 3.49 and a variance of 12.18. What does this mean? As you progress through this course, the meaning of these statistics will become clearer. However, for now, knowing how to generate these statistics in STATA is sufficient. We also see that we have a range of 25 by subtracting the highest value (30) from the smallest value (5) for this variable. This means that the distance between the highest level of education to the lowest level of education is 25 years. Since this number is plausible, we should have faith that the data have no errors, or that we didn't do anything wrong (not trivial occurrences in statistics!).

Let's look at one more example to illustrate the difference between the measures of central tendency. Figure 4 shows the frequency distribution for the variable "If an election were held today, how would you vote federally?" (k16a).

`. tab k16a`

If an election were held today, how would you vote federally?	Freq.	Percent	Cum.
Liberal Party of Canada	207	17.09	17.09
Conservative Party of Canada	535	44.18	61.27
Canada's NDP	52	4.29	65.57
Green Party of Canada	45	3.72	69.28
Other	19	1.57	70.85
Would not vote	41	3.39	74.24
Not Eligible	23	1.90	76.14
Don't Know	182	15.03	91.16
No Response/Refused	107	8.84	100.00
Total	1,211	100.00	

FIGURE 4 | Frequency Distribution of Variable k16a

This variable is a nominal level variable because the categories cannot be ranked. Referring back to the material presented in Chapter 6, we know that the mode is most commonly used for nominal or ordinal level data. This is a good rule to memorize and here is the reason. When we look at the mean (Figure 5), we have a value of 3.74. If we were to translate that value into words, it would mean that, on average, Albertans would vote NDP with a slight tendency toward the Green Party. If you have ever voted in a federal election, you know that you have to pick one, and only one, party or your ballot will be deemed invalid. Furthermore, the frequency in

Figure 4 reveals a strong preference for the Conservatives. Therefore, the mathematical mean does not make sense for nominal level data. Instead, we should pick the mode that tells us that the most frequently selected category is "2," the Conservative Party of Canada. Can you see why this is the case?

. **sum k16a**

Variable	Obs	Mean	Std. Dev.	Min	Max
k16a	1211	3.744013	2.867983	1	9

FIGURE 5 | Statistics Box

Now it's your turn!

Putting Information into Practice

1. For each variable, identify the level of measurement of the variable.
   a) "e22"   f) "k8a"
   b) "age"   g) "d13"
   c) "k10"   h) "d6"
   d) "k6"   i) "e9"
   e) "k3b"   j) "h15"

2. For each of the ten variables, run both a frequency distribution and *appropriate* measures of central tendency and dispersion (i.e., mean, median, mode, standard deviation, variance, and/or range).

3. Based on your analysis of your output, complete the following table by writing in the values of the *appropriate* measures of central tendency and dispersion. Leave the boxes blank where the statistic is inappropriate.

Variable	Mean	Median	Mode	Standard Deviation	Variance	Range
e22						
age						
k10						
k6						
k3b						
k8a						
d13						
d6						
e9						
h15						

LAB #7: STANDARD DEVIATIONS, STANDARD SCORES, AND THE NORMAL DISTRIBUTION

The focus of this lab is to introduce you to z-scores and help you further understand how the standard deviation relates to the normal curve. Z-scores are the most commonly used standard score and are a measure of the relative location in a distribution. Specifically, z-scores, in standard deviation units, give the distance a particular score is from the mean. In this lab, you will learn how to generate various z-scores within STATA. This lab corresponds with the material presented in Chapter 7.

LEARNING OBJECTIVES

The following lab is directed at helping you understand how z-scores relate to the normal curve and the standard deviation. Specifically, this lab assignment challenges you to clarify your understanding of:

1. The shape of distributions and the normal curve
2. The relationship between z-scores and the normal curve
3. How to use z-scores to mathematically calculate the percentage of cases that fall between two values.

Part 1: Reviewing the Shape and Characteristics of Distributions

Before learning to calculate z-scores, let's first refresh our memories on the shape and characteristics of distributions.

In Figure 1, we see a histogram for the variable "In total, how many years of schooling do you have?"

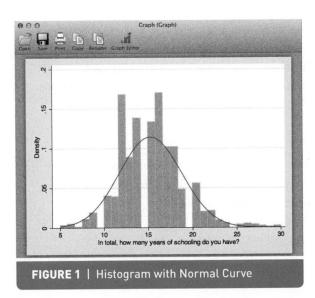

FIGURE 1 | Histogram with Normal Curve

Now, what can we say about this distribution? It is **bimodal** because there are two spikes, one at the 12 years of schooling mark and the other at the 16 years of schooling mark. The curve appears to have a slight **negative skew** because there are more people with higher levels of education than lower levels. The two peaks of the distribution are higher than the rest of the distribution, suggesting that the distribution has positive kurtosis.

When we look at the statistics box in Figure 2, we see that, on average, respondents have 15.26 years of school, with a standard deviation of 3.49.

```
. sum k7 if k7> -1 & k7<40, detail

           In total, how many years of schooling do you have?

            Percentiles      Smallest
      1%          8               5
      5%         10               5
     10%         12               5        Obs                1198
     25%         13               6        Sum of Wgt.        1198

     50%         15                        Mean            15.2571
                              Largest      Std. Dev.      3.490387
     75%         17              28
     90%         20              29        Variance        12.1828
     95%         21              30        Skewness        .5225816
     99%         26              30        Kurtosis       4.156461
```

FIGURE 2 | Statistics for "In total, how many years of schooling do you have?"

All right, so now we have refreshed our memory regarding the shape and characteristics of distributions. Keeping these elements in mind will help us to further understand z-scores and what it means to standardize a distribution.

Part 2: Calculating Z-Scores

Calculating a z-score is very similar to other commands you have learned up to this point, except that we must rely on one of STATA's extensions to complete:

Step 1: Within your command box, enter:

egen k7z = std(k7) if k7> -1 & k7<40

By imposing the restriction to values of −1 and 40, STATA will automatically assign the missing value code "." to all values outside this range. You should see that 13 missing values were created after executing the command above.

Step 2: Make sure that your new variable contains z-values by running a frequency (Figure 3):

tab k7z

Standardized values of (k7)	Freq.	Percent	Cum.
−2.93867	3	0.25	0.25
−2.652169	5	0.42	0.67
−2.365667	1	0.08	0.75
−2.079166	11	0.92	1.67
−1.792665	19	1.59	3.26
−1.506164	40	3.34	6.59
−1.219663	39	3.26	9.85
−.9331616	168	14.02	23.87
−.6466604	89	7.43	31.30
−.3601592	138	11.52	42.82
−.0736581	133	11.10	53.92
.2128431	170	14.19	68.11
.4993443	102	8.51	76.63
.7858455	102	8.51	85.14
1.072347	48	4.01	89.15
1.358848	56	4.67	93.82
1.645349	20	1.67	95.49
1.93185	21	1.75	97.25
2.218351	9	0.75	98.00
2.504853	6	0.50	98.50
2.791354	4	0.33	98.83
3.077855	5	0.42	99.25
3.364356	4	0.33	99.58
3.650857	2	0.17	99.75
3.937358	1	0.08	99.83
4.223859	2	0.17	100.00
Total	1,198	100.00	

FIGURE 3 | Frequency of k7z

Step 3: Run summary stats for your new variable k7z (Figure 4). Be sure to ask for details so that you get the mean, standard deviation, and variance.

sum k7z, detail

```
. sum k7z, detail
```

                    Standardized values of (k7)

	Percentiles	Smallest		
1%	-2.079166	-2.93867		
5%	-1.506164	-2.93867		
10%	-.9331616	-2.93867	Obs	1198
25%	-.6466604	-2.652169	Sum of Wgt.	1198
50%	-.0736581		Mean	-1.73e-09
		Largest	Std. Dev.	1
75%	.4993443	3.650857		
90%	1.358848	3.937358	Variance	1
95%	1.645349	4.223859	Skewness	.5225817
99%	3.077855	4.223859	Kurtosis	4.156461

FIGURE 4 | Summary Statistics for k7z

In our statistics box, you will first notice that we have a mean of (nearly) 0 and a standard deviation of 1 and a variance of 1.

To convince yourself of the accuracy of the calculations, feel free to manually calculate the z-score for an observation by using the equation presented below (and taken from Chapter 7). Remember that you need to use the standard deviation from the actual variable, not the z-score variable.

$$z = \frac{X - \mu}{\sigma}$$

Now it's your turn!

Putting Information into Practice

1. Run a frequency distribution for "age." Be sure to include a histogram, the mean, standard deviation, and variance.

    a) Are your respondents' ages normally distributed? What evidence supports your answer (consider the shape and characteristics of your distribution).

2. Create a new variable called "zage."

3. In your data editor window, on data view, find respondent # 7. (Hint: Use the variable called "respnum$." This variable assigns a number that is unique to each respondent who participated in the survey.) What are respondent #7's values for "age" and "zage"?

4. In your data editor window, on data view, find respondent # 32. What are respondent #32's values for "age" and "zage"?

5. What percentage of respondents are older than respondent #7?

6. What percentage of respondents are younger than respondent #32?

7. What percentage of respondents are older than respondent #7 but younger than respondent #82?

LAB #8: SAMPLING

The focus of this lab is to introduce you to introduce you to case selection within STATA and to help you to further understand how larger sampling distributions improve data accuracy. A sample that is accurately and carefully selected without a lot of sampling error allows for a more precise analysis, without including the full population. Because we are often unable to survey every individual, we make decisions about how much of the population to include based on our knowledge of the population parameter. In this lab, we are going to pretend that the total number of respondents who participated in this survey represent the entire population of Alberta (as though the survey was a census). This lab corresponds with the material presented in Chapters 8 and 9.

LEARNING OBJECTIVES

The following lab is directed at helping you understand what effect sample size has on the accuracy of sample values. Specifically, this lab assignment challenges you to clarify your understanding of:

1. The relationship between samples and populations
2. How increasing a sample size will reduce sampling error

Part 1: How to Select Cases in STATA

Before we begin, run a frequency distribution on the sex variable.

```
. tab sex1
```

Respondent Gender	Freq.	Percent	Cum.
Male	603	49.79	49.79
Female	608	50.21	100.00
Total	1,211	100.00	

Note that we have 603 males and 608 females. This will be the basis of our population parameters. However, remember, these numbers, in reality, do not represent the true population of Alberta. We are only using them as a population for illustrative purposes.

Step 1: Within your command box, type the following:

sample 5

This will give you a 5 per cent random sample of observations. To prove it, rerun frequencies.

```
. tab sex1
```

Respondent Gender	Freq.	Percent	Cum.
Male	30	49.18	49.18
Female	31	50.82	100.00
Total	61	100.00	

Can you see how your sample size is much smaller than what's in the full dataset? What's more, given that the sample is randomly drawn each and every time, it is possible that your frequencies differ from those above. Can you see why this might be the case?

Standard Error of a Sample Mean

The next thing we're going to do is use STATA to help us calculate the standard error of a sample mean. Recall from Chapter 9 that the equation is

$$S_{\bar{x}} = \frac{S_x}{\sqrt{n - 1}}$$

Using this, it is possible to estimate the distance that your sample is likely to be from a population mean. You can do this even though you don't know what the population mean actually is, using statistical theory and what we know about the normal distribution (which is how we're assuming the data from the Alberta Survey are distributed).

Suppose that you wanted to know the average age of your 5 per cent sample. Remember that you would do this by using the summary command (often abbreviated as "sum"), then selecting your variable of interest ("age"). The resulting output will give you the mean, the standard deviation, and the number of observations necessary to calculate the standard error.

It is important to note that STATA discards all unselected observations, and that the only way to get them back is to reopen the dataset. If you want to temporarily create a sample, simply type "preserve" in the command box, then sample your observations and perform your analysis on the subset. Once you are finished with your sample and want to return to the larger dataset, type "restore" and STATA will retrieve the original dataset.

Now it's your turn!

Putting Information into Practice

Run a frequency distribution for the "Area of the Province" variable (STRATA) for the population.

Use the select cases procedure to take a random sample of 2 per cent of the cases from the "population" (hint: Use "preserve" and "restore" each time to avoid having to reopen the dataset multiple times).

Run a frequency distribution on "STRATA" and record the percentage of respondents living in Edmonton. Calculate the standard error of the sample mean, using the standard deviation estimates generated by STATA.

Repeat this process to complete the following table.

%	% in Edmonton	Sampling error
5%		
10%		
25%		
50%		
75%		

1. Which percentage of cases would you choose if you were under budget and time constraints to complete your survey? In other words, which percentage begins to most closely resemble your population and at what point does your distribution start to level off?

LAB #9: HYPOTHESIS TESTING: TESTING THE SIGNIFICANCE OF THE DIFFERENCE BETWEEN TWO MEANS

The focus of this lab is to introduce you to the **one sample *t*-tests** function within STATA and help you to further understand how we use confidence intervals to determine generalizing our samples to populations. This lab corresponds with the material presented in Chapter 10.

LEARNING OBJECTIVES

The following lab is directed at helping you understand what effect sample size has on the accuracy of sample values. Specifically, this lab assignment challenges you to clarify your understanding of:

1. How to use a *t*-test to approximate the mean for a population from your sample
2. The relationship between confidence intervals and statistical significance

Part 1: Calculating a One Sample *t*-Test in STATA

Let's pretend we are interested in knowing whether the average years of schooling of our sample differs significantly from the population mean of 16 years (high school plus an undergraduate degree) at the 95 per cent confidence level (Figure 1). Suppose that we got this number from the Canadian census, and that it accurately represents the entire population.

Step 1: Enter the following syntax in your command window:

ttest k7 = 16 if k7>−1 & k7<40

```
One-sample t test
```

Variable	Obs	Mean	Std. Err.	Std. Dev.	[95% Conf. Interval]	
k7	1198	15.2571	.1008429	3.490387	15.05925	15.45494

```
    mean = mean(k7)                                          t =  -7.3670
Ho: mean = 16                          degrees of freedom =      1197

   Ha: mean < 16              Ha: mean != 16              Ha: mean > 16
 Pr(T < t) = 0.0000        Pr(|T| > |t|) = 0.0000        Pr(T > t) = 1.0000
```

FIGURE 1 | One-Sample *T*-Test: Options Dialogue Box

First, we can note that we have 1,198 cases and a mean of 15.26 years of schooling. The standard deviation is 3.49. In the next piece of output, we see we have a t-value of -7.367 with 1,197 degrees of freedom. This is the equivalent of our t-obtained value. By looking at the Sig. (2-tailed) (the middle of the bottom row where you see $Pr(|T| > |T|)=0.000$), we can see that we have a significance level of .000. This means that we can be more than 99 per cent confident that the average of our sample is significantly different than a sample with a mean of 16 years of schooling. Can you use these numbers to do the t-test manually, by looking at the student's t-table in Appendix B of your textbook?

Don't despair if you can't, because STATA does the work for you. If you go to the top right-hand side of your output, you can see at the 95 per cent confidence interval that our lower boundary is -15.06 and our upper boundary is 15.45. This means that 95 times out of 100, our sample mean difference will be between these two values.

If you wanted to (and who wouldn't want to?), you could use the information in the STATA output to calculate the confidence intervals yourself, and compare them to the numbers that STATA generated.

OK, now it's your turn!

Putting Information into Practice

1. Let's imagine that the average age of someone living in Alberta is 27 years old. We want to know if the average age of our sample differs significantly from the average age of someone living in Alberta at the 95 per cent confidence level. Conduct a one-sample t-test.

2. Can you be 95 per cent confident that the average age of our respondents differs significantly from the average age of someone living in Alberta?

3. What is your confidence interval? What does this mean?

LAB #10: HYPOTHESIS TESTING WITH INDEPENDENT SAMPLES

The focus of this lab is to introduce you to the **_t_-tests with two samples** function within STATA. For this type of analysis, you need to have a dichotomous independent variable and a interval/scale for your dependent variable. This lab corresponds with the material presented in Chapter 11.

LEARNING OBJECTIVES

The following lab is directed at helping you understand how you can use a t-test to compare the means of two independent samples. Specifically, this lab assignment challenges you to clarify your understanding of:

1. Stating the null and research hypotheses
2. How to establish a sampling distribution and critical region

Part 1: Calculating a _t_-Test with Two Samples in STATA

Let's pretend we are interested in knowing whether the average years of schooling of our sample differ significantly between males and females. Since both are samples and scores on the outcome of interest are independent of each other (presumably, the education level of women has nothing to do with the education level of men), it is most appropriate to conduct a _t_-test on independent samples.

Step 1: State the null and research hypotheses.

In this case, we are going to make the claim that men will have higher education than women.

Therefore, we are claiming that,

> H_0: In the population, the mean level of education for men and women does not differ. ($\mu_{MEN} = \mu_{WOMEN}$)
>
> H_1: In the population, the mean level of education for men is higher than that of women. ($\mu_{MEN} \neq \mu_{WOMEN}$)

Step 2: Select the sampling distribution and establish the critical region.

On a _z_-score distribution, the critical region that corresponds to a _p_-value < 0.05 will be represented by a t-score of $+/-1.96$ (Figure 1).

Should our test statistic be found in the 5 per cent of the distribution that is bounded by the two critical regions of our _t_-score distribution, we can be 95 per cent confident that we can reject our null hypothesis. Since we are only hypothesizing that there will be a difference in H_1, without saying anything about the direction of the difference (such as $\bar{X}_{MEN} < \bar{X}_{WOMEN}$), we're conducting a two-tailed test. If we were conducting a one-tailed test (and we were hypothesizing a direction of the relationship,), remember from Chapter 10 that we'd have a critical *t*-score of +/−1.65.

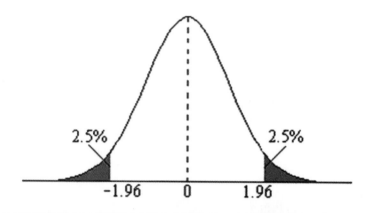

FIGURE 1 | The Critical Region at the 95 per cent Confidence Interval

Step 3: In your command box, type the following:

ttest k7 if k7>−1 & k7<40, by(sex1)

Our test variable will be k7 or **"how many years of schooling do you have"** and our grouping variable is sex1 or **sex of respondent**.

You should get the output shown in Figure 2:

```
. ttest k7 if k7>-1 & k7<40, by(sex1)

Two-sample t test with equal variances

    Group |     Obs        Mean    Std. Err.   Std. Dev.   [95% Conf. Interval]
----------+--------------------------------------------------------------------
     Male |     595    15.33613    .1442557    3.518774    15.05282    15.61945
   Female |     603     15.1791    .1410365      3.4633    14.90212    15.45609
----------+--------------------------------------------------------------------
 combined |    1198     15.2571    .1008429    3.490387    15.05925    15.45494
----------+--------------------------------------------------------------------
     diff |              .15703    .2017234                -.2387412    .5528012
--------------------------------------------------------------------------------
    diff = mean(Male) - mean(Female)                            t =   0.7784
Ho: diff = 0                                 degrees of freedom =     1196

    Ha: diff < 0                  Ha: diff != 0                  Ha: diff > 0
 Pr(T < t) = 0.7818       Pr(|T| > |t|) = 0.4365         Pr(T > t) = 0.2182
```

FIGURE 2 | Independent Sample *t*-Test

Looking at Figure 2, we can see that our groups both had approximately the same sample size, 595 males and 603 females.

Already we can see that the mean values of years of education are quite similar, although men are slightly more consistent with our hypothesis. However, this difference in means may be due to chance so we have to check the t-tests in the next table.

The tables give us the 95 per cent confidence intervals for both groups, then both the groups combined. Next, the t-value is listed as 0.7784 with 1,196 degrees of freedom. This number is rather low, which suggests that we might be failing to reject the null hypothesis.

Earlier we said that we needed a t-score of $> +/-1.96$. Here we see that we have a t-value of 0.778. Since this score falls outside our lower critical region, we can conclude that the mean years of education for our two sample groups (males and females) are not significantly different. Therefore, we can fail to reject the null hypothesis of no differences between groups. Similarly, if we were conducting a one-tailed test, we also fail to reject the null hypothesis, as the bottom row indicates (our p-value would have to be 0.05 or lower to reject the null hypothesis).

Now it's your turn!

Putting Information into Practice

Let's pretend we are interested in knowing whether the average number of children under the age of 18 differs significantly between those who live on a farm and those who do not.

We will use variables "Do you live on a farm?" (k15) and "How many children under the age of 18 live at this number?" (k3b).

1. Identify your dependent and independent variable.

2. State your null and research hypotheses.

3. Run an independent samples t-test.

4. What is the average number of children under the age of 18 living on a farm?

5. What is the average number of children under the age of 18 not living on a farm?

6. Using a t-test, do you accept or reject the null hypothesis? Why?

LAB #11: BIVARIATE STATISTICS FOR NOMINAL DATA

The focus of this lab is to introduce you to the **association or relationship between nominal variables**. Specifically, this lab will help clarify your understanding of independent and dependent variables and how to interpret the chi-square test of statistical significance. This lab corresponds with the material presented in Chapter 12.

LEARNING OBJECTIVES

The following lab is directed at helping you understand how to interpret the relationship between two nominal variables (bivariate relationships). Specifically, this lab assignment challenges you to clarify your understanding of:

1. Dependent and independent variables
2. How to create a cross-tabulation or a contingency table
3. How to interpret your findings and determine statistical significance

Part 1: Creating Contingency Tables within STATA

Now let's learn how to create contingency tables in STATA. For this example, we will ask the question, "Who is more likely to have driven while impaired, males or females?".

Step 1: Identify your dependent and independent variables.

An independent variable can be thought of as the modifying outcome. The dependent variable can be thought of as the outcome of interest. In this situation, we are interested in seeing if sex (sex1) will modify patterns of impaired driving (h1); therefore, it is our independent variable. The outcome we are interested in is impaired driving; therefore, it is our dependent variable.

Step 2: Enter the following in your command box:

tab sex1 h1

```
. tab sex1 h1
```

Respondent Gender	In the past 12 months, have you driven while impaired?				Total
	No Respon	Yes	No	Don't Kno	
Male	5	37	560	1	603
Female	2	11	595	0	608
Total	7	48	1,155	1	1,211

Step 3: Select the appropriate measure of association.

Since we are dealing with nominal data, we want to use an appropriate measure of association, such as **phi and Cramer's V**. It is also good practice to request chi-square so that we know if the differences are statistically significant. To do this, all we need to do is modify the above syntax slightly:

tab sex1 h1 if h1==1 | h1==2, chi2 V

chi2 after the comma refers to chi-square and V refers to Cramer's V. Recall that Cramer's V reverts to phi in a 2 by 2 table, so it is possible to obtain phi values by requesting only Cramer's V. Also, it is necessary to restrict h1 so that it only contains valid values (which, as you can see from the codebook, is 1 and 2).

```
. tab sex1 h1 if h1==1 | h1==2, chi2 V
```

Respondent Gender	In the past 12 months, have you driven while impaired?		Total
	Yes	No	
Male	37	560	597
Female	11	595	606
Total	48	1,155	1,203

$$\text{Pearson chi2(1)} = 15.0775 \quad \text{Pr} = 0.000$$
$$\text{Cramér's V} = 0.1120$$

Let's look first at chi-square. A **chi-square test**, as discussed in Chapter 8 of the textbook, is a hypothesis test that measures whether or not a relationship exists. This measure is suitable for all levels of measurement and all distributions. It tests the **null hypothesis** and measures the discrepancy between observed and expected events. The events are assumed to be independent and have the same distribution, and the outcomes of each event must be mutually exclusive.

To evaluate whether we will reject the null hypothesis that no differences exist between males and females, we need to determine the degrees of freedom, which can be found in the STATA output. Our chi-square value is 15.078, which exceeds the critical chi-square value (not shown, but in Appendix C of your text), so we can reject the null hypothesis and conclude that there are statistically significant differences between males and females about whether or not they have driven while impaired in the past 12 months.

Sometimes, you are interested in identifying the *strength* of a relationship (not just its existence), and this is what measures of association are for.

Remembering the classification criteria covered in Chapter 12, you can see that since the value of 0.112 is below 0.3 the relationship is weak.

Now's it's your turn!

Putting Information into Practice

Continuing with the theme of this chapter, we are going to ask the question: Who is more likely to act as a designated driver, males or females?

1. Answer the following questions:
   a) What is your null hypothesis?
   b) What is your research hypothesis?
   c) What is your dependent variable?
   d) What is your independent variable?
   e) What are the levels of measurement of your variables?

2. Produce a contingency table. Be sure to include the chi-square statistic and Cramer's *V*.

3. Based on your output, answer the following questions:
   a) What is the total valid sample size for this table?
   b) How many missing cases do you have?
   c) What percentage of females indicate they have been a designated driver in the past 12 months? What percentage of males indicate the same?
   d) How much difference (variance) is there between males and females with respect to the percentage that have been a designated driver in the past 12 months?
   e) What is the value of your chi-square statistic?
   f) What is the critical chi-square value for this table?
   g) Are your findings statistically significant? Why?
   h) What is the nature of the relationship? Why?

LAB #12: BIVARIATE STATISTICS FOR ORDINAL DATA

The focus of this lab is to introduce you to the **association or relationship between ordinal variables**. Specifically, this lab will help clarify your understanding of independent and dependent variables, how to interpret the chi-square test of statistical significance, as well as other measures of association (i.e., gamma and Kendall's tau-*b*). This lab corresponds with the material presented in Chapter 13.

LEARNING OBJECTIVES

The following lab is directed at helping you understand how to interpret the relationship between two variables (bivariate relationships). Specifically, this lab assignment challenges you to clarify your understanding of:

1. Dependent and independent variables
2. How to create a cross-tabulation or a contingency table
3. How to interpret your findings and determine statistical significance

Part 1: Establishing Your Research Question and Identifying Your Variables

In this example, we will ask the question: Does level of education affect an individual's opinion about whether having a disability lowers an individual's quality of life? (d2).

Step 1: Identify your dependent and independent variables.

An independent variable can be thought of as the modifying outcome and the dependent variable can be thought of as the outcome of interest. In this situation, we are interested in seeing if highest level of education will modify opinions on quality of life among those who have disabilities; therefore, it is our independent variable. The outcome we are interested in is opinions on quality of life among those with disabilities; therefore, it is our dependent variable.

Step 2: Recode your independent variable.

In this example, we are going to recode our independent variable from a 15 category variable into a 4 category variable measuring highest level of education. In Lab #4 you were introduced to the recode function. Let's review by recoding our highest level of education variable (k6) according to the specifications below.

Old Value → New Value

1, 2, 3, 4, 5, 6 → 1 (less than high school)

7, 8, 10 → 2 (high school)

9, 11 → 3 (College, certificate, diploma)

12, 13, 14, 15 → 4 (University degree or higher)

This will give you a variable that is collapsed into four categories:

1. Less than high school
2. High school
3. College/certificate/diploma
4. University degree or higher

In addition to this, the people with no response (there are 5) will need to be set to missing. You will need to tell STATA that this is what you want.

Step 1: In the command box, enter:

recode k6 (1 2 3 4 5 6=1) (7 8 10=2) (9 11=3) (12/15=4) (*=.), gen(k6recode)

A few things to note here: first, a shortcut was used to denote the value 12 through 15 (12/15). This can be done to speed things up, or you can type in every value that you want recode (as was done with values 1, 2, 3, 4, 5, and 6). Second, we set all remaining values to be missing with (*=.). This is a very handy and potentially dangerous option in STATA. You should always be sure that you have recoded every value you're interested in, because if you forget one, it will be recoded as missing. In STATA, the "*" means "all other values," and if you forget one it will end up as another value.

Step 2: As a final check on your coding, run a frequency distribution on the new variable, k6recode, and the original variable, k6, to confirm your new values add up to the values in the original variable. This is done by creating a contingency table and entering the following syntax:

tab k6 k6recode

You should get the following output:

```
. tab k6 k6recode
```

What is your highest level of education?	RECODE of k6 (What is your highest level of education?)				Total
	1	2	3	4	
No Schooling	1	0	0	0	1
Elementary – incomple	3	0	0	0	3
Elementary – complete	4	0	0	0	4
Junior High – incompl	9	0	0	0	9
Junior High – complet	19	0	0	0	19
High School – incompl	77	0	0	0	77
High School – complet	0	197	0	0	197
College/Technical Ins	0	65	0	0	65
College/Technical Ins	0	0	290	0	290
University – incomple	0	69	0	0	69
University – Diploma/	0	0	41	0	41
University – Bachelor	0	0	0	278	278
University – Professi	0	0	0	28	28
University – Master's	0	0	0	94	94
University – Doctorat	0	0	0	31	31
Total	113	331	331	431	1,206

Notice that the total number of observations equals 1,206 instead of 1,211. This is because the missing values have been removed by STATA. Otherwise, the coding looks good.

Step 3: Recode variable d2.

A quick look at the codebook suggests that we need to remove some values from variable d2 ("Having a disability necessarily lowers a person's quality of life"). All other values can remain as they are, since they're already appropriately structured as ordinal data.

recode d2 (8 0 =.), gen(d2recode)

A quick crosstab confirms that our recode was done properly:

Having a disability necessarily lowers a person's quality of life.	RECODE of d2 (Having a disability necessarily lowers a person's quality of life.					Total
	1	2	3	4	5	
Strongly Disagree	221	0	0	0	0	221
Somewhat Disagree	0	235	0	0	0	235
Neither Disagree nor	0	0	130	0	0	130
Somewhat Agree	0	0	0	353	0	353
Strongly Agree	0	0	0	0	237	237
Total	221	235	130	353	237	1,176

Now we're ready to measure association with gamma and Kendall's tau-*b*.

Step 4: Select your statistics.

Remember from the last lab that we used "tab" to measure association. The same is true here, except that asking for Cramer's *V* we'll ask for gamma and tau-*b*. We'll also ask for chi-square with the following command.

tab k6recode d2recode, chi2 gamma taub

We should have output that resembles the following:

```
. tab k6recode d2recode, chi2 gamma taub
```

RECODE of k6 (What is your highest level of education?)	RECODE of d2 (Having a disability necessarily lowers a person's quality of life.					Total
	1	2	3	4	5	
1	4	16	10	41	33	104
2	70	52	26	111	64	323
3	59	74	40	91	59	323
4	88	93	54	110	76	421
Total	221	235	130	353	232	1,171

```
        Pearson chi2(12) =  41.1726   Pr = 0.000
                   gamma =  -0.1271   ASE = 0.032
         Kendall's tau-b =  -0.0948   ASE = 0.024
```

The first thing to look at is the chi-square test. Our chi-square value is 41.1726 with p = 0.000. Therefore, since our chi-square value is statistically significant, we can reject the null hypothesis and conclude that there are statistically significant differences between highest level of education and opinion on whether having a disability lowers a person's quality of life. This should give us confidence as we move on to look at the measures of association.

Under the chi-square value are the gamma and tau-*b* statistics. Looking at gamma first, the negative value means that we have a discordant relationship between our independent and dependent variable where high values of the independent value correspond with low values of the dependent variable. In other words, as educational values increase, attitudes toward the deleterious effects of quality of life decrease, and vice versa.

The value of .1271 means that we are 12.71 per cent better at predicting the score on the dependent variable when we know the value of our independent variable. Furthermore, a score of .1271 means that the association between our dependent and independent value is moderate. Recall from Chapter 13 that the gamma statistic is more liberal in its calculation. If you want to err on the side of caution, it is recommended that you use tau-*b*.

We can see that we have a tau-*b* value of −.0948. The negative value means that we have a discordant relationship between our independent and dependent variable, where a high school on the independent value (higher levels of education) results in a lower score on our dependent variable (strongly disagree). The value of .0948 suggests that the association between our dependent and independent value is weak.

Now's it's your turn!

Putting Information into Practice

Continuing with the theme of this chapter, we are going to ask the question, does level of education affect an individual's opinion on whether involuntary sterilization is justifiable for people with chronic mental or intellectual disabilities who rely on government support?

1. Answer the following questions:
   a) What is your null hypothesis?
   b) What is your research hypothesis?
   c) What is your dependent variable?
   d) What is your independent variable?
   e) What are the levels of measurement of your variables?

2. Produce a contingency table. Be sure to include percentages and the chi-square statistic, gamma, and Somers' *d*.

3. Based on your output, answer the following questions:
   a) What is the total valid sample size for this table?
   b) How many missing cases do you have?

c)   What percentage of individuals with less than a high school education indicate that they strongly disagree? What percentage of individuals with a university degree or higher indicate the same?

d)   How much difference (variance) is there between those with less than a high school education and those with a university degree or higher with respect to the percentage that strongly agree that people with chronic mental or intellectual disabilities who rely on government support should be involuntarily sterilized?

e)   What is the value of your chi-square statistic?

f)   How many degrees of freedom do you have?

g)   What is the critical chi-square value for this table?

h)   Are your findings statistically significant? Why?

i)   What is the value of your gamma and your Somers' d? What do these statistics tell you?

LAB #13: BIVARIATE STATISTICS FOR INTERVAL/RATIO DATA

The focus of this lab is to introduce you to the **association or relationship between interval/ratio level variables**. Specifically, this lab will help clarify your understanding of Pearson's *r* and explained variance. This lab corresponds with the material presented in Chapter 14.

LEARNING OBJECTIVES

The following lab is directed at helping you understand how to interpret the relationship between two variables (bivariate relationships). Specifically, this lab assignment challenges you to clarify your understanding of:

1. Dependent and independent variables
2. How to calculate and interpret Pearson's *r*
3. How to interpret explained variance

Part 1: Calculating Pearson's *r* in STATA

When calculating Pearson's *r*, we make the assumption that the two variables we are correlating (evaluating the extent to which the variables are related) have a linear relationship. That is, the relationship between the two variables is the same, regardless of what the value of either of these variables is. So, the first step in calculating Pearson's *r* is to evaluate whether the relationship between the two variables is linear.

In this example, we are interested in whether an individual's age is correlated with the number of years of education they have obtained. In this case, our dependent variable is years of educational attainment (k7) and our independent variable is an individual's age (age).

Step 1: Recode variables.

Since both age and education have missing values, we need to recode them:

> **recode age (−1=.), gen(agerecode)**
> **recode k7 (−6/−1 98=.), gen(k7recode)**

We can check our coding with cross-tabulations:

RECODE of k7 (In total, how many years of schooling do you have?)	Freq.	Percent	Cum.
5	3	0.25	0.25
6	5	0.42	0.67
7	1	0.08	0.75
8	11	0.92	1.67
9	19	1.59	3.26
10	40	3.34	6.59
11	39	3.26	9.85
12	168	14.02	23.87
13	89	7.43	31.30
14	138	11.52	42.82
15	133	11.10	53.92
16	170	14.19	68.11
17	102	8.51	76.63
18	102	8.51	85.14
19	48	4.01	89.15
20	56	4.67	93.82
21	20	1.67	95.49
22	21	1.75	97.25
23	9	0.75	98.00
24	6	0.50	98.50
25	4	0.33	98.83
26	5	0.42	99.25
27	4	0.33	99.58
28	2	0.17	99.75
29	1	0.08	99.83
30	2	0.17	100.00
Total	1,198	100.00	

The tabulation for age is too long to print here, but it should be ok as well.

Step 2: Evaluate for linearity.

To evaluate for linearity, we will use a scatterplot. To create a scatterplot in STATA, click on

scatter agerecode k7recode

Figure 1 shows the scatterplot that should have been produced:

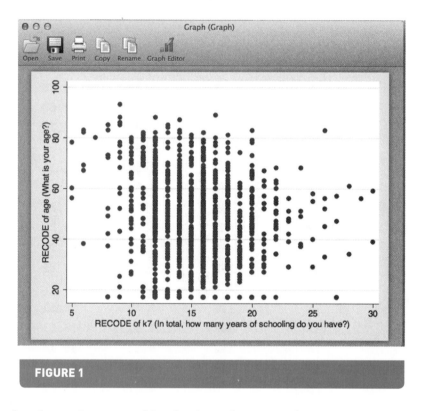

FIGURE 1

Here are a few observations we could make about this scatterplot:

1. Though not as linear as we may have liked, the dots do not appear to be arranged in a "shotgun" fashion, which means that there is no initial reason to suspect non-linearity. Thus, for our purposes, there's no reason to suspect non-linearity, so we can proceed with calculating Pearson's correlation.

2. There are likely to be quite a few outliers both above and below the line . . .

Now that we've done the necessary diagnostics, we are ready to calculate Pearson's r in STATA.

The computation of our Pearson's r is done "behind the scenes" by STATA, and is quite complex despite its easy implementation. In a nutshell, it considers the amount of covariation between your X variable (independent variable) and your Y variable (dependent variable).

Pearson's *r* ranges from −1.00 to +1.00

    −1.0 = a perfect negative relationship or association

    −0.5 = a moderate negative relationship or association

     0.0 = no correlation between two variables

    +0.5 = a moderate positive relationship or association

    +1.0 = a perfect positive relationship or association

Step 2: In your command box, type:

    pwcorr agerecode k7recode, sig obs

where "sig" requests that STATA reports the significance levels, and "obs" asks for the number of observations.

You should see a screen that looks like the one in Figure 2.

```
. pwcorr agerecode k7recode, sig obs

                 |  agerec~e  k7recode
       ----------+----------------------
       agerecode |   1.0000

                 |      1211


        k7recode |  -0.1746    1.0000
                 |   0.0000
                 |      1198       1198
```

FIGURE 2 | Pairwise Correlation Between Age and Years of Schooling

Looking at the first table, we observe that 1,198 people have valid values on both variables, a necessary condition for the calculation of correlation.

This table is called a correlation matrix. Refering to the lower-left hand cell, we see that we get a Pearson's *r* of −.1746. This means that the relationship between our two variables is negative but weak. However, looking at the value immediately below our Pearson's *r* coefficient, we see that our results are statistically significant at the 0.000 level.

Now it's your turn!

Putting the Information into Practice

In this example, we are interested in whether the number of children in the household (k3c) is correlated with the number of years of education they have obtained (k7).

1. Answer the following questions:
    a) What is your null hypothesis?
    b) What is your research hypothesis?
    c) What is your dependent variable?
    d) What is your independent variable?
    e) What are the levels of measurement of your variables?

2. Produce a scatterplot.
    a) Does the relationship between your two variables meet the assumption of linearity?

3. Calculate Pearson's r. Be sure to include the mean and standard deviation of your variables.
    a) What sample size did STATA use to calculate the Pearson correlation coefficient between k7 and k3c?
    b) What is the mean value of k7? What is the mean value of k3c?
    c) What is the Pearson correlation coefficient? Is it significant? Is it small, large?
    d) In terms of our two variables, what does the Pearson correlation coefficient mean? (Hint: Is the Pearson correlation coefficient positive or negative?)

LAB #14: ANALYSIS OF VARIANCE

The focus of this lab is to introduce you to a procedure known as ANOVA, or, **analysis of variance**. Specifically, this lab will help clarify your understanding of when this procedure should be used, AND how to calculate within-group sum of squares, between-group sum of squares, and the total sum of squares, which are the three major components of ANOVA. Finally, this lab will teach you how to interpret the F-distribution with ANOVA. This lab corresponds with the material presented in Chapter 15.

LEARNING OBJECTIVES

The following lab is directed at helping you understand how to interpret the relationship between two variables by using a procedure called ANOVA. Specifically, this lab assignment challenges you to clarify your understanding of:

1. Dependent and independent variables
2. Null and research hypotheses
3. How to interpret your findings and determine statistical significance

Analysis of variance, or ANOVA, is like a *t*-test but allows us to compare more than two groups. Conceptually, ANOVA compares three things:

1. Differences between means
2. Differences in values within samples
3. Differences in values across samples

Essentially, ANOVA is used to compare the variation caused by the independent variable and randomly occurring variations around the mean within groups to the variation across groups.

Part 1: Calculating ANOVA with STATA

In this example, we will ask the question: Are there significant differences in years of schooling (k7) by city, village, town or rural residence (k14)?

Step 1: Recode variables as necessary.

> **recode k7 (−6/−1 98=.), gen(k7recode)**
> **recode k14 (0 =.), gen(k14recode)**

Step 2: Run ANOVA by typing the following into your command box

> **oneway k7recode k14recode, tabulate means standard**

where "oneway" is the basic command, and "tabulate means standard" requests a table that contains means and standard deviations.

This will give you the output shown in Figure 1:

```
. oneway k7recode k14recode, tabulate means standard

 RECODE of    Summary of RECODE of k7
 k14 (Do you   (In total, how many
  presently    years of schooling do
    live in        you have?)
      a...)       Mean    Std. Dev.
-----------+------------------------
         1      15.835427  3.3779606
         2      14.405556  3.2626158
         3      13.382353  3.9158938
         4      13.967568  3.4858451
-----------+------------------------
     Total      15.261088  3.4899401


                      Analysis of Variance
    Source              SS         df      MS             F      Prob > F
------------------------------------------------------------------------
Between groups      823.870369     3    274.623456      23.84    0.0000
Within groups      13718.6702    1191   11.5186148
------------------------------------------------------------------------
    Total          14542.5406    1194   12.1796822

Bartlett's test for equal variances:  chi2(3) =   2.3243  Prob>chi2 = 0.508
```

FIGURE 1 | ANOVA Output of k7recode and k14 recode

There are a few things to note here. First, let's look at the means. You will notice that those who live in a city (k14recode=1), had, on average, 15.84 years of schooling. On the opposite end of the spectrum, those who lived in a rural part of Alberta had 13.97 years of schooling on average.

There are differences in the means of all the different groups, but are they statistically significant? ANOVA can begin to answer this question by comparing the variance within groups with the variance between groups. To risk overgeneralization, we could say that if the average person is no more similar to someone in their own category than they are to those in another response category, we would conclude that the there is no statistically significant pattern in the data.

To determine this, we need to look at the second table in the output above. For our between-group sum of squares, we can see that we have 3 degrees of freedom, and for our within-group sum of squares we have 1,191 degrees of freedom. If we go to Appendix D at the back of the textbook, we find that the critical F-distribution score for three degrees of freedom for the between groups score and for more than 120 degrees of freedom for the within-group value is less than 2.61. We can see in our table that our F score (F-observed) is 23.84. Because this number exceeds the critical F-score of 2.45, we can conclude with 95 per cent confidence that there are significant differences between at least two groups.

Now it's your turn!

Putting the Information into Practice

In this assignment, we will ask the question: Do urban Albertans have different incomes from rural Albertans? Use K12b to measure income (pretend that the variable is suitable for ANOVA, even though technically it is not), and k14 to measure how urban a person is. Be sure to handle all missing values appropriately.

1. Answer the following questions:
   a) What is your null hypothesis?
   b) What is your research hypothesis?
   c) What is your dependent variable?
   d) What is your independent variable?
   e) What are the levels of measurement of your variables?

2. Calculate ANOVA (remember to include your descriptive statistics).

3. In your output, using the table called descriptives, calculate the difference between mean income for
   a) Those who live in a city and those who live in a rural area: _____
   b) Those who live in a town and those who live in a village: _____
   c) Those who live in a village and those who live in a rural area: _____

4. What do these data suggest about the relationship between the degree of rurality and income?

5. State the value of the total sum of squares, the within-groups sum of squares, and the between-groups sum of squares.

6. What is the value of your *F*-statistic?
   a) Does this mean your results are statistically significant?
   b) Do you accept or reject your null hypothesis? Why?

LAB #15: OLS REGRESSION: MODELLING CONTINUOUS OUTCOMES

The focus of this lab is to introduce you to a form of multivariate analysis called **regression analysis**. Specifically, this lab will help clarify your understanding about when this procedure should be used, how to calculate and interpret ordinary least squares (OLS) regression, and how to compute dummy variables. This lab corresponds with the material presented in Chapter 16.

LEARNING OBJECTIVES

The following lab is directed at helping you understand how to interpret the relationship between multiple variables by using OLS regression. Specifically, this lab assignment challenges you to clarify your understanding of:

1. Dummy variables
2. Standardized partial slopes
3. How to interpret your findings and determine statistical significance

Part 1: Calculating OLS Regression with STATA

In this example, we are interested in which variables might affect the number of years of education an individual has obtained. For various reasons, we think that the number of years of education an individual has obtained may vary by gender (sex1) and by what part of Alberta they live in (strata).

Step 1: Code your variables.

Because one of the conditions of OLS regression states that all variables must be interval, ratio, or dummy variables, we will need to recode our variables to meet these conditions.

First, gender is a nominal level variable where the values are coded 1 "male" and 2 "female." We will need to recode this variable into a dummy variable where the response categories are 1 "male" and 0 "female."

STATA has a very efficient way to create dummy variables:

gen male = (sex==1)

Next, we will need to create a series of dummy variables for our area of the province variable (strata). As you recall from Chapter 16, you need to leave out one category of your independent variable (strata) as a reference category. Because we are most interested in the differences between Edmonton and Calgary, as compared to the rest of the province, we will make "other Alberta" our reference category. We will call these new variables "Edmonton" and "Calgary." We know by clicking the **values** tab in our data editor screen for the variable strata that "Edmonton" is coded as a "1," "Calgary" is coded as a "2," and "Other Alberta" is coded as a "3."

gen edmonton = (strata==1)
gen calgary = (strata==2)

As always, you'll want to check your coding by looking at tabulations of the data.

Step 2: Conduct an OLS regression in STATA.

STATA syntax for estimating regression is very concise, and always requires that you enter your dependent variable first, followed by all independent variables:

regress k7recode male edmonton calgary

This will give you the following output:

. regress k7recode male edmonton calgary

Source	SS	df	MS			
Model	905.73298	3	301.910993			
Residual	13677.0817	1194	11.4548423			
Total	14582.8147	1197	12.1828026			

Number of obs =	1198
F(3, 1194) =	26.36
Prob > F =	0.0000
R-squared =	0.0621
Adj R-squared =	0.0598
Root MSE =	3.3845

k7recode	Coef.	Std. Err.	t	P>|t|	[95% Conf. Interval]	
male	.1580169	.1955726	0.81	0.419	-.2256873	.541721
edmonton	1.333528	.2393216	5.57	0.000	.8639902	1.803065
calgary	2.094051	.2394718	8.74	0.000	1.624219	2.563884
_cons	14.03879	.1948982	72.03	0.000	13.65641	14.42117

First, look at the R-squared value in the top right-hand corner. R-squared measures how well the model fits your data; it tells you how much of the variation in the dependent variable can be explained by all the independent variables. In our example, we have explained 6.21 per cent of the variation in educational attainment. Adjusted R-squared values, though we didn't cover them in the text, are a modification of R-square that adjusts for the number of terms in a model. R-square almost always increases when a new term is added to a model, but adjusted R-square increases only if the new term improves the model more than would be expected by chance.

Second, the bottom table of the output above provides the regression coefficients. Now, if you recall, the regression equation is as follows:

$$y = a + bx + \varepsilon$$

A regression equation expresses the relationship between two or more variables. The variable a is the constant term (expressed as _cons in STATA), the intercept value when all independent values are set to zero, and it equals 14.03879. This means that our respondents in the reference category (females, other Alberta) have, on average, 14.04 years of schooling, a finding that is statistically significant at the .000 level. The other coefficients in the equation above represent the effect that each independent variable has on the dependent variable when all other independent variable values are 0. We can see from the output that men have .158 years more schooling than females. However, this finding is not statistically significant ($p = .419$, which is greater than .05). Next, individuals living in Edmonton have 1.333 more years of schooling than those living in "Other Alberta" and this finding is statistically significant at the .000 level. Finally, individuals living in Calgary have 2.094 more years of schooling than those living in "Other Alberta" and this finding is statistically significant at the .000 level. Confidence intervals are provided for each coefficient.

Now it's your turn!

Putting the Information into Practice

In this assignment, we are interested in whether age affects behaviours surrounding alcohol consumption. Specifically, we are interested in whether an individual has driven while impaired (h1), whether an individual has consumed alcohol while driving a motor vehicle (h4), and whether an individual has been involved in a traffic accident because of an impaired driver (h7).

1. Answer the following questions:
   a) What is your null hypothesis?
   b) What is your research hypothesis?
   c) What is your dependent variable?
   d) What is your independent variable?

2. Recode h1, h4, and h7 into dummy variables (make "yes" your reference category, i.e., equal to "1").

3. Conduct an OLS regression analysis using STATA.

4. What is the value of your R-squared? What does this mean?

5. Write the equation for your regression equation.

6. What is the average age of someone who has driven while impaired? Is this finding statistically significant?

7. What is the average age of someone who has consumed alcohol while driving a motor vehicle? Is this finding statistically significant?

8. What is the average age of someone who has been involved in a traffic accident because of an impaired driver? Is this finding statistically significant?

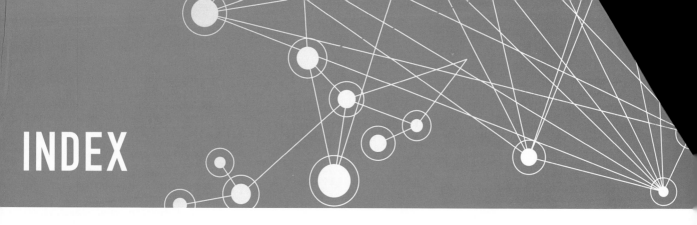

INDEX